Organizational Issues
in Health Care Management

Health Systems Management

Edited by Samuel Levey, Ph.D. and Alan Sheldon, M.D.

Organizational Issues in Health Care Management

By **Alan Sheldon**,
Graduate School of Business Administration
Harvard University

S P Books Division of
SPECTRUM PUBLICATIONS, INC.
New York

Distributed by Halsted Press
A Division of John Wiley & Sons

New York   Toronto   London   Sydney

TO MY PARENTS

Library of Congress Cataloging in Publication Data

Sheldon, Alan, 1933-
    Organizational issues in health care management

    (Health systems management)
    Bibliography: p.
    1. Health services administration - - Case studies.
I. Title. [DNLM: 1. Health services - - U.S.
2. Organization and administration. W84 AA1 S50]
RA393.S47   658'.91'3621   74-12357
ISBN 0-470-78275-7

Spectrum Publications, Inc.
86-19 Sancho Street, Holliswood, N.Y. 11423

Distributed solely by the Halsted Press Division of John Wiley & Sons Inc., New York

Printed in the United States of America

ACKNOWLEDGMENTS

I would like to thank the National Institutes of Health, Division of Allied Health Manpower, Public Health Professions Branch, who supported the development of The Philadelphia Blue Cross 1971 Contract Negotiations, Children's Hospital Medical Center, The Foundation for Health Care Evaluation, The Peer Review Problem, Stephen Doyle, and The State Laboratory Institute of Massachusetts cases with Contract # NIH 72.4221, Harvard Business School, who supported the remainder of the cases and Harvard College, who kindly gave me permission for the reproduction of the cases.

I would like to express my appreciation to Martin Charns, Assistant Professor at Carnegie Mellon Graduate School of Industrial Administration, who allowed me to reproduce the Canton State Series, to Stanton Peele, Assistant Professor at Harvard Business School for the Department of Health, Education, and Welfare series, and to Katharine Bauer, Associate at Harvard Center for Community Health and Medical Care and John Diffenbach, Research Assistant at Harvard Business School for The Philadelphia Blue Cross 1971 Contract Negotiations case and note.

The rest of the cases and notes were written under my supervision. I would like to thank Jeanne Stanton, Research Assistant at Harvard Business School, who wrote a case, and Lynda Diane Baydin and Ardis Burst, also Research Assistants at Harvard Business School, who wrote the remainder of the cases used herein. I am deeply grateful to them for the superb job they have done. Also, to Donna Maier, my secretary, who both edited and typed versions of the

v

manuscript, and to my wife, who, as always, was there to help when I needed her.

Some of the material appearing in the text has been previously published. Permission to reprint is gratefully acknowledged. "The Individual in the Organization" by Jay Lorsch and Alan Sheldon from Lorsch and Lawrence, eds., *Managing Group and Intergroup Relations*, (Homewood, Illinois: Richard D. Irwin, Inc., 1972c), pp. 161-82.

"Professionalization, A Necessary Evil" and "Research on Research on Research," *Social Science and Medicine*, (1970, 1971).

"Psychiatric Care in Crosscultural Perspective" by Alan Sheldon and Douglas Hooper, *Human Organization*, (1966).

"Personal Reaction to Organizational Change" by Gregory St. L. O'Brien, Alan Sheldon, and Susan G. Willard, *Mental Hygiene*, (1972).

The notes on groups in chapter four were prepared and written by Eric Neilsen, Assistant Professor at Harvard Business School, and I am greatly in his debt for allowing me to reproduce them here.

Finally, I would like to thank all the people and institutions, named and anonymous, who allowed us to write about them so that others could learn. I appreciate enormously their openness and longsuffering cooperation.

PREFACE

This is intended primarily to be a case book of selected real (if disguised occasionally), managerial situations drawn from a variety of health institutions. In over two hundred health care management cases available from the Intercollegiate Case Clearing House, they are the best examples of characteristic organizational behavior and design issues in the health field. They are taught as such, in the Harvard Business School Program for Health Systems Management. It is hoped that managers will benefit by reading them, and that teachers of management might find them useful in their courses. The note appearing before each case briefly describes the case itself, and the issues that the reader (or teacher) might consider. Harvard Business School cases are not case studies, i.e., exhaustive descriptions of situations. They are highly edited presentations of managerial dilemmas requiring the reader (or student) to put himself in the manager's situation and consider what action he would take. I should add that I use the pronoun 'he', here and throughout the book, in a sexually neuter sense.

The intent of the text is to provide a succinct account of current theory and techniques which will give managers some ideas on how to approach the kinds of situations depicted in the cases. Teachers will no doubt have their own preferences for theory, but may find it a useful overview. The text is also highly selective and is not intended to be, nor is it, comprehensive. There are innumerable perfectly good textbooks of human behavior and organizational design available. I have attempted to complement these, where I felt it to be necessary, to briefly survey, where I felt guilty, and to indulge my whims and idiosyncrasies, where I felt the urge. It is therefore brief, but covers some points that are important and I do not think are well covered elsewhere. I have tried to provide a good bibliography of further reading in the references for those so inclined.

Alan Sheldon, M.D.
1975

CONTENTS

Organizational Issues
in Health Care Management

CHAPTER 1

THE JOB OF
THE MANAGER

Now that technology and good intentions are seen to be insufficient to provide good affordable health care for all, the effective disposition of resources against objectives has become critical. Essentially, this is the job of the manager. It is curious to note, however, that even in industry surprisingly little attention has been paid to what a manager does. Thus, only this year Drucker (1974a) has produced an 800 page tome on the job of the manager. For too long in the health field a prevailing attitude has been one of reaction rather than proaction. While defensive management is all very well because every manager has to protect himself some-times, proaction should be stressed above all; a manager is someone who makes decisions and takes action, someone who makes things happen, someone who converts constraints into opportunities.

In this first chapter, the roles and tasks of the manager (Mintzberg, 1972) are described. The distinction between managership and leadership is left for later (Chapter 5). There is a discussion of the influences on a manager, the conscious or unconscious forces affecting his decisions, and, finally, the influences that he may use to help him make things happen.

One assumption is made throughout this book: there is not that much difference between a manager in the health field, whether he be physician or not, and a manager in industry. To some degree, of course, there are differences in the kinds of organizations but these are, when it comes down to it, differences of degree. Even in industry the senior manager has to juggle community forces, regulatory bodies, and political considerations just as much as the top administrator of a community hospital. Even the supposed complication of multiple hierarchical authority structures in health are by no means unique, for the widely prevalent matrix organization in industry presents the same problem of differing functional specialties who report through their own hierarchies, but work together on a program.

THE ROLES AND TASKS OF A MANAGER

Mintzberg (1972) defines the manager as that person in charge of a formal organization or one of its subunits. The manager has formal authority over his organizational unit and this leads to his two basic purposes. First, the manager must ensure that his organization produces its specific goods or services efficiently. He must design and maintain the stability of its basic operations, and he must adapt it in a controlled way to its changing environment. Second, the manager must ensure that his organization serves the ends of those persons who control it (the ''influencers''). He must interpret their particular preferences and combine these to produce statements of organizational preference which guide its decision-making. Due to his formal authority, the manager must serve two other basic purposes as well. He must act as the key communication link between his organization and its environment, and he must assume responsibility for the operation of his organization's status system. These basic purposes are operationalized through ten interrelated roles which are performed by all managers. These roles fall into three groupings—three interpersonal roles which derive from the manager's authority and status, three informational roles which derive from the interpersonal roles and the access they provide to information, and four decisional roles which derive from the manager's authority and information. Mintzberg goes on to discuss these roles.

The manager's simplest role is that of figurehead, which describes him as a symbol. This role is required because of his responsibility to carry out duties which are social, inspirational, legal, and ceremonial in nature. The manager's interpersonal relationships with his subordinates are described as his leader role. Interaction with people outside his own organizational unit is characterized as the manager's liaison role. In order to develop a thorough knowledge of his milieu, the manager acts as a monitor continually seeking and receiving internal and external information from a variety of sources. The manager functions as disseminator by transmitting some of his internal and external information to subordinates. Information is transmitted to individuals outside the manager's organizational unit through his role as spokesman. As entrepreneur, the manager initiates and designs much of the controlled change which takes place in his organization. When his organization faces a major disturbance, the manager must take charge by assuming his disturbance handler role. Maintaining control of the organization's strategy-making process is achieved through overseeing the allocation of all resources. This task is described as the manager's resource allocator role. Finally, the manager assumes the role of negotiator and takes charge when his organization must have important negotiations with another organization.

Mintzberg also identifies several managerial skills that he regards as important for effectiveness. Sharing information, dealing consciously with superficiality, sharing the job, making the most of necessary obligations, but freeing himself of those he can, emphasizing the role that fits the situation, seeking a comprehensive picture in terms of its details, recognizing his own influence, and dealing with a pending coalition.

In the State Laboratory Institute of Massachusetts, it would appear that previous incumbents of the directorship essentially regarded their task as that of presiding over the status quo. However, Dr. Madoff defines his job differently. He feels that he should be more than a skilled public health professional who takes the attitude that he has a limited budget and limited resources and therefore will go on doing what he has done before. Instead, he questions whether SLIM should do it at all or whether perhaps it should have a much expanded or altered role for which he should energetically seek additional funding. It is this attitude toward his job and his organization that suggests that Dr. Madoff is not only an effective manager but an effective leader. It is this attitude that is becoming more and more frequent in the health system.

INFLUENCES ON THE MANAGER

The day when the manager could make most of his critical decisions independently, the day when he had unlimited authority to make things happen, perhaps never existed except in the rosy recollections of reminiscing retirees. But to whatever extent it may have, it does no longer. Decisions are highly interdependent, relationships must be managed, influences proliferate, and thus the political aspect of decision-making is important. A manager has to contend also with less apparent forces which may not often be in his consciousness and therefore are largely unheeded. The effective manager should pay at least some attention to these, for in the form of values and personality attributes, they may have a not insignificant part to play in the choices that he characteristically makes.

Organizational Influences

The sources of influence on a manager's behavior are summarized in the figure (page 5). Clearly those with most impact will be those most proximate in time and space and of greatest importance to the individual manager. The key organizational forces with which the general manager has to cope are well discussed by Uyterhoeven (1972). The typical general manager in industry, and this is certainly as true of managers in the health field, basically works through relationships, upward, downward, and laterally. A key task is to integrate specialists and functions. But a major problem is that he often has somewhat limited authority but full responsibility. He needs the cooperation of others but has limited power and great vulnerability in a highly political environment. This may be his first job and typically he may have been a specialist of some kind, for example a physician who becomes department chairman or heads up an out-patient department. There is a maze of accommodation and compromise. It is critical for him to define for himself and to make explicit the network of relationships that he has to manage and to identify the requirements on him from superiors, subordinates, and peers. He has to communicate his understanding of his job to them and, while consistency is difficult, attempt to be as consistent as possible. Roethlisberger (1965), in a now classic earlier work, deals with the dilemma of the first line supervisor, not at all dissimilar to that of the general manager, but with the added complication of being recently promoted from a group of workers to whom residual loyalties continue to make demands. There is very real role conflict and ambiguity in the dilemma of this job (see below), where the supervisor is supposedly a part of management yet can only function effectively with the support of a group from whom he may now be alienated.

The influences so far mentioned emanate from the demands that other organizational members may make on the manager. The organizational system itself exerts pressure on the manager by measuring his performance in certain ways and rewarding that performance or punishing it. This is discussed in Chapters 2 and 3. A more intangible organizational influence is that of climate, in which certain organizational expectations and norms about standards of behavior get communicated. This process of influence begins at the time a manager joins an organization. At this time he explicitly or implicitly develops a psychological contract with the organization, negotiating the kind of relationship he both expects and wishes to participate in. During the early months of his membership in the new organization, he becomes socialized and learns what is expected of him and what he may expect. This is as true of an employee joining a hospital as it is of a medical student becoming a physician. Influences on the manager may also come from the demands of the task itself. Certain kinds of tasks require rigorous clear thinking, others require a flexible patience. Some require great tolerance of ambiguity, some authoritarian action. Of this, also there is more later.

Extraorganizational Influences

Socially the manager is a system and is as well a subsystem of larger social systems. The manager participates in many activities and in many areas. The family, work, and the group of activities called "social life" are probably the most important of these. In each of these areas or systems, the manager has a part to play—his role. This role is in part determined by his own preferences and personality and in part by the system in which he is an actor. Thus a man plays a part as father, community leader, etc., as well as manager. His behavior may differ to varying degrees as he assumes different roles, but nevertheless the underlying consistency of his personality is present.

Figure 1

Sources of Influence on Manager's Behavior

(Past, Present, Future)

Organizational

                individuals

    people   groups — work, peer

                hierarchy — superiors, subordinates, peer

    operating mechanisms — selection, evaluation, reward

    climate — socialization

    task

Extraorganizational

    family

    reference groups — e.g., profession

                community — e.g., local, state, federal

    society

    culture

Manager

    internal to self

    external — feedback from effects of behavior — organizational and

                extraorganizational

The demands that the various roles make on the individual may be harmonious and consonant with each other, or may be in conflict. A conflict may be apparent and external, for example, a man may be on shift work which involves his being at work when his children are at home. Here his role in the family system as a father and his role as a manager are clearly in conflict. But such conflicts may be much more subtle. His role as manager may require him to be aggressive, determined, and exacting, while his family role as father requires him to be gentle, patient, and tolerant.

The manifestations of such conflict may be obvious to others or barely evident even to oneself. Furthermore, such conflict may turn up in unexpected places, for frequently, conflict within a particular system which cannot be dealt with there can appear in other systems. Thus, as a psychological defense, a man who for very good reasons finds it difficult to speak up to his boss may displace his resentments into his family life.

Influences from Within and Without

Every manager makes choices based on his personality and his particular set of experiences. These past experiences shape his behavior and his values. Some sense of who one is, what characteristic choices one makes, and why are crucial to the effective manager. This does not imply self-indulgent navel gazing. Sometimes a manager makes choices which he may believe are in the best interests of his organization, but are really in his own self interest, or vice versa. All people have mixed motives much of the time, although few ever really come to terms with this. Some reflective self-knowledge may at least reduce painful rumination if not avoid idiosyncratic and questionable decisions. The chairman of the board of trustees of a Canadian hospital was also a senior manager of a multinational industrial company. He had become reconciled to the fact that he would never head this company, so being president of the hospital meant a great deal to him. He was considering making some very major capital investments on improvements in this hospital; but before he did so, he reflected on whether these in fact would be in the best interests of the hospital and of the community which it served or whether they were really a function of his own very human desire to leave behind him some concrete and visible accomplishments.

Another top administrator of a major federal institution had worked effectively in his job for many years. Now he was faced with a federal edict that the hospital should be handed over to the local community. Employees were concerned about loss of jobs and benefits. He felt torn between his personal values of straight dealing and of loyalty to the federal system that had rewarded him and equally powerful loyalties to his employees. The alternative of attempting to manipulate possibly powerful political constituencies to affect the decision was, because of who he was, enormously distasteful.

A last source of influence are the effects of feedback about one's behavior. As the manager does, he sees the effects of what he does. This may take the form of successfully completed tasks or more or less welcome comments by others. The extent to which this feedback becomes a source of influence depends on many factors. These include the value that the manager places on the source of the feedback, the perceived meaning and intensity of the feedback, and the degree to which the manager has a clear sense of himself and a high self-esteem. Professional growth as a manager depends on the degree of openness to signals about behavior and willingness to learn from them. This is not necessarily easy because feedback is so often painful and unwelcome, and it is tempting to stop hearing it or distort it. So the source of the feedback may be discounted by putting down the person who is telling unwelcome news, or a low self-opinion may be reinforced as less demanding than doing something about oneself. People with very low or high self-esteem tend to ignore feedback, not unsurprisingly.

Figure 2

Managerial Influence Model

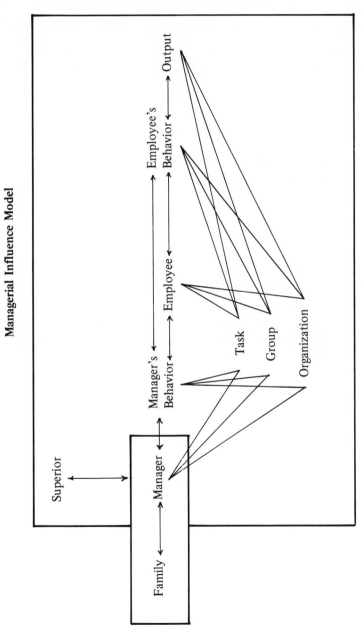

Figure 3

Types and Forms of Power/Influence

Authority
     ascribed
     positional
     personal
         charisma
         moral

Experience
     knowledge/information
     skills
     referent — reference groups
     constituencies

Control over resources/opportunities

Control over/exchange of — satisfaction of needs, e.g., need to be influential (need for affirmation)

Control over rules

Control over fate

Normative (by setting example or model)

Influences Available to the Manager

The model (Fig. 2) shows that sources of influence on the manager are also amenable to influence by him. In the end he has to get people to produce some output (goods or services). He can influence them directly, through his own behavior, or via his control over desired resources. He can change their task, affect the group of which they are a member, or change the organization. There are often more alternative routes of influence available than are considered.

The major forms of power and influence are listed in Fig. 3. The manager may give or withhold reward or punishment. He may merely threaten to withhold, or promise to give (expectations). A powerful influence is that of exchange—especially the satisfaction of the ubiquitous need for affirmation (see below). Motivation is discussed further in the next chapter.

Note for State Laboratory Institute of Massachusetts

Description

This case describes the situation facing the director of the State Laboratory Institute of Mass. (SLIM) a state laboratory system providing certain free services for residents of Massachussetts. The director, who is entering his second year in that position, is considering possible future roles and directions for SLIM as part of the total health delivery system in the state.

Teaching Objectives

The main question raised in the case involves the process of making a decision: How can the director set a course for SLIM when he does not have enough information available to completely assess the situation, when he and his subordinates have very little training in managerial decision-making, and when there is neither time nor money to explore health systems and management issues more thoroughly.

A number of related issues, such as the role and responsibilities of such providers of services and the future of health care delivery systems, can also be raised. In fact, this case is extremely open ended because it reflects the enormous complexity and interrelatedness of health institutions.

This case is well suited to providing an introduction to major issues in the health field because it deals with a variety of topics. An extensive set of exhibits provides an opportunity for the student to analyze the same data available to the director and formulate his or her own conclusions and recommendations.

STATE LABORATORY INSTITUTE OF MASSACHUSETTS

In the spring of 1973, Dr. Morton Madoff, superintendent of the State Laboratory Institute of Massachusetts (SLIM), decided that he needed some advice in determining the future direction of his organization. The laboratory would shortly be moving from its present modest quarters into a large new multi-million dollar building. Dr. Madoff felt that the physical move provided an excellent opportunity for reassessing the tasks and goals of the laboratory and its role in the total health care system in Massachusetts. He particularly wanted to consider the implications of rising health care costs in the nation and possible changes in the way care was delivered and paid for, such as the introduction of national health insurance. But he felt that he did not have the managerial skills necessary to analyze what changes were possible and desirable for the Institute or to make accurate predictions about what future role the Institute should play.

At the advice of a professional colleague, Dr. Madoff approached a professor from the Harvard Business School and asked him to help him sort out the problems Dr. Madoff had to deal with. The two men met in Dr. Madoff's office one March afternoon with Dr. Mitchell, principal physician, and Dr. Grady, Biologic Laboratories Director. Dr. Madoff explained his situation to the consultant:

> Our new building was designed around the status quo and that status quo needs to be changed. I am in a good position to bring about change because I am new in the job, having been here only a year.

> Yet I don't have the time or background to actually make the changes myself. I'm not a trained manager nor is any of my staff. Only three or four of us here function at a true managerial level. Most of the administrative staff work more or less as bookkeepers. I have to explore new directions for the labs while being bound down to handling day-to-day problems.

The Structure of the State Laboratory Institute

SLIM received its operating budget primarily from the Commonwealth of Massachusetts. This budget remained essentially unchanged from year to year, the only increases being cost of living allowances. The budget for fiscal year 1973 was $2.7 million, $2.1 million coming from the state and $600,000 from federal sources. The proposed state allocation for FY 1974 was $2.7 million, and it was unlikely that this would be increased.

The labs employed 237 people, 167 of whom were civil service appointees. (See Exhibit 1 for an organization chart in 1973 and Exhibit 2 for a list of employee salary levels.) The labs were divided into two major functional areas. The biologic laboratories, employing 100 people, 80 of whom were funded by the state, manufactured non-virus immunizing agents and fractional plasma. The diagnostic laboratories, which employed 118 people, provided testing primarily in the areas of venereal disease, bacteriology, metabolic disorders, and other basic tests. In addition, the diagnostic laboratories also specialized in a few intricate limited-demand areas such as salmonella and shigella typing and virus isolation and antibody testing. SLIM, because it covered a very broad population base, could run these tests more efficiently, accurately, and economically than could the average clinical lab.

SLIM's services were free to anyone in the state. The practice of providing free lab service dated particularly from the department of diphtheria antitoxin in 1896. At the time, diphtheria was most common among the poor and to meet this health problem, it was felt necessary to provide the antitoxin free.

The Role of SLIM in the State

Dr. Madoff felt that it was necessary for him to have a clear picture of the role that SLIM played in the total Massachusetts health care system. His knowledge was limited, however, primarily by a lack of information on who constituted the ultimate recipients of the lab's free services. Individual tests were identified only by the name of the clinic or hospital which submitted them. Dr. Madoff consequently did not know if tests were being sent in for individuals unable to pay commercial laboratory fees or if doctors used SLIM because of the lab's high quality testing or specialized services.

Only one small survey had been conducted to date to determine the identity of recipients. This survey had shown that a disproportionately high number of samples in one area, the streptococcal throat culture program, had come from the suburbs west and south of Boston. Because these were mainly middle to upper-middle class communities, Dr. Madoff was concerned that samples SLIM received may reflect the fact that more affluent families sent their children to doctors more often. He felt that this suggested that SLIM was serving the people who needed free services least.

In light of this possibility, Dr. Madoff hoped the consultant could help him determine first, how he could find out why the lab was used, and second, how he could find out who the ultimate recipients of services were. He wanted to test his hunches before deciding what, if any, action to take on serving a different segment of the community.

Cost Standards

Another area in which Dr. Madoff felt he needed more data was that of costs standards. He used SLIM as an example of variations in costs for a single test.

> Why are there differences between the costs of performing certain tests at SLIM and at some allied lab in central Massachusetts, for instance? We contract with two other labs to provide streptococcal throat cultures for their immediate geographic areas. While we do 100,000 cultures a year at $1.07 per culture, one lab does 50,000 a year at 80¢ per culture (a $35,000 contract) and the other does 25,000 a year for only 60¢ per culture (a $14,000 contract). Even if there are extraneous factors, the cost differences are still significant.

He thought that a full-scale clinical lab pilot project, established under optimal conditions with a team of professional managers as well as scientists, could be used to develop realistic data on costs, guidelines, and advice on maximizing cost efficiency. SLIM could use this data to tighten their cost controls, but more importantly could make such information available to commercial labs, both to help them increase efficiency and to provide some standards for their charges. With the latter in mind, the superintendent considered publishing a list of relative laboratory costs in the state to distribute to both consumers and providers, thus engaging consumer support of labs which were following these guidelines.

But SLIM did not have the money to establish such a project, the superintendent told the consultant. Unless present programs were cut back, the most SLIM could contribute to a pilot project would be some of the additional space in the new building.

Quality Control

The superintendent felt that a program of lab quality control would also be valuable to the state. He explained:

> At present, we do some work in quality control. For example, periodically we send samples of streptococcal throat cultures to commercial and hospital labs to be tested and reported on. In these cases, the labs know they are being tested and undoubtedly do their best to identify the cultures. But even then, only 65% of the samples are correctly identified even as positive or negative. And when it comes to identifying the type of streptococcus, results are even poorer.

> Obviously we need a better program of quality control and we need an education program to train lab staffs so their performance will improve. But the same financial and staff limitations exist for establishing such programs as for the cost standards program.

Should Programs Be Cut Back?

The superintendent saw cutbacks in present programs as the only way to find money within the present SLIM budget to use for X new programs. He was reluctant to take this step, however.

> Sometimes I ask myself what difference it would make in the state health care picture if we stopped doing anything we now do. We had to cut back our streptococcal testing program because of budget cuts. Instead of serving the total population, we were only working with the 0-12 age group. This resulted in about a 35% reduction of our testing. We have complaints about this but they have been relatively few, and to the best of my knowledge, it has had no apparent effect on medical care. (See Exhibit 4 for data on this program.)
>
> But we could be wrong and I don't know whether similar cuts in other testing would have as little effect on the public or on medical care. Moreover, further cutbacks might influence the good will of the community, especially the physicians, with whom we have had excellent relations until now.
>
> I don't know if viable alternatives exist for testing, for example. And yet I have to ask questions about cutting back because the only way I can obtain the resources to do anything new is to cease doing other things. There is no excess capacity.

Even while he was considering cutting back some present programs to provide funds for what he considered vital new programs, the superintendent was being approached by various groups in the state who wanted SLIM to provide new or expanded services for their special health interests. One organization, for example, was proposing that all school children in the state be tested routinely for streptococcal infection in order to prevent the occurrence of rheumatic fever, a disease which can develop from untreated streptococcal infection. Processing cultures from these programs would result in a tremendous increase in the streptococcal culture program at SLIM and would thus make it impossible for SLIM to expand into any new programs.

Making Decisions

Although the superintendent had outlined five goals for SLIM in his 1972 Annual Report (see Exhibit 5 for excerpts), he was not certain that meeting these goals was most crucial to the health care system in Massachusetts. Nor did he know how he could find the money to meet these goals if he chose to pursue them.

Meanwhile, he felt that he had to begin making decisions at once, even if he did not have all the information he needed. As the end of the meeting with the consultant approached, he stressed again that he needed help both in identifying the direction to take and in creating sources of funds to implement his decisions.

Exhibit 1

State Laboratory Institute of Massachusetts

State Biologic Laboratories of Massachusetts Partial Organization Chart

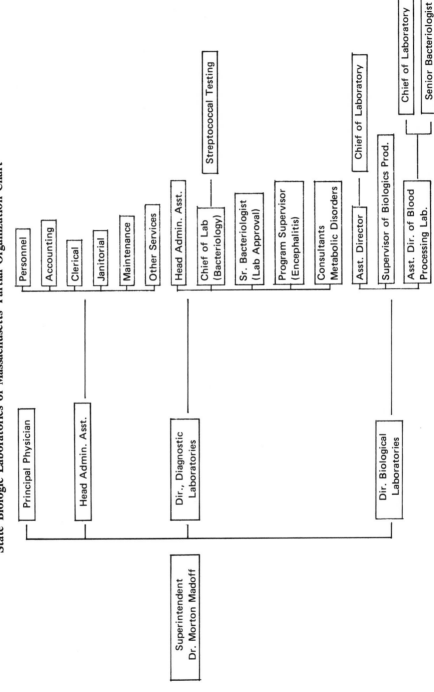

Exhibit 2

State Laboratory Institute
of Massachusetts

Number of Employees by Salary Level

Salary Level (Grades)	Representative Salary (at step 3 in $)	No. of Employees in Category*	Representative Jobs in Category
1	5400	9	Cleaner
2	5500	0	—
3	5700	29	Jr. Clerk/Typist
4	5900	3	Jr. Clerk/Stenographer
5	6100	50	Laboratory Asst.
6	6500	16	Janitor
7	6700	10	Truck Driver
8	7000	2	Stable Foreman
9	7500	21	Lab Technician
10	7900	10	Supervising Lab. Tech.
11	8300	5	3rd Class Engineer
12	8800	3	2nd Class Engineer
13	9400	32	Jr. Bacteriologist
14	10100	1	Chief Engineer
15	10800	14	Asst. Bacteriologist
16	11500	0	—
17	12300	15	Sr. Bacteriologist
18	13000	1	Epidemiologist
19	13800	4	Laboratory Chief
20	14500	0	—
21	15300	1	Program Supervisor
22	16200	0	—
23	17000	2	Asst. Lab. Director
24	18000	3	Asst. Lab. Director
25	18800	0	—
26	19500	0	—
27	20400	2	Laboratory Director
28	21300	0	—
29	22200	1	Laboratory Director
30	23300	1	Institute Superintendent

*Includes a total of ten part-time employees in all categories

Exhibit 3

State Laboratory Institute
of Massachusetts

Selected Employee Data by Lab and Job*

	Lab Chief	Sr. Bacteriologist	Sr. Chemist	Asst. Bacteriologists	Jr. Bacteriologists	Asst. Chemist	Jr. Chemist	Supervising Lab. Tech.	Lab Tech.	Lab Asst.	Animal Room Staff	Service and Domestic Workers	Stable Workers	Sr. Clerk/Typist–Stenographer	Jr. Clerk/Typist
Biologic Prod.	1	2	1	–	1	–	4	1	–	12	4	2	–	–	–
Plasma Products	1	2	–	–	–	1	2	2	2	6	–	–	–	–	–
RH Globulin	–	½	–	1	2	–	1	–	1	–	–	2	–	–	–
Kidney Transplant Serum	–	½	1	–	–	–	–	–	–	–	–	–	5	–	–
Bacteriology Lab	1	3	–	2	11	–	–	–	4	5	–	3	–	2	4
Virus Lab	1	–	–	2	3	1	–	–	3	1	–	–	–	–	–
Wassermann Lab	–	1	–	1	1	–	–	1	3	10	–	–	–	2	5
Lab Approval	–	1	–	–	–	–	–	–	1	–	–	–	–	–	1
Encephalitis	1	–	–	–	1	–	–	–	–	–	–	1	–	–	1
Metabolic Disorders	–	–	1	1	4	1	–	1	3	3	–	–	–	2	2

*Individuals were assigned to work on a particular test (such as streptococcal) generally. Those who worked in more than one area had their time allotted to different areas on a percentage basis. Therefore tests could be costed.

Exhibit 4

State Laboratory Institute
of Massachusetts

Data for a Representative Testing Program*

Personnel assigned currently

  1 Senior Bacteriologist
  5 Junior Bacteriologists
  3 Laboratory Technicians (full-time)
  1 Laboratory Technician (1/2 time)
  1 Laboratory Technician (1/3 time)
  3 Laboratory Assistants (1/2 time)
  2 Institution Domestic Aides (1/2 time)
  1 Senior Clerk/Stenographer (1/4 time)
  5 Junior Clerk/Typists (1/2 time)

Assigned on a rotating basis

  1 Assistant Bacteriologist
  4 Junior Bacteriologists

Saturday and holiday assignment (usual)

  5 Bacteriologists
  3 Laboratory technicians or assistants
  3 Clerks

Federally funded assigned personnel and date of funding

  1 Senior Bacteriologist (Dec. 1967)
  1 Assistant Bacteriologist (1962)
  3 Jr. Bacteriologists (1–1962, 2–1966)
  2 Lab Tech. (1–1966, 1–1967)
  1 Sr. Clerk–Stenographer (1967)
  1 Inst. Domestic Aide (1965)
  2 Lab Tech. (full-time) (1–1970, 1–1971)
  2 Lab Tech. (part-time) (1970)
  3 Lab Asst. (part-time) (3–1966)
  1 Lab Asst. (full-time) (1967)

Work Load Statistics

Fiscal Year	1966	1967	1968	1969	1970	1971
No. Throat Cultures	54,029	99,041	113,858	114,485	143,157	166,586
% Increase		83.3	14.9	.09	24.6	16.3

*This data refers to the streptococcal program.

Quarterly Work Load

Fiscal Year	1970	1971	1972
July–Sept.	35,073	33,205	33,406
Oct.–Dec.	25,876	42,352	44,349
Jan.–Mar.	42,874	51,032	
Apr.–June	38,671	39,997	

February Work Load

	Number Culture Received	Number Positive	Percent Positive
1972	14,617	3,304	22.6
1971	15,324	3,343	21.8
1970	12,860	3,262	25.4

Exhibit 5

Annual Report

Fiscal Year 1972

State Laboratory Institute

General Statement

In February, 1972, Dr. Morton A. Madoff, who had previously served the Department in various capacities (as a staff physician at the Lemuel Shattuck Hospital, Director of the Division of Biologic Laboratories, and Director of Adult and Maternal Health Services), succeeded Dr. Geoffrey Edsall as Superintendent of the State Laboratory Institute. Dr. Edsall retired after many years of State and Federal services to become Professor and Chairman of the Department of Microbiology at the London School of Hygiene and Tropical Medicine.

Dr. Madoff has outlined five major objectives which he feels the State Laboratory Institute must achieve:

(1) Increased assistance to public and private laboratories in the areas of laboratory improvement and quality control, to assure the highest level of laboratory services at reasonable cost for the citizens of the Commonwealth.

(2) Provision of more ready access to laboratory tests of an unusual or highly specialized nature.

(3) Greater emphasis on the rapid development and general introduction of newer laboratory tests and techniques of potential public health benefit.

(4) Full utilization of the unique capabilities of the Division of Biologic Laboratories as both a state and national resource to assure the quality and continuing availability of immunizing agents and specialized blood products.

(5) More effective use of contemporary data processing methods to assist Departmental divisions and other concerned agencies in the recognition and management of problems of disease surveillance and control.

Exhibit 5 (continued)

Annual Report – July 1, 1971–June 30, 1972

Division of Biologic Laboratories

1. The Biologic Laboratories took a leading role in a national series of studies to determine whether a special immune serum globulin is more effective than conventional gamma globulin in preventing type B hepatitis (formerly known as serum hepatitis). The new globulin for the entire national program was produced at the Massachusetts Laboratories.

2. Rh globulin, given to mothers to prevent Rh disease of their newborns, received a Federal license and reached full scale distribution to all Massachusetts hospitals having obstetrical services. A team of Polish-scientists visited the Laboratories to learn how to institute a similar program in Poland.

3. A new method of producing Smallpox Vaccine was devised to yield a better product. The demand for Smallpox Vaccine remained relatively strong (despite Federal recommendations that routine childhood vaccination be discontinued) especially for the large number of medical personnel and travelers in the Boston area.

4. Approximately 200,000 doses of vaccines were sent to aid flood-stricken Pennsylvania residents cut off from traditional sources of supply. The episode illustrates the value of the Laboratories in the event Massachusetts should experience a similar disaster.

5. The Biologic Laboratories acquired a new Assistant Director, Dr. George Wright, who is highly experienced in vaccine production and testing. Dr. Wright was previously the Chief of Immunology at Fort Detrick, Maryland.

Exhibit 5

Biologic Laboratories

Distribution of Products

5 Year Comparative Chart

	Fiscal Year 1967–68	Fiscal Year 1968–69	Fiscal Year 1969–70	Fiscal Year 1970–71	Fiscal Year 1971–72
Diptheria					
Antitoxin, units	1,467,000	2,162,000	1,063,500	649,500	291,500
Schick Outfits, 2 – 50 dose vials	934	634	562	400	397
Toxin – Bulk ml	1,190	585	662	10	310
Diptheria–Tetanus, adsorbed ml	105,499	88,858	68,236	68,573	62,045
Diptheria–Tetanus–Pertussis adsorbed ml	308,436	324,556	278,991	279,226	250,390
Diphtheria Toxoid, concentrated purified ml	1,190	945	430	400	630
Enteric Fevers					
Typhoid Vaccine ml	60,419	46,105	45,295	40,540	34,480
Typhoid & Paratyphoid Vaccine ml	2,749	—	—	—	—
Measles, Hepatitis					
Immune Serum Globulin ml					
State	84,250	114,336	127,924	120,462	110,770
American Red Cross	1,464	17,710	138,078	49,932	97,736
Total	85,714	132,046	266,002	170,394	208,500
Smallpox					
Smallpox Vaccine capillaries	429,451	448,785	448,577	372,395	258,630

Tetanus

Antitoxin, units	4,752,000	1,294,720	268,500	60,000	31,500
Toxoid, fluid ml	249,975	73,045	—	—	320
Antitoxin, bovine ml	—	—	—	135	200
Tetanus–Diphtheria Toxoid, Adult adsorbed ml	65,685	101,840	79,255	116,590	93,575
Immune Globulin, units	165,750	539,750	844,250	614,250	660,250
Tetanus–Diphtheria Toxoid Booster ml	40,790	19,835	—	—	—
Tetanus Toxoid, adsorbed ml	—	135,030	176,125	172,955	166,000
Tetanus Toxoid, concentrated, purified ml	—	—	1,970	1,588	950

Tuberculin

Tuberculin Concentrated, ml	92	114	58	—	—
Diluted 1:2000 Tuberculin, ml	28,370	30,157	15,043	9,402	26,044
Tuberculin Tine Test	203,219	268,175	300,900	371,960	368,334
P.P.D. Tuberculin – ml	—	—	26,480	38,980	1,600
P.P.D. – Battery – ml	—	—	400	1,610	1,280

Gonorrheal Ophthalmia

Silver Nitrate Solution ampoules	122,510	125,550	134,940	176,950	207,890

Syphilis

Penicillin, 600,000 unit vials	20,898	8,585	5,109	4,747	4,425
Frei Antigen 10 test	21	29	28	23	22
Benzathine Penicillin G					
1,200,000 unit vials	1,240	6,296	2,145	3,090	3,670
Penicillin, 1,200,000 unit vials	—	—	33,255	47,870	54,550

Transfusion Therapy

Normal Serum Albumin ml	348,500	357,400	387,000	576,300	888,450
Plasma Protein Fraction ml	—	—	—	—	—

Whooping Cough

Pertussis Vaccine ml	430	—	55	475	590
Inc. Antihemophilus Pertussis					
Rabbit Serum ml	—	—	—	—	—

	Fiscal Year 1967–68	Fiscal Year 1968–69	Fiscal Year 1969–70	Fiscal Year 1970–71	Fiscal Year 1971–72
Miscellaneous Other Products					
Antihemophilus Influenza Serum rabbit typing serum ml	50	58	36	90	138
Whole Blood ml (Horse)	162,500	10,500	—	—	—
Defibrinated horse blood ml	732,750	695,380	512,070	56,310	55,000
Normal Horse Serum ml	142,000	122,310	157,750	134,700	145,200
Serum Sensitivity 3 ml Outfits – Horse	287	—	—	—	—
Oral Polio Vaccine – Trivalent ml	60,592	49,621	33,782	37,540	36,666
Measles Vaccine – Schwarz Strain ml	89,100	77,072	69,024	62,754	78,490
Mumps Vaccine ml	—	96,140	80,977	55,401	84,020
Rubella Vaccine ml	—	—	299,568	169,003	162,090
Measles & Rubella Combined ml					41,720
Red Cross Contract Distribution					
Immune Serum Globulin ml	88,054	17,710	138,078	49,932	97,736
Normal Serum Albumin ml	404,100	383,300	546,700	491,600	279,200

22

Exhibit 5 (continued)

Annual Narrative Report of the Diagnostic Laboratories

July 1971 — June 1972

Introduction

The program of the Diagnostic Laboratories consists primarily in the provision of routine and special diagnostic services in the areas of communicable diseases control and congenital metabolic disorders screening. In recent years the traditional confinement of our public health diagnostic laboratories to the diagnosis of the communicable and venereal diseases has been lifted to include not only the detection of metabolic disorders, but also other areas, providing a more broadened and balanced service capability. Surveillance of the quality of tests performed by local clinical laboratories certified under Medicare and/or enrolled in the Laboratory Improvement Program is a further activity, not new, but increasing in scope and importance. Likewise, the screening program begun in 1962 to detect PKU in neonates continues to further develop and has been expanded to include nearly all other detectable inborn errors of metabolism.

The overall program has four major components:

1) *Large scale performance of routine services,* i.e., Hinton test, screening of newborns for PKU and other metabolic disorders, identification of group A streptococci, screening for enteric pathogens such as Salmonella and Shigella, rubella immunity testing, etc.

2) The provision of highly technical services not ordinarily available in local laboratories, e.g. certain viruses, typing of salmonella organisms, identification of atypical mycobacteria, certain special tests for syphilis, rabies testing, etc.

3) Maintenance of a diagnostic service guaranteeing the availability of the latest, most rapid and effective techniques for the recognition of unusual infections which nevertheless may occur in Massachusetts, e.g. cholera, plague, tularemia, psittacosis, anthrax, eastern viral encephalitis, leptospirosis, glanders, melioidosis, malaria, etc.

4) Assistance to local laboratories throughout the State to achieve a high degree of excellence in the performance of clinical laboratory tests.

Table 1

Five Year Summary of Number and Kinds of Specimens Examined by the Diagnostic Laboratories

	1968	1969	1970	1971	1972
Bacteriology					
Agglutinations	4,580	2,566	2,535	2,420	2,247
Enteric Pathogens	11,979	12,512	13,830	13,019	13,126
Gonorrhea	7,107	5,614	6,451	13,463xxx	17,373xxx
Malaria	3	3	—	—	183
Mycology	221	154	195	147	—
Throat Cultures	113,858	114,845	143,157	166,586	168,075
Tuberculosis	4,122	4,115	4,687	5,152	2,345
Vincent's Cingivitis	21	16	10	18	34
Food	x	53	68	45	20
Miscellaneous	458	370	1,270xx	460	817
Totals	142,349	140,248	172,213	201,310	204,220
Wassermann					
Syphilis Serology	489,726	455,190	415,162	376,559	370,019
Rabies	672	616	632	691	696
Totals	490,398	455,806	415,794	377,250	370,715

Virus

Virus Isolations	400	528	280	331	779
Virus Serology	528	2,423	6,172	5,416	2,581
Encephalitis Program	1,904	3,633	3,687	4,260	1,567
Rubella Program	975	1,166	4,791	4,832	7,700
Totals	3,807	7,750	14,930	14,839	12,627

Metabolic Disorders

PKU Screening	190,527	204,761	203,540	229,945	203,939
Special Studies	16,719	114,933	131,583	3,588	3,756
Totals	207,246	319,694	335,123	233,533	207,695
Grand Totals	843,800	923,498	938,060	826,932	795,257

x Included under Miscellaneous prior to Fiscal 1969
xx Includes 900 Gonococcus Cultures
xxx Includes Gonococcus cultures plus smears

Exhibit 5 (continued)

Laboratory Improvement Program

During FY 1972 a total of 277 local laboratories — 30 more than FY 1971 — were evaluated for the performance of one or more specified test categories. The total number of proficiency test specimens sent out by the Program throughout the year was 23, 138, and the average number received by each participating laboratory was 83. Evaluations were conducted in 6 different broad testing categories: *Bacteriology Cultures, Clinical Chemistry, Hematology, Immunohematology, Syphilis Serology,* and *Miscellaneous - (non-syphilis) Serology*.

For the first time, blood specimens that were positive and negative for hepatitis-associated antigen (HAA) were sent to all laboratories in institutions having blood banks. In general the participating laboratories performed quite well using this relatively new test procedure. The percentage of laboratories approved for streptococcal cultures dropped from 91% in 1971 to 83% in 1972. Instead of pure cultures, mixed cultures resembling actual clinical specimens were used and laboratories seem to have more difficulty detecting the beta strep than previously. However, the use of simulated throat cultures, though more challenging, probably provides better index of laboratory proficiency than do pure cultures. In enteric bacteriology there was noticeable general improvement in overall performance as compared with the previous year. This apparent improvement may be due to the availability of improved commercial rapid-test media that now seems to be working quite well. With regard to clinical chemistry, arrangements were made to join the New England Regional Proficiency Testing Program conducted by the Connecticut State Health Department Laboratories. This will be advantageous to us in several ways, e.g.

a) It will remove the burden and time involved in the preparation of these test specimens.

b) It will broaden the basis for statistical analyses by incorporating Massachusetts laboratories with those in Connecticut and Maine already participating.

c) It will provide more time for on-site visits to local laboratories for trouble-shooting and follow-up services.

In immunohematology although 100% proficiency is required for successful participation only one of 145 laboratories failed to achieve approval this year. In syphilis serology 22 local laboratories and 3 reference laboratories each received 6 consignments of 10 serum specimens between September and April. In all, 13, 260 such specimens were prepared and forwarded to participating laboratories. Of the total (221) 95% or 210 laboratories were approved, and 11 were not.

A total of seven formal workshops were held for 55 students in hematology, syphilis serology and antibiotic sensitivity testing. In addition, individual bench-type instruction was provided for 30 students and 28 laboratory visits were made by program personnel.

A PHS federal grant supporting the major portion of the program amounting to $55,574 in financial assistance was renewed to June 1, 1973.

Licensure of Independent Clinical Laboratories Under Medicare

During FY 1972 the number of local Massachusetts laboratories certified by the Program increased from 91 to 104. Furthermore new regulations instituted in January 1972 by Social Security Administration required that deficiency reports be sent to each laboratory classified as 7b, i.e., in substantial compliance with regulations but with correctable deficiencies. These deficiency reports must then be returned by each laboratory director along with an acceptable plan of correction of such deficiencies before the certification process can be completed.

One of the new major changes scheduled to go into effect soon will require that all laboratories successfully participate in approved proficiency testing programs in all specialties in which they request (or have) approval. (Under present conditions, doctoral directed laboratories are exempt in those specialties for which the State does not offer a program.) To facilitate the greatly increased workload caused by these new federal requirements in addition to the 13 newly enrolled laboratories, Mrs. Regina Merenda, an experienced medical technologist, was added to the staff, beginning in January 1972.

Summary

In the tests which have to do with infectious diseases, progress has been made over the years in use of more accurate, more definitive, or otherwise more satisfactory tests. In Bacteriology, for example, we are using refinements that methodologists have devised particularly in the diagnosis of enteric pathogens, so important in food poisoning outbreaks, in streptococci, the treatment of which is so important in the control of heart and kidney complications, and in tuberculosis and the other mycobacteria. The Wasser-mann Laboratory is looking forward to further modernizing its program through automation and other means although faced with serious problems of

27

Exhibit 5 (continued)

personnel retraining, retooling, inadequate space, and a severely limited budget. The Virology Laboratory, under the new leadership of Dr. Gilfillan, has an on-going, greatly expanded, capability to aid the diagnosis of nearly all important viral agents. The Encephalitis Field Station is continuing dedicated efforts on its surveillance program and has with the Virus Laboratory been instrumental in the isolation of arthropod-borne viruses of potential importance in the spread of epidemic encephalitis in this area among humans. The Metabolic Disorders Laboratory has continued to expand its search for disorders of metabolism that can be effectively screened in the newborn, along with its routine testing for phenylketonuria (PKU). Finally, the Laboratory Improvement and Medicare Certification Program reports reveal continued progress toward increased proficiency of the clinical laboratories in the State, so necessary for prompt and accurate diagnosis, treatment and prevention of the infectious diseases, as well as for other disabilities.

Important future plans naturally gravitate around the projected new building and the promise it brings for greatly improved facilities, for we have already more than utilized all available space for present operations. Equally urgent, however, is the resolution, or at least amelioration, of the huge administrative problem posed by the enormously increased paper work. While certain reports, reviews, and memoranda, when put in writing, can be of great value — if one can keep up with them in addition to the mass of letters and minor administrative matters that take up so much of the day anyhow — the professional scientist, in his administrative capacity, tends too much to do so at the expense of not being able to use his professional knowledge in the even more important day-to-day running of the laboratory itself. This need for available time for the Division Director (or Acting Director) and the Chiefs of Laboratories to insure real quality in the laboratory work as a whole, whether it is in the field of accuracy, needed change, or to develop new programs, is so important that a plea is made that somehow means be devised to very substantially decrease the total exchange of written reports, communications, and even a number of routine meetings, wherever it is at all feasible to do so.

SOME MANAGEMENT QUESTIONS

1. Marketing: Who is really the market for the state labs—the community, the physicians, the end users?

How would one find out about the nature and the extent of the market?

To what extent is goodwill tied up with use of services or products?

What does it cost to provide a given level of service or product?

What would the effect be if any of these were stopped? i.e., what is the interdependency of the current market?

What is likely to be the future market of products or services? He is talking about moving from providing lab testing and certain kinds of hard products to providing a new kind of service, i.e., quality and cost control.

To what extent is this realistic, is there indeed a market for this kind of service?

Who would determine this market, i.e., can he determine it or will it have to be determined by legislative action?

How would he mobilize to get support for such legislative action if required?

2. Operations Management: What are the current operations of the labs and how efficient are they?

To what extent is he making best use of the skill resources available? To what extent could he increase productivity in some areas with fewer personnel, thus releasing resources?

What kinds of simple studies might be performed to find out about productivity and work flow?

To what extent could he contract out further services to others under some kind of supervision, i.e., is the cost differential he describes inevitable in certain kinds of size operation?

How would he find out about the relationship between size of a lab operation and costs? How feasible would it be to set up a pilot operation to look into methods of obtaining higher productivities and establishing the relationship between cost and volume?

3. Finance: To what extent is Madoff locked into certain patterns of functioning because of the poverty concept?

How would he be affected by future competition in this area?

Would it be feasible or possible politically or financially to begin to charge for any of the services that he performs? Should this be on a fee for service basis or on a contract basis or on a user basis?

How would he establish the costs of doing some of the new functions he talks about? Where could he raise the money for doing so; would it have to be the state or could he obtain other kinds of financing, i.e., federal or even private? If he wanted to go into R and D on marginal areas, would it be feasible or possible or politically desirable to obtain support from some of the large pharmaceutical companies and do this under some kind of contract for them?

4. Organizational: What are the current feelings of his staff about the situation that they are in right now, and how much do they know about the kinds of questions that he is raising?

How would he take an inventory of his professional and managerial skills?

How would he enable some of his middle and senior people to acquire management skills so that they could take a look themselves at their own operation?

Would this involve the acquisition of new kinds of personnel or could he retain the ones that he has? To what extent is civil service likely to stultify this?

How transferable are the current professional skills in his labs?

To what extent would there be likely to be resistance to any of the changes he proposes and how might he ascertain this and deal with it?

Could he set up a different kind of organization no longer based on functional distinctions but along some other kind of lines that might be more compatible with the goal that he is setting, i.e., is the current organizational setup appropriate to the future objectives?

To what extent should he set up any kind of control system?

What are the incentives currently existing to reinforce present behavior and how could he set up new kinds of incentives to encourage the change to the kind of behavior that he feels might be desirable?

Should a retraining or management program be inhouse or out of house?

CHAPTER 2

MANAGERIAL VALUES AND ORGANIZATIONAL MOTIVATION

Values permeate organizations; and conflicts between ends and means, between this group and that, between this organization and that are as much rooted in value differences as in questions of fact (Harrison, 1972). Conflicts erupt which take the form of dialogue (or diatribe) about fact, but really represent different values, especially values concerning power, who should have it and how it should be exercised. More subtle may be the erosion of personal by organizational values where the conflict is latent.

This chapter starts with a discussion of values and value conflict. A manager makes characteristic choices and decisions in any situation where alternatives may be available, as much on the basis of personal and professional values as on the dictates of the task. Since there is usually no one best way to do anything, nor any single technology which may be used to accomplish results, choices must be made between equally effective alternatives, and these choices usually get made on a value basis. There is nothing wrong with this although it is better to be aware that values are involved and to be explicit about them, rather than implicit and unconscious. These values may often be cultural or professional in origin. This chapter contrasts U.S. and British values as they have influenced, for example, mental health services in the two countries, and outlines the particular values of physicians and researchers. Successful organizational change may depend on recognition of value consonance and dissonance (Chapter 5).

Last, values determine motivation. What someone cares about is what turns him on. If a manager wishes to motivate people, he must be aware of their values either as sources of support or resistance of his intentions. This chapter concludes with a brief survey of motivational approaches.

VALUES AND VALUE CONFLICT

Thomas More became for me a man with an adamatine sense of his own self. He knew where he began and left off, what area of himself he could yield to the encroachments of his enemies, and what to the encroachments of those he loved. It was a substantial area in both cases, for he had a proper sense of fear and he was a very busy lover. Since he was a clever man and a great lawyer he was able to retire from those areas in wonderfully good order, but at length he was asked to retreat from that final area where he located his self. And there this supple, humorous, unassuming and sophisticated person set like metal, was overtaken by an absolutely primitive rigor, and could no more be budged than a cliff.

(Bolt, 1960)

The issue of managerial values is critical not only because characteristic managerial decisions are value-based, but because any manager has to be something of a politician to successfully reconcile the conflicting values of others. Once a politician, there is the necessity for compromise, for the subordination of cherished values to those of others and to the dictates of expediency. Thomas More was the manager-politician par excellence who knew where and when he had to compromise and he was enormously successful. But he knew also that small important area of himself which could not be yielded up to others. In these days of expediency, it is only too easy to make a succession of small compromises without realizing that one has lost oneself at some point along the way. Silent loyalty has limits, and at some point, personal distaste for organizational acts may necessitate exit, or the perhaps more difficult step of public dissent (Bennis, 1973a).

In the face of uncertainty and complexity, decisions and choices require making simplifying assumptions about the world. These embody central values, personal or professional, and stake out interests. This is often forgotten, and the assumptions are treated as though real, and therefore based on fact rather than value and interest.

Take the concept of need. Health care systems are supposed better to reflect the patient's need, or the community's need. But the physician defines need as what he happens to treat and like treating (his territory). The epidemiologist defines need as what he happens to be able to measure, e.g., incidence and prevalence. The planner likewise defines need as anything that he can measure in some halfway convincing fashion. The community defines need as those conditions that they wish would go away, like the drug addict on the corner. These are usually visible conditions and it is ironic that there may be innumerable alcoholics invisible in middle class living rooms, but there is much more fuss about the much smaller number of drug addicts. The patient defines need as what he has at the moment. The politician defines need as whatever is fashionable right now, i.e., who is screaming loudest about what. The academic defines need as what is currently being funded for grants. So need reflects a set of powerful interests and values and is a relative concept. It is absurd to attempt to define it operationally as though it existed as some absolute and objective phenomenon.

These simplifying assumptions about the world do provide stability and continuity and reflect tradition as they become embodied in ways of operating. But they inevitably also fall short of reflecting the true complexity of the world, and so are impervious to change, however much needed, when the world changes.

When the ways of operating are challenged, what is really at stake are values and interests. Symptomatic of their underlying the apparent issues, is that instead of problem solving taking place (what shall we do for the best), there is a regurgitation of rhetoric and mouthing of myths. Dialogue is characterized by pseudosemantics, in which people believe they are talking about the same thing but no one really bothers, or wishes, to find out. Rather than real change, there tends to be pseudo reorganization with only the appearance of change. What "loss of autonomy" or "evils of centralization (regionalization, federalization)" means, whether said by industrial manager or physician, is leave me alone.

Many physicians have a high value for autonomy, and believe that they should have unchallenged authority to make clinical medical decisions. This is reflected in their protection of the doctor-patient relationship (e.g., in law) and the form of reimbursement of fee for service deriving from that relationship. Challenge of cost structures and methods potentially undermines that authority. The Peer Review Problem Case contrasts the traditional medical (A.M.A.) view of controls, which states that only the physician's peers understand what he does well enough to control the controls, with that of Nader who is skeptical about the effectiveness of this and believes that others should have a hand on the controls. The Medical Foundation (Foundation for Health Evaluation Case) is an example of a new kind of organization which allows physicians to practice in traditional ways while being eligible for new forms of funding such as HMO grants.

The problem of differing values, known or unknown, expressed or unexpressed, based on different assumptions, may well lead to conflict. This conflict, involving turbulence and discomfort, is inevitable because different interests and identities are involved. Coping with it is crucial for any effective manager, for too often the response of one to another's value difference is to argue against it on a point of fact or to put down the other's position as one both foreign and offensive. Since these differences of view may well be coming from people who are in fact strange to oneself, and this experience must now be common for many members of boards of trustees joined by representatives of ghettos, or hospital administrators attempting to cope with community boards, a defensive attitude is only too understandable. Yet a real attempt to comprehend the other's position and not only this but to demonstrate to them an acceptance or their point of view, while acknowledging that one's own is different seems to be crucial.

VALUES AND CULTURE

A complex organization is the product of interaction between a social system and a technological system. Since there is generally a range of technologies available (or of their elements) and of organizational structures, there will be a range of choices limited in some degree by the specificity of the technology or by the efficiency required. Thus Trist *et al.* (1963) demonstrated that a relatively specific technology—coal mining—still allowed for two distinct social organizations to develop in highly proximate mines. The less limited the choices between technological alternatives and between social system alternatives, the more strongly will they be influenced by social and cultural factors.

Psychiatric treatment, regarded as a technology, is highly nonspecific. There is no evidence which unequivocally supports a preferred technique for treating any specific disorder or any specific psychiatric patient, let alone all psychiatric patients. Nor is there any evidence to support any particular organization of psychiatric services. Psychiatric services could be expected to be heavily influenced by the prevailing social and cultural norms in society.

The use of a technology—the actual effectiveness of which is ambiguous at least—leads to a rationalization of its function and there will be a tendency for its value to be seen in terms of social utility rather than any more specific function. For example, it is important to differentiate between the use of E.S.T. as a method of social control and as a specific treatment for depression, if its use in a milieu is being assessed. One reason for techniques to outlive their proved (or disproved) usefulness lies in a failure to make just this distinction.

In general, in the United States, psychiatric care is characterized by fairly rigid legislative control of a large segment of patients and decentralization of power and authority. In Britain there is far less legislative control of the patient and a much greater degree of centralization of authority. Relationships between facilities in the United States (often under different administrative controls) tend to be informal while in Great Britain, such facilities tend to be under single formal administrative control. There is much greater emphasis in the United States on private practice and less on the administrative responsibilities in the professional, while in Great Britain the reverse is true. Treatment in the United States tends to be split between a psychotherapeutic approach for the higher socioeconomic groups and an organic, institutional approach for the lower socioeconomic groups. In Britain there is a greater emphasis on the social milieu and on a somewhat more catholic approach to treatment. In the United States, individuals at all levels participate in the planning process, and services reflect the needs of communities to a greater extent than in Britain.

The American political system reflects a particular view of the citizen which is taken by the body politic and which is well summarized by Banfield and Wilson (1963) who say:

It is characteristic of the American political system that everyone has a right and even a positive obligation to 'get in on the act' of running the government. As heirs to the Protestant tradition, a great many Americans believe that they owe a debt of service to the community: participating in public affairs is one of the ways in which those Americans discharge their obligation to 'do good.' As heirs to the frontier and Jacksonian democracy, they believe, too, that the ordinary citizen is qualified to decide any matter of public importance. And, as we have just seen, politics in America has always been a form of mass entertainment. For all these reasons and more, the public business is everybody's business to an extent that would astonish other democratic peoples, even the English.

The British system stands in interesting contrast to this. Of course, the population is much smaller (it has not always been), and some political institutions are much older, but even allowing for this the genre of political actions is much different. In general, it has become more and more true that power and authority have become centralized into a single legislating administration. The judiciary is rarely drawn into the political arena because there are no constitutional issues at stake. There is, of course, a developed system of local government, but, in general, this is equally concerned with carrying through centrally made and legislated plans as with initiating purely local business. Thus in many activities such as education and health, the local government acts as the agent of national government. The relationship is a discreetly balanced one, but initiative in general is from the center to the periphery and not vice versa.

While the will of the people is preserved in open elections, the choice of candidate is not up to the individual but to a small and select group from within either of the major parties. In addition, the parties are differentiated on a number of major doctrinal issues, and party whips ensure that Members of Parliament vote the party line.

Generally, in America, political action is a means used to forward social action; in Britain social action may be the means to advance party policy. The committed citizen in the United States may belong to the Civil Rights' movement or to the D.A.R., but his counterpart in Great Britain is a socialist or a tory. Although both societies adhere to the democratic ideal, in the United States this is perceived as requiring a complex dispersion of power and authority while in Britain the tendency is to arrange things on a fairly simple hierarchical system, which leads to the centralization of power.

The political parties in the United States frequently call upon the idealized values of freedom and democracy in support of their various programs, and emphasize the individualism, independence, and autonomy of the individual. However, the need to maintain simple unifying values in a pluralistic society leads to considerable conflict for the political system, let alone society itself, covertly denies the realization of these values.

In Britain, values tend to be much less homogeneous and like society itself, despite recent movement, are still class-stratified, and so reflected in the two major parties. Willmott and Young (1960), in their study of a London suburb, say:

> The two classes live in the same kind of district, often in the same kind of houses and have much the same kind of hopes for their children. One can see what Hoggart meant when he talked about 'our emerging classlessness.'
>
> And yet these are only the outward and visible signs of class. Inside people's minds, the boundaries of class are still closely drawn. Classlessness is not emerging there. On the contrary, the nearer the classes are drawn by the objective facts of income, style of life and housing, the more are middle-class people liable to pull them apart by exaggerating the differences subjectively regarded.

These value differences are reflected in a study by Barker (1961), in which similar locations in the United States and Britain were compared. He found that there were relatively many more "settings" for people in a small U.S. town ("Midwest") than in a similar town in Britain ("Yoredale") and that there was a much greater degree of homogeneity. Thus he concludes:

> The importance of all kinds of people, including children, is clearly visible in Midwest . . . In the Midwest system the all-round person, the adjustable person, the person who is willing to do his part even when he cannot do it very well, has a higher value than in the Yoredale system. It is these versatile willing people who make the Midwest system function, and they reap much approval and many satisfactions within the town's behavior settings . . . we can summarize these findings in two general statements:
> 1) People are functionally more important in Midwest than in Yoredale; and
> 2) Differences between people are functionally less important in Midwest than in Yoredale.

In America, this emphasis on individualism and autonomy and distaste for dependency is paralleled by an informality and a gregariousness which is quite consonant with the conflicting demands deriving from the value given to equality on the one hand and the necessity for some form of differentiation on the other hand. Lerner (1958) commented that:

> By joining [a person] finds status, and means for measuring social distance.

In Britain, values are locked into the social structure and people are able to "place" each other quite simply, regardless of the social context. There is thus less necessity to "belong" since the structure itself provides a means for estimating social distance, and the structural limits indeed may allow for a greater degree of individuality, amounting even to eccentricity.

The values of individualism and autonomy and participation seen both in the political system (in the behavior of electorate and elected) and as a general value running through American society are reflected in the participation of the individual citizen at many levels in the psychiatric care system and in the informality and decentralization of the administrative structure. The primary form of treatment again emphasizes the value set on the independence of the individual, while the distaste for dependency is reflected perhaps in the paucity of after-care services for those who have returned to society. In Britain, society itself provides the structure as does the highly centralized psychiatric care system and there is relatively little concern for the expression of needs on the part of the individual (who knows his place) or of the community.

PHYSICIANS:
PROFESSIONALIZATION AND VALUE SYSTEMS

The major professions, medicine, law, and the church, emerged in the 19th century from the trades and crafts. In those early days, patronage and a liberal education (the education of a gentleman, not that of a trader or an artisan) were all that were required and the physician's chief professional asset was:

> . . . an impressive manner, bolstered by experience and guarded by elaborate etiquette, of which one of the cardinal rules was to make certain that the patient knew of no difference of opinion that might arise in consultation. No doubt that was good for the patient's peace of mind, but was that the only consideration? "I was dining at the Duke of Richmond's one day last winter," wrote the physician Thomas Young about 1800, "and there came in two notes, one from Sir W. Farquhar, and the other from Dr. Hunter, in answer to an enquiry whether or not His Grace might venture to eat fruit pies or strawberries. I trembled for the honour of the profession, and could not conceal my apprehension from the company; luckily, however, they agreed tolerably well, the only difference of opinion being on the subject of the pie-crust."
>
> (Reader, 1966)

By 1860 or thereabouts,

> . . . the elements of professional standing were tolerably clear. You needed a professional association to focus opinion, work up a body of knowledge, and insist upon a decent standard of conduct. If possible, and so soon as possible, it should have a Royal Charter as a mark of recognition. The final step, if you could manage it—it was very difficult—was to persuade Parliament to pass an Act conferring something like monopoly powers on duly qualified practitioners, which meant practitioners who had followed a recognized course of training and passed recognized examinations.
>
> (Ibid.)

A profession is an occupation based on specialized intellectual study and training, involving the practice of a definite technique, and supported by a fund of knowledge organized in an internally consistent system called a body of theory (Vollmer and Mills, 1966). Hitherto, the professional has assumed authority in the specific sphere of his expertise and the client has not been considered able to diagnose his own needs, discriminate among the range of possibilities for meeting them, or evaluate the results. These assumptions are now open to question, as the power of the expert diminishes where difficulties become amenable to rational prediction (Crozier,

1964). Professions could once be differentiated on the basis of the "most character-istic professional act," but not so any longer (Vollmer and Mills, 1966). The surgeon today must be as adept at the handling of electronic equipment as at operating, and the senior physician or medical school dean must be more a manager than a physician. The equation of specific skill or technique with profession is rendered obsolete under the impact of the rapidly changing technologies of today.

These traditional professions developed a specialized variety of business morality called professional ethics or etiquette, since what a professional man sells is expert advice, generally on confidential matters, where probity is essential. The profes-sional code of ethics serves not only to regulate the professional's possibly erring behavior, but also to regulate deviations of a more positive kind.

The informal milieu of the profession also serves to control variance and entry into the profession at all points of the career. The practice of ritual (to diminish risk) and the exercise of power by an energetic minority are further constraints not only on the profession but the health care system in general. (Vollmer and Mills, 1966). These constraints are now being attacked by the consumer sector of society.

Traditionally, physicians have been solo practitioners charging a fee for service, (Freidson, 1970b). The economics of this led to a concern for pleasing the patient, giving them essentially the treatment they wished, and a referral system in which there was pressure on the specialist to please the general practitioner. The setting affects performance much more than personality or education. The system leads to an increase in the number of services and a lower quality. Professionals are free to control content although the terms of work may vary. There is control of perform-ance by the professional and professional bureaucracies. There is not really that much uncertainty, risk, or judgment involved. The prevailing values are those of independence, autonomy, and action, and the physician has reached a legal position of privilege through licensing. The professions provide an esoteric service to a client who cannot handle it, whose judgment of need is amateur, and thus there is secrecy in formal institutions. The professional dominance of authority requires faith and trust.

The segmental view, the need to control and monopolize, the eradication of emotion, the educated incapacity to realize that one will be old or sick or die or a grieving member of a family are all brought into question by the newer technologies and by needs now being voiced. The broad view, interdependency, the serial acquisition of skills exercised by capacity rather than by membership, the com-mitment to caring, and credibility based on who one is and how competent rather than on a label are now more cogent. It is more important to help someone face death than to practice the ritual (and safe) exercise of dramatic and futile techniques.

The need for legitimating new skills, especially expertise in the management of human behavior at all levels (ask a physician and he says he teaches, researches, or gives service but rarely that he manages), brings into serious question whether the solution is change in the professions, new professions or subprofessions (inevitably under the thumb of medicine since only a doctor supposedly has ultimate responsibility), or the radical remaking of an outmoded mechanism. Perhaps the whole notion of a profession, residing in the acquisition of so much useless knowledge, with so much concern for status and so much futile bickering, as a fruitful societal mechanism should be questioned. This is yet virgin territory. Tentative nudges have been made at the established curriculum—ironically in the direction of yet earlier specialization.

There is, though, a serious problem that has to be faced in thinking about such a radical remaking. The development of professional identity is a source of stability, and if it is usurped by a serial skill approach, individuals will need a matrix which offers much greater emotional support than the current framework. Assumptions learned early are difficult to question later when enmeshed in the system, and when they are attacked from without, however justifiably, they tend to be met with defensiveness.

RESEARCHERS: VALUES AND MOTIVATION

Gordon (1966a,b), a prolific "early" writer on the subject, points out that science has been institutionalized as a management-free operation with a high degree of autonomy. It is difficult to measure scientific accomplishments. It may be desirable to organize research successfully, but how do we know when we have done it? Gordon suggests four criteria: (1) the importance of the research problem; (2) its productiveness; (3) its innovativeness; and (4) its overall significance. Commonly used criteria include acknowledged major contributions, assessment by co-workers, and number of publications or patients. Gordon's review of the field found that the major values of science included the freedom to do what one cared about, free from administration, open access to the literature of one's colleagues, and an organization that places emphasis on the individual rather than the team. Thus, scientists reject the very controls which were found (in both his own studies and those of a number of others) to facilitate major breakthroughs rather than hinder innovation. Conclusions include the suggestion that for predictable research, group responsibility is desirable, but unpredictable research requires individual responsibility. A research team should not only include the usual mixture of disciplines where required, but recognize that different people possessed different skills and that in particular there were problem solvers and problem recognizers and both were required.

Much of the research on research has been done in industry where the research and development department has to pay off. Scientists in industry have a problem shared by some of their fellows in the academic world in that they have to pursue simultaneous organizational and professional careers. Perhaps for them the issue is a little more clear-cut, for in academia the prominent researcher often finds himself willy-nilly consumed by administration, while in industry a more vivid choice must be made at some point. Glaser (1964) studied the professional careers of organizational scientists and found that highly motivated scientists valued both research and nonresearch activities. He compared contrasting reward systems and felt that a routine mechanism stabilized more than one depending on the recommendations of one's superiors. In addition, an important reward was a succession of constellations of working conditions that provided opportunities. Pelz and Andrews (1966), in a classic study, came to somewhat similar conclusions summarized below:

> Effective scientists were self-directed by their own ideas, and valued freedom. But at the time, they allowed several other people a voice in shaping their directions; they interacted vigorously with colleagues.

> Effective scientists did not limit their activities either to the world of 'application' or to the world of 'pure science' but maintained an interest in both; their work was diversified.

> Effective scientists were not fully in agreement with their organization in terms of their interests; what they personally enjoyed did not necessarily help them advance in the structure.

> Effective scientists tended to be motivated by the same kinds of things as their colleagues. At the same time, however, they differed from their colleagues in the styles and strategies with which they approached their work.

> In effective older groups, the members interacted vigorously and preferred each other as collaborators, yet they held each other at an emotional distance and felt free to disagree on technical strategies. Thus in numerous ways, the scientists and engineers whom we studied did effective work under conditions that were not completely comfortable, but contained 'creative tensions' among forces pulling in different directions.

Crosby (1968) studied creativity and performance in industrial organizations and concluded that original persons prefer complexity and some imbalance in phenomena; they are more complex as persons, more independent in judgment, more self-assertive, and reject suppression as a means of controlling impulse. He concluded that:

> Traits of the creative person seen in his perceptual behavior:
> (a) tolerance of ambiguity
>   (1) preference for complexity in phenomena
>   (2) preference for imbalance in phenomena
>   (3) openness for variety in phenomena
> (b) breadth of interest
> (c) perceptual control
>   (1) flexibility
>   (2) deferment of judgment.

> Traits of the creative person seen in his awareness of himself:
> (a) personal complexity

(b) rejection of suppression as a means of controlling impulses
(c) accommodation of some feminine interests and impulses
(d) exploitation of hedonic response,

And his traits seen in interaction with others are:
(a) self-assertion; tendency to dominate through drive
(b) verbal fluency
(c) impulsiveness
(d) expansiveness
(e) non-conformity
(f) tendency to release tension readily through motor activity
(g) feminity in some interests and reactions
(h) independence of judgment.

Traits of the creative person seen in his motivation:
(a) rapid personal tempo
(b) high level of drive.

One can easily see from this why creative scientists reject controls. But since stable organizations develop mechanistic forms with a high degree of control, this is inevitably inimical to innovation. He therefore suggests that under such circumstances innovative task activities should be centralized in a single unit to form a locus of influence. This, of course, facilitates creativeness, but potentially creates a barrier between the creative group and the rest of the organization.

Smith's work (1966) is interesting for its revelation of the administrative contrivances by which the Rand Corporation was able to institutionalize the needs of creative scientists and yet maintain some semblance of control. The organizational hierarchy was inevitably quite flat; but this created problems, while reducing the prevalence of authority, because the units were based on disciplines and projects requiring inter-unit collaboration received lower priority than those engaging only the unit. The reason for this preference was that status obviously lay in the peer group and in professional recognition. This imbalance was to some degree counteracted by the establishment of an advisory board which had some power to legitimate inter-unit collaboration and to sanction resources for such projects.

Among the organizational solutions to the technology transfer problem are Bell's use (Cockcroft, 1965) of organizational separation but physical proximity of basic research and applied groups. Another alternative is the shifting of those who invent over to the application phase so that they take their ideas with them.

MOTIVATION

A manager's job involves acting largely through, or with, others and that almost invariably means getting others to behave in some way that he regards as appropriate to the organization's ends. Any organization will have natural incentives and disincentives built in. Thus, Freidson (1970b) points out that fee for service as an incentive encourages the physician to please the patient and give him whatever treatment he wishes. But in health organizations these incentives have, for the most part, never been harnessed systematically towards defined ends. The design of control and incentive systems are discussed in part of Chapter 3 on the structure of organizations and the function of operating mechanisms. The two main inputs to incentive system design are (1) desired ends (behavior), and (2) the motivation of the organization's members. While the specific values of researchers and physicians have been discussed above, the major general approaches to motivation need no more than brief treatment, since these have been well covered in many textbooks.

The importance of well-designed motivational systems should be only too apparent. Health maintenance organizations (HMO) are being set up at considerable cost all over the United States. While one purpose is to prevent expensive hospitalization by developing alternatives, another is to get health care professionals to treat people while they are well and thus minimize morbidity and its expense. For an HMO to function effectively, the health professionals involved will have to behave towards the patient, towards their task, and towards each other differently from usual, or they will largely fail. If a patient is discharged from a hospital late in the afternoon, it is not unknown for nurses to fail to inform the discharge office until the following morning because they dislike admitting new patients with all the tedious form filling involved toward the end of the day. The result may well be one unfilled patient bed that night; over many weeks a not insignificant loss in revenue can be attributed to this very human failing. Physicians dislike the bureaucratic necessity of completing discharge summaries. The mere cost of having to remind them is not insubstantial, let alone possible delays in billing and collecting reimbursements. In each instance, an effective manager would have to consider how, in the knowledge of the values and motivations of these groups of people, he could improve his organization's performance by encouraging an appropriate change in behavior.

In the Stephen Doyle case, a hospital administrator faces a common problem. Selection and recruitment were not particularly amiss, for the emergency room clerks are neither over- nor under qualified for their jobs. Apparently no measurement or reward system exists to encourage adequate performance. There are many possible solutions, covering the gamut from giving clerks more money, through providing some kind of group incentive, to giving them a more challenging job.

Schein (1969) feels that the underlying assumptions behind most major approaches to motivation can be summarized as four approaches to man.

The first of these is the rational-economic man approach. The assumption is that man, driven by economic need, requires incentives from outside, and that workers need to be disciplined for otherwise they will not work. This approach is oriented to the performance of tasks and concerned with organizational structure and authority. It is very much a traditional approach to motivation, popularly referred to as Theory X, and one which Levinson (1973a) has criticized as the great jackass fallacy. Levinson points out that this motivational approach relies on the carrot and the stick and asks the manager to imagine what lies between. Examples of the rational-economic approach include job redesign, competition and bonuses for individuals, and external controls.

The second is the social man approach. This suggests that the manager should meet workers' social needs and be concerned with people. Derivations of this approach have led to such developments as participative management, industrial democracy, and Theory Y. Encounter groups and training groups (T-groups) are based on the principle that effective interpersonal skills are felt to be necessary for good organizational performance. Other examples include group bonuses, bowling teams, and profit sharing such as the Scanlon plan.

The third approach is that of the self-actualizing man. This approach suggests that most people in organizations have in fact secured the satisfaction of many basic needs and are mainly motivated by the opportunity to grow and be challenged. Herzberg (1968) is one of the more prolific writers on this theme and proposes two sets of quite distinct factors. Hygienic factors remedy job disatisfaction, improvement in salary, work conditions, or job security, while motivators increase job satisfaction and essentially provide opportunities for growth and increase in competence (job enrichment).

These approaches really treat all men as alike. They essentially imply that most people are motivated by similar kinds of drives and, therefore, an incentive system based on them will usually work. They treat people as black boxes where it is not particularly necessary to know a great deal about what is in any given black box. The Doyle case is an example of a fashionable Skinnerian positive reinforcement technique in which the manager seeks to influence the desired behavior directly by rewarding it consistently. This is black box par excellence, for it does not even involve the assumptions made by the three motivational approaches above. This approach usually is highly controversial, for it arouses concerns about dehumanization. But it works, and it is cheap. The circumstances under which it might be used, organizational and ethical, are worth considering by the reader.

The problem with each of these approaches is that they are partly right and partly wrong, for while most people have some needs corresponding to each, few people are driven totally by one set of needs. Moreover, each runs the danger of becoming normative, and workers failing to respond to motivational schemes based upon these approaches may well find themselves regarded as deviant.

The most sophisticated and most difficult approach for the manager is that of complex man. This no longer treats the individual as a black box but says that it is the job of the manager to find out the particular motivation of each individual for whom he is responsible, and to use whatever schemes and systems will turn that person on. Thus Thompson and Dalton (1970) point out in a critique of performance appraisal techniques, that different kinds of objectives should be used and different kinds of systems devised to satisfy different individual needs. These systems should not be rigid or zero sum. By zero sum is meant a comparison with others in which one individual can only be rewarded at the expense of another, as compared with a system using measurement against the attainment of management or personal objectives. Motivational approaches describe means by which managers may influence people (see model in Chapter 1). Paradoxically, May (1972) has pointed out that a powerful need that most people have is the need for affirmation. People feel affirmed when they feel that they have been able to influence others. So one of the most powerful tools that the manager has available is to demonstrate to others that they can influence him.

The advantage of these relatively simple approaches (which have certainly grown complex in their application) as described by Schein is that organizations can set up fairly simple systems based on them. The more managers move toward some complex man type of approach, in which they recognize that individuals or groups of individuals may be driven by very different needs, the more there is the need for a broad and flexible range of measurement and incentive systems. The industrial company, Texas Instruments, has done work which shows that there are no less than six categories of workers: the tribalistic, which includes those who respond to strong leadership, who can be happy and dedicated if shown genuine care and concern. The existential group, on the other hand, is comprised for the most part of employees who will do a job only if it is meaningful. While perhaps contentious, the existential employee is usually the brainiest and most creative. Other types are egocentric (entrepreneurial), conformist (tradition-oriented), manipulative (achievement-oriented), and sociocentric (socially-oriented). The implication of these complex approaches to motivation is that different kinds of managers are going to be needed for different kinds of workers, for no one manager can satisfy all these differing needs. This is not impossible in an industrial organization where one may be able to group people by their motivational needs and supply them with supervision suited to them. If there is, as suggested earlier, some commonality of motivation among professional types and yet a need to mix professional skills in a working team, this raises some interesting questions for the ideal kind of managerial style for a health care organization.

The Peer Review Problem

In 1970 both Ralph Nader and the Federal Government challenged the medical profession's age-old privilege of monitoring its own work. This practice, which has doctors monitor the work of their colleagues, is usually referred to as "peer review." Doctors have traditionally been responsible for judgment and quality control in the area of medical practice, and, except in the case of rare malpractice suits, answerable to no one in the event of error.

Nader's "Center for Study of Responsive Law" published a document titled *One Life—One Physician: An Inquiry Into the Medical Profession's Performance in Self-Regulation,* which for the first time examined the "professional, legal, ethical, and moral questions raised by the present system of medical self-policing." The following statement appeared in the preface:

> Both the public and the profession agree that none can better judge the quality of care rendered
> by a physician than a group of his professional peers. Because this delegation of authority has

been accepted by the medical profession, the exercise of this authority becomes an important subject for study: to discover what systems of quality control the profession has established to monitor each physician's service to his patients, to evaluate how well these systems perform, and to determine whether the profession merits the trust with which society has placed itself into the hands, and relied on the hearts, of all its physicians.[1]

Concurrent with the preparation of the Nader study, the quality of health care in the United States was posed as a serious problem by sources as diverse as *Fortune* magazine, President Nixon, and the American Medical Association. Consequently legislation was introduced in Congress which would transfer the responsibility for evaluation of medical practice to government agencies. The AMA, viewing peer review as something of a God-given right, hotly contested this legislation.

The following pages contain a description of the peer review issue as viewed by both the Center for Study of Responsive Law and by the American Medical Association. The first section is a brief review of the continued education of practicing physicians, and the practice of medicine in both hospitals and doctors' offices. Particular notice is paid to related deficiencies in quality control. The Center's conclusions about the quality of physicians' performance are then summarized, and the recommendations presented in *One Life—One Physician* are reproduced in full. Finally, excerpts from the *American Medical News,* are reproduced in full. Finally, excerpts from the *American Medical News,* a weekly AMA sponsored publication, are used to depict the medical profession's position on the subject of peer review.

Part One: The Education, Training and Licensing of Physicians*

Entry to the Profession

The physician practicing in the United States has normally completed four years of undergraduate work, four years of medical school, and one year of internship. (Dr. Osler Peterson of North Carolina has carried out one of the few studies of physician training in which he attempted to measure the correlation between medical school performance, nature of postgraduate training, and subsequent performance as a practicing doctor. The study, reported in 1956 in the *Journal of American Education,* found no significant relationship between quality of practice and grades in medical school.) After obtaining their MD degree, doctors must also pass a licensing examination for the state in which they intend to practice. Almost all graduates of U.S. medical schools pass the examination on the first attempt.[2] Specialists train for an additional 5-6 years, of which at least 3 are residency, and may then eventually join one of the prestigious specialist societies, such as the American College of Surgeons, by

---

*Much of the information used in this section was taken from *One Life-One Physician,* copyright © 1970 by the Center for Study of Responsive Law, Washington, D.C. Material has been reprinted by special permission.

taking an examination administered by the boards of these socieities.

Formal control and evaluation of physicians' performance began in the United States immediately following the Civil War, when laws were passed to establish state boards of medical examiners. These laws have remained virtually unchanged since their passage in the 1870's. The purpose of state boards was to protect both the public and the profession, although some in the profession feel that an unfortunate side effect has been professional stultification, as access to the occupation becomes restricted and the role of the physician becomes more rigidly defined.[3]

The licensing statutes in the 50 states vary considerably in content, but all usually call for the creation of a medical licensing board, appointed by the governor and composed of practicing members of the profession. According to George A. Woodhouse, writing for the *Federation Bulletin:*

> Their function is to assure compliance with minimum qualifications specified in the statutes by supervising the licensure process and policing the practice of medicine. They are empowered to determine the eligibility of candidates for licensure (including review of character and moral fitness, assessment of educational qualifications, administration of examinations, and approval of postgraduate internships); to accredit or approve medical schools; to issue, register, and renew medical licenses; to decide the recognition to be given to licenses of other jurisdictions; to make administrative rules and regulations concerning professional standards; and to suspend, revoke and reinstate licenses in disciplinary proceedings.[4]

The Center for Study of Responsive Law has reported that licensing boards are primarily composed of general practitioners. Although the state statutes define personal and educational qualifications for candidates, often in great detail, the licensing physicians seldom have any previous experience in administering such examinations. Approximately two-fifths of the states require candidates to pass a basic science exam. Physicians may also be tested and licensed by the National Board of Medical Examiners, whose certification is accepted by all the states except Arkansas, Florida, and Georgia; Delaware, Indiana, Louisiana, North Carolina and Texas only accept the certification if the doctors have been licensed in another state as well.

The authors of the *One Life—One Physician* document feel that, particularly given the mobility of today's physicians, more uniform licensing procedures should be established. They include the following reasons: . . . some states are more lenient than others . . . state practices do not always relate to competence. Often they are picayune or appear to be ways of controlling competition.[5]

One possible failing of the current licensing system may be its inability to evaluate the competence of foreign educated doctors who wish to practice medicine in the United States. Foreign graduates frequently fail state licensing exams, yet these tests are at present the only measure of professional competence accepted by state boards.

Recently a great deal of criticism has been directed at the licensing process. Cities have been particularly adamant about the ill-conceived methods of medical discipline. Dr. Robert C. Derbyshire, past president of the Federation of State Medical Boards, commented in the preface to his study of medical licensure:

> As a result of many years of observing medical licensing and discipline in America I have concluded that there is no system. My criticism is similar to that of the people who say that there is no system for the delivery of medical care to the people of America. There are so many variable laws and regulations concerning both initial licensure and discipline of physicians that for all practical purposes the United States is composed of a group of tightly organized kingdoms.[6]

Continuing Education

Because of the constant generation of new scientific knowledge, which often refutes former beliefs and practices, it is essential that practicing doctors continually expose themselves to technical advances in their field. A study of 2090 physicians living in Kansas between 1956 and 1965 revealed, however, that in-state continuing education courses were attended by only half of the state's general practicitioners. Motivating doctors to improve their professional knowledge has been a problem to several American Medical Association officers, as they have consistently found that a significant number of physicians seem uninterested in further education. Although some state medical societies have begun to require continuing education of their members, doctors do not have to be members of a medical society in order to practice and so these requirements do not ensure that doctors will keep up-to-date.

The Physician and the Law

Both the Federal Government and professional medical organizations have recognized the need to protect patients from the incompetent and/or the unethical of the nation's 325,000 doctors. The state licensing boards, in addition to examining prospective physicians, are charged with monitoring the quality of ongoing medical practice. Almost all states require a regular renewal of the physician's license. However, Forgatson, Rolney and Newman reported that this renewal is merely a formality:

> The significant feature of license renewal is not what it entails but what it does not entail. A routine and clerical measure, renewal requires only the signature of the physician and the payment of a nominal fee. No other information is required—no showing of continuing education undertaken or its effect on the physician's skills, and no evidence of the physician's having updated his knowledge and credentials to keep pace with medical progress. Not a single state attempts to prevent educational obsolescence by requiring evidence of further education or professional growth as a condition for maintaining licenses in good standing.[7]

A survey made through the auspices of the American Medical Association in 1961 verified this opinion in a statement about discipline in the medical profession: . . . Medicine's efforts have largely ceased with the discharge of the licensing function. All too seldom are licensed physicians called to task by boards, societies, or colleagues.[8]

The Center for Study of Responsive Law, as part of its inquiry into self-regulation in the medical profession, described the magnitude of the medical discipline problem:

> Frequently, the concept of what medical discipline means in the context of the medical practice acts is at best a confusing matter. The activities of state and county medical societies, hospital staffs and local grievance committees, when they exist, often overlap with state licensing boards in this area. They are all concerned with the conduct of practitioners. But punishing violators of the licensing statute should not be the function of the medical societies or the grievance committee. Only the state boards have jurisdiction over all practitioners in the state. Whether they can or do adequately exercise their disciplinary tasks is another question.[9]

The problem is complicated by differences in the grounds listed by the various states on which a physician's license may be revoked. Dr. Edwin J. Holman, in "The Complex of Unprofessional Conduct," gave the following breakdown:

No one ground, stated in the same words, is to be found in all of the acts, and no law contains all grounds. Nine grounds were found repeatedly in 30 or more state laws. They are: drug addiction, 47; unprofessional conduct, specifically or generally, 45; fraud in connection with examination or licensure, 44; alcoholism, 42; advertising, 40; abortion, 39; conviction of a felony, 38; conviction for an offense involving moral turpitude, 36; mental incapacity, 33.[10]

Several of the above listed grounds, such as "unprofessional conduct," are sufficiently vague that licensing boards have difficulty prosecuting, and, according to the *One Life—One Physician* document, "obvious violations may go unpunished if the statutory language is vague and does not satisfy due process requirements." Unfortunately, most discipline problems are not acted upon by state boards until they reach grave proportions, since the confusing language of state laws leaves licensing boards anxious to act only in clear-cut, and often extreme, situations. State boards are further hindered in their exercise of disciplinary authority by lack of funds, lack of competent investigators, and state legal systems which provide severe penalties rather than rehabilitation for offenders.

When the medical profession's own disciplinary regulations have failed him, the ill-treated patient has recourse to legal action. Malpractice is a civil suit filed by the patient against his hospital or doctor or both. The obvious drawback to this defense against medical incompetence is that it is an action which can be taken by a patient only *after* he has suffered at the hands of a doctor. (Doctors are now required by law to carry malpractice insurance, and the cost of these policies is becoming quite high.)

The American Medical Association and the Local Medical Societies

Out of approximately 325,000 physicians in the United States, 219,570 were members of the American Medical Association (AMA) as of December 1969. As a national organization the AMA does not itself exercise any control of physicians, but instead acts as a consultant to state and county medical societies. AMA proposals and policies may be either accepted or rejected by these local groups. However, membership in the local medical society is often a prerequisite for obtaining hospital staff privileges.

Local medical societies generally include a grievance committee, whose task is to review complaints against a physician by patients, third parties, or another physician. Often these complaints concern medical fees exclusively. The authors of *One Life—One Physician* felt that these committees did little to make themselves known to the public. Once charged with incompetence, however, usually a doctor challenged by his medical society has only been dropped from the ranks of membership; he could, of course, continue to practice medicine. Furthermore, these committees have had no jurisdiction over nonmembers; "Because state medical societies are voluntary professional organizations, they can only impose disciplinary sanctions against those physicians who are members of the medical society."[11] However, "the state or county medical society is the only body other than the state licensing board to which a doctor exclusively engaged in office practice is responsible."[12]

Hospital Regulatory Practices

Physicians who are admitted to the staffs of hospitals come under the jurisdiction of the hospital's Board of Trustees. These governing boards, through the responsibility vested in them by the state, determine who gets what staff privileges. They have, in effect, an employer-employee type of relationship with the doctors, and thus are responsible for the quality of activities performed by their hospital staff.

According to Dr. Avedis Donabedian, a professor in the School of Public Health at the University of Michigan, "Patients' records are almost always the source of information in formal procedures of evaluating care."[13] He inferred, however, that the type and extent of information given varied from record to record, making reviews difficult in terms of set standards.

The Joint Commission on Accreditation of Hospitals (JCAH) was formed in 1952 to serve as, in the words of the *One Life—One Physician* document, "the quasi-official medical auditing organization for hospital practice." The JCAH was really a continuation of American College of Surgeons' activities practiced since the early part of the century. It is sponsored by the American Medical Association, the American Hospital Association (each of which appoints seven commissioners), and the American College of Physicians and American College of Surgeons (which appont three commissioners each). The study by the Center for the Study of Responsive Law reports:

"The seven AMA members are constituted as an ad hoc Committee of the Board of Trustees of the AMA, and as such report to and are advised by the Board of Trustees on all policy matters coming before the Joint Commission."[14] The commissioners determine what the policies of JCAH will be. Of the current 22 commissioners, 18 are MD's. Further, "The extent to which the commissioners act as representatives of their organizations, rather than as individuals, varies both with the question on the table and with the man." Dr. John D. Porterfield, JCAH director, has said that 'where an organization's house of delegates has taken a firm stand on a question, its commissioners feel obliged to vote that position, regardless of their own opinions. Often the commissioners from the AMA and the AHA are polarized, leaving the specialists either to arrange a compromise or to cast the swing votes."[15]

Participation in the JCAH is voluntary, and so desire for professional prestige is a major factor in motivating hospitals to seek accreditation, as well as eligibility for internship and residency programs. In 1969, 4906 hospitals (out of 7137), or 69% of all U.S. hospitals, had sought and received JCAH accreditation. Dr. Porterfield, JCAH director, had said that accreditation is directed at the hospital environment rather than with quality of medical care, since direct interference with the activities of the doctors themselves is not politically possible. However, in 1970 a new set of standards was approved for use by the JCAH, and according to Dr. Porterfield, "the one most fundamental requirement in the whole code is that each organized hospital medical staff regularly, currently, conscientiously, and critically review and evaluate the clinical work done in the hospital by each of its members."[16] Several of the standards included in this code are fairly specific on the subject of peer review:

Criteria for evaluating medical care must be established . . . the formal means . . . varies with the size and organizational structure of the hospital . . . the medical staff must provide an appropriate peer group method by which the required basic functions of medical, surgical and obstetrical audit are thoroughly performed at least monthly. Included in this audit must be the analysis of necropsy reports and a tissue review.

There *shall* be regular medical staff and departmental meetings to review clinical work of members . . . [D]epartmental meetings must be held monthly to review the care and treatment of patients served by the hospital. This review *should* include consideration of selected deaths, unimproved patients, patients with infections, complications, errors in diagnosis and treatment.[17]

Dr. Porterfield noted, however, that "the survey procedures are as important as the code." Dr. Stone, assistant director of JCAH, explained that there were no set standards for surveyors who were mostly older and/or retired physicians. Surveyors spend from two to four days at a hospital, depending on its size, although JCAH will soon begin to use survey teams rather than individuals for approximately half of the accreditation visits.

Most hospitals currently practice a form of peer review in their use of tissue committees. The *One Life—One Physician* report describes these monitoring devices as follows: "The function of this type of committee is to reduce needless surgery by careful review—and criticism, if necessary—of operations in which tissue has been removed." These groups, however, are voluntary and not subject to review by outsiders.

Commission on Professional and Hospital Activities

The Commission on Professional and Hospital Activities, with a voluntary membership of over 1300 hospitals, is sponsored by the American College of Physicians, American College of Surgeons, American Hospital Association, and the Southwestern Michigan Hospital Council. The Center for the Study of Responsive Law describes its activities as follows:

> The major services provided by CPHA are the Professional Activity Study (PAS) and the Medical Audit Program (MAP). PAS is a program in which the medical recording personnel of a participating hospital use the usual clinical records of a patient's stay in the hospital to fill out a PAS case abstract form. These case abstract forms are mailed to the CPHA offices in Ann Arbor, Michigan, where they are processed by computer systems. Standard reports are prepared and mailed to each participating hospital for analysis by the administration and staff of the hospital. The tabulations, providing a display of practice, are mailed out monthly and semi-annually.

> At the same time, CPHA is accumulating a huge library of case abstracts, now numbering over 50 million individual records of hospitalizations. This body of data is computer analyzed and is used in comparisons among the various hospitals participating in the study.

> The second major service provided by CPHA is the Medical Audit Program (MAP). CPHA defines a medical audit as a system of continuing medical education based on the evaluation of the quality of medical care as reflected in the medical records. The quality of the medical care delivered is to be determined by comparing the care given in a particular hospital to previously agreed upon written standards. These standards are to be the widely accepted principles and practices such as those found in textbooks.

> The system works in this way. The CPHA computer processes the case abstracts submitted by the hospital and produces quarterly tabulations called PAS-MAP reports. These reports, which are analyses of hospitalizations during a three month period of time, consist of eight separate packages organized by clinical services and types of surgery. The reports are then given to the hospital internal medical audit committees. These committees are to compare the tabulations of services provided at their hospital with written standards of quality care which the committee staff previously agreed upon. The purpose of the internal audit is to raise the quality of care given at the hospital and to serve as an educational experience for the members of the staff.[18]

All reports are kept confidential between the CPHA and the hospital. CPHA also distributes a report to all participating hospitals which contains computer-derived statistical summaries of various parameters of the care being provided in member hospitals (hospitals are not identified by name). CPHA does not pretend, however, to be more than an aid to hospitals trying to ensure high quality medical care themselves.

The Private Physician

In the March-April 1968 issue of *Medical Care,* Dr. Kerr L. White summed up the situation regarding review of privately practicing physicians:

> When it comes to disease and problems seen by doctors in their offices or in clinics, emergency rooms, or outpatient departments, an ever greater mystery is encountered. Virtually nothing is known about what doctors and nurses do for ambulatory patients. This is not a matter of invading the privacy and confidentiality of the patient-physician relationship, but of developing information about the content of medical practice, the accomplishment of end-results and the organization of responsible health services arrangements to meet the needs of the people . . . Apart from the National Disease and Therapeutic Index, a marketing survey, the desultory reporting of notifiable communicable disease and data collected by a few group health plans, there is virtually no information available about complaints, symptoms, problems, or diseases brought to doctors in their offices and clinics.[19]

Part Two: The Center for the Study of Responsive Law on Peer Review*

The authors of *One Life—One Physician* cite the fragmented nature of the medical system in the United States as a cause of difficulty in assessing the general quality of medical care. Differences in state licensing standards, hospital practices, and the total nonregulation of private physicians contribute to this lack of uniformity. Examples of case studies are given which reveal differing quality between types of hospitals (university, community, and private). The study concludes that:

> No one knows the full extent of the consequent unnecessary disability and death which seriously impair the right of each person to "life, liberty, and the pursuit of happiness." No one knows because no system of data collection exists by which the extent might be determined . . .

> While the poor and rural segments of the population may suffer most by being deprived of any health care, no citizen can be secure in the belief that he will automatically receive good care. Every citizen is at the mercy of a system devoid of uniform, enforced standards of quality and must run risks implied in the statistics of uneven level of care and hospital and physicians.[20]

With respect to the licensing of physicians, the Center for the Study of Responsive Law criticized the current practice of licensing all physicians via a general examination. The Center felt that licensing boards set only minimum requirements for the specialist, and contained no safeguard against obsolescence of a doctor's medical knowledge. The report states, "Most of the medical practice acts require annual or biennial license renewal that is nothing more than payment of a fee. The physician need not indicate whether he has done anything to keep abreast of medical advances. Even if he received his license in 1930 and has learned nothing since, he is free to practice almost totally unimpeded by law.[21]

The authors of *One Life—One Physician* conclude that medical graduates should be tested on their particular specialized field prior to licensing, and the boards "would

---

*As described in *One Life-One Physician,* © 1970 by the Center for Study of Responsive Law, Washington, Material used by special permission.

grant the physician a license limited to practice in a specified field of medical care." In order to ensure that physicians would keep abreast of medical advances, the study recommends periodic re-examination for doctors who wish to maintain their license to practice. Doctors should:

. . . be re-examined periodically in the narrow or broad field he "professes," that, as a condition to recurrent admittance to examination, he present evidence of continuing formal postgraduate education.[22]

In the case of physicians giving poor quality care to their patients, the authors of *One Life—One Physician* feel that the current disciplinary system is quite inadequate, resulting in action against only the worst offenders. The vague wording of statistics, inadequate staffing and financing of state boards, and harsh punishment for violators are cited as reasons for the ineffectiveness of the system.

The American Medical Association calls itself "a federation of state and local medical organizations." The Center for the Study of Responsive Law contends that, as such, the AMA has certain leadership responsibility. However,

Nothing discovered by our group indicates subsequent AMA fulfillment of responsibility to lead its member societies into more effective use of their disciplinary power to improve the quality of physician performance.[23]

In 1967 a permanent committee for planning and development was founded, called the "Himler Committee" after its chairman. A report was submitted to the AMA Board of Trustees in July of 1969, and made public at the winter meeting of the AMA House of Delegates. The report contained 57 recommendations for changing the AMA's approach to health needs, and emphasized that,

Until and unless the Association addresses itself publicly, actively, and objectively to the resolution of the very concrete problems that exist in health care, its attempts to justify present delivery systems and payment mechanisms will be incomprehensible both to the public and government, and will be interpreted as self-seeking on the part of the profession.[24]

The Himler Committee's report was apparently offensive to a large number of the delegates and further consideration of the proposals was postponed until the annual meeting of the House of Delegates the following June. At this meeting the proposals were rejected. According to the Center study, the Himler Report was "a landmark document of tremendous scope and importance in regard to its subject matter," and the AMA's refusal to accept the recommendation that "the AMA adopt an active role and take the initiative in developing all plans and programs for health care in *all* their ramifications" was seen by the Center as indicative of the Association's general attitude concerning leadership of organized medicine. The Center concluded that "organized medicine is reacting in alarm, and beginning the change in reforms to broad public concern about the cost, availability, and quality of medical care," but, "by 1970 the record clearly demonstrates that organized medicine has not faced up to the responsibilities to, in the words of the AMA Judicial Council, maintain high standards of ethical and professional competence."[25]

In a section titled "Effect of Present Self-Regulatory System," the authors of *One Life—One Physician* ask the question, "Why is it that nothing has been done in self-regulation of treatment given in physicians' offices, where such a major portion of all medical care takes place?" They conclude that an ineffective record-keeping system, plus the unwillingness of physicians to intrude on their colleagues and thus hamper them in their work, are factors preventing any audit of private practices.

The Joint Commission on Accreditation of Hospitals is cited as "the only organization that the medical profession has established to monitor the quality of care, and therefore the only quality control mechanism, for hospitalized patients." Although the JCAH is regarded as effective in its purview of the hospital environment, the Center contends that the JCAH is unable to monitor the quality of physician performance. Peer review is relegated by the JCAH to the medical staff of accredited hospitals, via such mechanisms as tissue committees, but the Center staff feels that the resources of the JCAH are entirely inadequate to judge hospitals on the subject of peer review. They conclude that "the JCAH simply does not know, does not try to know, whether the medical staffs of accredited hospitals, in fact, virtually hold effective peer group reviews." They add that since JCAH was a voluntary organization, it has no legal status, and the wording of its regulations tend to the use of "should" rather than "shall," and since all accreditation surveys are confidential, the JCAH is virtually useless to the consumer as a self-regulatory device.[26]

Recommendations

The Nader group, after a thorough analysis of existing systems of quality control within the medical profession, concludes that current systems are inadequte. The authors of *One Life—One Physician* also conclude that the profession has failed to "merit the trust with which society has placed itself into the hands, and relied on the hearts, of all its physicians." The Nader group further implies that the Federal Government is not yet ready to take the radical steps necessary to correct this situation.

In their conclusions about the current status of medical auditing, the authors of *One Life—One Physician* identify certain needs which, in their opinion, merit immediate public consideration. As listed in the study, these are the needs:

1. To develop standards of optimal care, as a basis for universal quality judgments, relative to the levels achieved in our university medical center clinics and hospitals.

2. To require standardized recording of medical care. Standards of optimal care cannot be developed until after the forms and records used by physicians are redesigned and standardized and the primary purpose of medical care evaluation. These will lend themselves to computer storage, retrieval, and statistical analyses, and thereby, to the development of standards of quality care.

3. To develop truly effective "peer group" evaluation by the medical profession that will afford protection to all patients in all hospitals (including the almost 3000 "nonaccredited") and physicians' offices.

4. To establish "para-peer" groups from the profession, outside of "organized medicine" and the local area pressures of friendship and economic rewards, which will periodically check on the function of the local peer groups.

5. To arouse and involve university medical faculties to their human and social responsibilities to become involved in this problem, because it is at least as essential to teaching and research.

6. To develop a national body of leading physicians to direct the establishment of acceptable standards of care, and to establish and administer a valid quality control system. This must be beyond the control of the politically oriented executive branch of government and of organized medicine.

7. To develop a system of controls to limit the entrance into, and continuation in, the practice of medicine to only those physicians who are sensible of the privilege of service, and

sensitive to the moral premise that either the life and health of every person is important, or that of no one is.[27]

One Life—One Physician ends with a series of recommendations which are posed as "suggested changes in the health care system that relate to its responsibility to afford each patient 'reasonable assurance' that any doctor he chooses will be competent to, and *will*, protect his life and return him to liberty and to his pursuit of happiness . . ." In order to assure implementation of their recommendations, the Center for Study of Responsive Law recommends, "as an essential beginning," establishment of a National Board of Medicine. They describe this Board as follows:

> The Board would have sole jurisdiction over all health care programs which the Federal Government funds. As a reasonable condition for participation in any federally funded health care program, the individual states would be required to bring their laws into conformity with acceptable standards of utilization and quality control, as established by the National Board of Medicine.
>
> The Board and its staff would have responsibility for the establishment of policies, programs, and standards, and for the administration and regulation of these, in the area of its jurisdiction.[28]

The report's final pages contain a series of specific recommendations. These proposals are presented for consideration by "a National Board of Medicine and/or Congress," as "elements of a system for quality control of physicians' performance and of hospital management." The complete list is given below:

A. Development of patient record forms, for use in hospitals and offices, standardized around the primary purpose of effective medical care evaluation.
   1. Development of regional and/or national computer data centers for storage, retrieval and statistical analysis.
B. Development of standards of optimal care as a basis for judgments of individual physican and hospital performance.
   1. Standards of optimal care to be developed from the results of treatment by disease category from a random sampling of university hospitals and clinics, and university faculty private office practice.
   2. An optimal standard of quality of care to be derived from these sources, and to be set at, for example, 70% of the 50th percentile of university-level results.
C. Development of licensing standards for admission of physicians and hospitals into the system.
   1. After the system is long enough in operation in respect to those graduating from medical schools, and an appropriately long "grandfather" period or charter membership for these now in practice, a variety of specialized licenses would be granted by the Board to all qualifying physicians, after differing examinations:
      a. Class A, for general practice.
      b. Class B, for specialists in the new field of Family Practice.
      c. Class C, etc., for specific licenses in the areas of the present 19 specialty Boards, and so on.
   2. Examinations could be taken only near the end of postgraduate clinical training in the equivalent of, at the least, a rotating internship of one year, or at the end of formal residency training.
   3. Licenses would specify the area and type of practice permitted to each license holder, and examinations for their granting would measure the applicant's information and clinical judgmental capacities in that field alone.

4. Hospitals would be required to measure up to JCAH "environmental" standards, participate in data collection required for the physician quality control mechanism, and for daily monitoring of admissions of all patients, to determine that the condition for which the patient was admitted properly came within the categories permitted within that physician's license.

No physician could be denied the privileges of that hospital on any grounds except that of competence, as measured by the parameters of his license.

D. Development of standards for continuation of physicians in the system.
   1. Determine the appropriate amount and form of continuing education related to each special license field of knowledge.
   2. Re-examine all license holders every five years, but only if the necessary continuing education requirements have been fulfilled. (Exam limited to license area.)
   3. Develop (and pay for) a quality control system on physician performance.
      a. Hospital Practice:

      First-line Peer Review:
      1) For hospitals of less than 100 beds, or for those without an adequate complement of specialized licentiates, monitoring to be performed by well-structured committees of the county medical societies (in some counties there may not be an appropriate complement of physicians, and there the State societies would have to fill the gap).
      2) For hospitals of 100 beds or more, or those with a full complement of licentiates, monitoring to be done by appropriate committees of that hospital staff.
      3) Monitoring to be performed at least once a month.
      Para-peer Review
      1) At the 4th and 8th months of each system year, appropriate committees of the State medical societies will review the work of the first-line peer review groups.
      2) At the 12th month, appropriate committees of the university medical school faculties (of that State, if possible) will review the work of the first-line peer review groups.
      3) The para-peer monitoring can be done to a large extent by a random selection from the data collection system, with on-site monitoring where needed, or for appropriate sampling verification.
      b. Office Practice:
      1) First-line peer review by committees of the county (and where needed, State) medical societies.
      2) Para-peer review—as for "Hospital practice."
      3) Review largely at both levels, by random sampling of records principally. On-site verification where needed.
   4. Causes for removal of licenses of physicians within the system, in addition to present statutory causes:
      a. Unexplained failure to refer patients whose condition is beyond the licentiate's area of competence, as defined by the parameters of his license.
      b. Failure to participate in the on-going schedule of the structured continuing education program appropriate to this license category.
      c. Failure to complete successfully the required re-examination for license maintenance.

d. Persistently falling below, for example, 70% performance of the 50th percentile level for the areas of disease therapy within his license. Performance below this level could result in probation, and require special educative efforts directed at the discovered areas of therapeutic weakness.[29]

Part Three: The AMA on Peer Review*

Impetus for a new peer review setup is the escalating cost of Medicare. Social Security shocked Congress with predictions that the price tag will be $213 billion more than originally estimated over the next 25 years. The Senate Finance Committee's staff report alleging widespread abuse by providers heightened demand for cost control.

The general agreement on both sides of the political aisle for economics spurred by letters from constituents complaining of health care costs, makes Congressional passage imminent this year of a new peer review mechanism to curb unnecessary services and too-high charges appear inevitable.[30]

In October of 1970, three proposals had been placed before Congress which contained outlines for a peer review mechanism for Medicare and Medicaid, designed primarily to cut medical costs. The plan submitted by the Administration gave the HEW secretary authority to establish "program review teams" at the state or local levels to check for abuses or over-utilization; the Senate Finance Committee had approved a peer review mechanism that would establish regional review teams in areas of 300 or more physicians and which would have broad powers to police utilization (these review teams would be staffed by physicians "whenever possible"); and, the AMA had proposed a plan similar to that advanced by the Senate Finance Committee, but with state medical societies made responsible for operation of the review teams. The AMA position with respect to their proposals was voiced by William O. LaMotte, Jr., M.D., Chairman of the Council for Legislation. According to the *American Medical News,* the AMA spokesman "objected 'most forcefully' to the provision (which included the Administration plan) which would have nonmedical groups act as review teams and make medical judgments." Further,

He recommended changes in PSRO (the Finance Committee supported Program, called the Professional Standards Review Organization) to assure that review of physicians' services is done by peers, to allow the state medical services to carry out the peer review systems, and to confine peer review to services of physicians.[31]

The AMA's main objection to the plans backed by the Administration and by the Senate Finance Committee was that they allowed for the intrusion of nonmedical personnel into the review process. The AMA position was described in detail in the October 19, 1970 *American Medical News,* in an article titled, "AMA's stand: review by MDs only":

The American Medical Association supports peer review administered by state and local medical socieities as part of Medicare-Medicaid.

---

*Material in this section is reproduced by special permission of the editors of the *American Medical News.*

The AMA's position was explained by its president, Walter C. Bornemeier, MD, who said many members and others are confused about the organization's stand.

The Senate Finance Committee accepted the Professional Standards Review Organization's (PSRO) amendment to HR 17550, the Social Security amendments bill (AMN, Oct. 12, 1970). The PSRO amendment was introduced by Sen. Wallace Bennett (R., Utah).

The bill is now being written by the committee for reporting to the Senate.

"The essence of peer review is that only physicians should review physicians," Dr. Bornemeier stated. "The AMA has said many times that abuses in Medicare and Medicaid should be eliminated. The most effective way to review the services of physicians is through the medium of other physicians.

"Professional services, whether they be legal, medical, or otherwise, should be evaluated by professional peers."

Since PSRO as originally proposed did not assure peer review, the AMA urged the committee to reject it, Dr. Bornemeier said.

The AMA's peer review plan (PRO) is part of its Medicredit bill, which would provide for a system of tax credits to provide for national health insurance. Medicredit has been introduced in both houses of Congress.

"Many members and others have been misled into believing that the AMA's PRO and Senator Bennett's PSRO are the same thing. That is not true," Dr. Bornemeier declared.

Under PRO, the Secretary of Health, Education, and Welfare would enter into agreements with state medical societies for a review of the need for and quality of services provided, and the reasonableness of charges. Local review plans would carry out immediate peer review functions. Physicians would review physicians, Dr. Bornemeier said. He pointed out that PRO provides for advisory councils that would include representatives of consumers, providers, and carriers.

"On the other hand," Dr. Bornemeier pointed out, "under PSRO there is no assurance that the review of physician's services will be done by his peers."

While the Bennett amendment gave first priority to the local medical society to act as the PSRO, if the secretary does not accept the medical society, he may designate a public or private agency to act.

"In that case it may or may not be a 'peer' group and the members of the group doing review need not be physicians," the AMA president said.

The AMA also objected to the original PSRO proposal because it:

• Requires pre-admission approval before hospitalization for an elective procedure, or a costly or long-term treatment program, or as to whether proposed institutionalization is the proper level of institutional service required for the patient's condition. The AMA believes that this section, raising many legal and medical questions, should not be adopted, as it would cause considerable confusion and would not be in the best medical interests of the patient.

• Creates national norms for care and treatment. The AMA believes that "norms" should be guidelines or criteria, developed and created locally, to operate as criteria for local evaluation. It was pointed out that, improperly enacted, standards could actually raise costs in the program, where the standards in effect become a "floor" for determination of acceptable practice.

• Sets penalty provisions (up to $5,000, or refund of charges for unnecessary services) as subverting the intent of peer review and removing the beneficial educational function of peer review.

- Requires federal ownership of data and information acquired by the PSRO which instead should remain with the reviewing board and be confidential.
- Requires physician review of services to extend beyond those services for which he has responsibility and control.
- Provides for demonstration projects under which the PSRO assumes the role of risk underwriter and also payment reviewing agent.

Dr. Bornemeier said that if the AMA peer review proposal is not acceptable to the Senate Finance Committee then the question of review of services as to quality and charges should lay over to the next Congress.

"The concept of peer review as structured mechanism is still new," he explained. "There are different approaches to this important problem and many organizations in the medical and paramedical fields are now becoming involved in varying plans for peer review. We suggest that it may be wise not to cast its future direction in statutory language at this time."

AMA Reaction to the Nader Report

The report of the Center for the Study of Responsive Law was issued in early November of 1970, and the November 16 *American Medical News* featured an article on the peer review recommendations posed by the Nader Committee. It was the opinion of the *American Medical News* that the Nader recommendations did not differ substantially from the plan which had been submitted to Congress by the AMA. AMA President Bornemeier, however, was reported to have made the following comment:

> We have not had an opportunity to study the report thoroughly and consequently are not in a position to make detailed comment on it at this time. However, the report appears to be comprehensive and deserving of the objective consideration which we will give it. On a hasty perusal, some of its recommendations appear to have merit while others raise questions. We are gratified that it recognized that peer review must be carried out by state and county medical societies, which is the fundamental principle of the AMA proposal.

Private Practice MD's

The November 23 issue of the *American Medical News* contained an article which described private practice physicians as being opposed to government-linked peer review: "The Congress of County Medical Societies, an outspoken voice of private practice physicians, has urged its members to oppose enactment of Professional Standards Review Organizations (PSRO) and any other form of peer review that involves a contract with a government agency."

At a seminar sponsored by the group, member physicians drafted a resolution to oppose outside intervention in peer review or any outside perusal of confidential medical records. (The seminar was attended by approximately 45 physicians representing 33 county medical societies and 21 states, according to the *American Medical News*.)

Senate Finance Committee Approves PSRO

In late November, a modified peer review mechanism had been developed which was expected to win Senate approval. This was the Professional Standards Review Organization's plan of Senator Bennett, which gave medical societies "first crack" at establishing regional review systems. According to the *American Medical News,* certain changes had been made in the bill which made it more palatable to physicians: "Spelled out was authorization for a PSRO to acknowledge and accept an individual hospital's own review of admissions and need for continued care, on a hospital-by-hospital basis, where it has determined that the 'in-house' review is effective. PSRO could accept a hospital's review in whole or in part."

In spite of this and other modifications in the bill, the AMA's position, as voiced by the *American Medical News,* remained opposed to this particular piece of legislation. One *American Medical News* editorial on the subject is reproduced below:

Not A Time for Haste

The frantic efforts in the "lame duck" session of Congress to enact peer review legislation are a hasty, ill-advised gamble with the future of the practice of medicine.

While organized medicine has espoused peer review, as embodied in the Peer Review Organization section of the American Medical Association's Medicredit Bill, some members of the Senate Finance Committee have committed themselves to the Professional Standards Review Organization (PSRO) measure sponsored by Sen. Wallace Bennett (R., Utah). Certain provisions of the legislation are of serious concern to physicians.

The AMA believes that state medical societies must have the prime responsibility in any formal peer review organization. Because it has not seen the language of the Senate bill and because of comments made by senators, the AMA is concerned about the roles to be given state and county medical societies. Indications are that the Senate Finance Committee may be considering approving a measure that would usurp the proper peer review functions of the medical societies.

In fact, Bennett's original bill contains no guarantee that the review of physicians' services will be done by physicians—which is the essence of peer review. Where the Secretary of Health, Education, and Welfare does not accept a medical society, he may designate a public or private agency to act.

Among other concerns of the medical profession is that protion (of the Bennett bill) which creates national norms for care and treatment. If it is necessary to establish norms, they should be developed and created locally, to operate as criteria for local evaluation. If improperly enacted, the national standards could actually raise costs of a program, since the standards could, in effect, become a "floor" for the determination of acceptable practice.

The AMA has urged that Congress delay any action on peer review until next year, pointing out that such a far-reaching measure should not be enacted without a great deal more study. The same sentiments—for different reasons—have been expressed by the American Hosital Assn., which has strong reservations about PSRO's power of hospital procedures, and by the AFL-CIO, which feels that too much power is vested in the medical profession, and that more should be given to consumer interests.

In view of the far-reaching nature of the Bennett proposal, such a delay seems the only adequate safeguard against precipitate action. While a carefully organized peer review system will contribute to the elimination of abuses of Medicare and Medicaid, and will bring greater awareness to physicians and hospitals of the rising cost of its health care, the concept as a structured, nation-wide mechanism is so new and so complex that Congress must give the matter thorough study to avoid enacting a measure containing shortcomings that outweigh benefits.

The 91st Congress

Congressional action on the Medicare-Medicaid bill, which included the PSRO plan, was ultimately blocked by Wilbur Mills, who objected that more time needed to be spent resolving differences between the new bill (which contained provision for a PSRO) and a measure passed months earlier by the House. The major differences to be resolved lay in the Senate's PSRO provision, and the issue was in fact debated in the Senate for more than an hour prior to adjournment of the 91st Congress. The chief opponent to the bill, Senator Carl Curtis, told the Senate that PSRO could produce "an organization with thousands of clerks who could take a blue pencil and direct the practice of medicine if we put one doctor at the top." Senator Bennett, who has sponsored the bill, defended it by saying that "the alternative to use of PSRO's is the beefed-up review of governmental employers and insurance company personnel. That is an alternative which holds little appeal to us or to the doctors." Bennett further stated,

> For obvious reasons there are many people in the American Medical Association who feel that the power should be lodged with the state medical society. I have opposed that because I do not believe it proper for any private organization supported by private funds . . . whose membership would be controlled by private rules . . . to administer such a law. Therefore, a program was established under which groups of local physicians in an area supporting 300 or more physicians would be invited to offer their services . . . to carry out the review.

> If PRSO is knocked out of the bill, the Senator maintained, the House provision would be left that "gives the (HEW) secretary full power to do anything he pleases. The doctors will have no opportunity to review their own professional activity."

In May of 1971 the AMA introduced to Congress a modified version of the Peer Review Organization legislation that it had proposed to the previous Congress. The new bill added a national council of 11 physicians—including the assistant secretary for health of HEW—who would establish administrative guidelines for peer review. An article in the May 31, 1971, *American Medical News* described the legislation:

AMA Introduces
New Peer Review Legislation

The American Medical Association has introduced in Congress a modified version of the Peer Review Organization (PRO) legislation proposed last session as part of Medicredit.

The new PRO bill, introduced in the Senate (S. 1898) by Clifford Hansen (R., Wyo.) and in the House by Rep. Joel T. Broyhill (R., Va.), adds a "national council" of 11 physicians—including the assistant secretary for health of HEW—who would establish administrative guidelines for peer review.

Another change would establish five-member state PRO Commissions, appointed by state medical societies to act as review tribunals. They would maintain final jurisdiction over disciplinary recommendations, and not the secretary of HEW as in last year's version.

The new bill stipulates that all cases could be subject to judicial review, with data collected by a PRO to be admissible as evidence.

The measure proposes agreements between state medical societies and the secretary of HEW under which the society would establish peer review systems for federal health care programs, including Medicare and Medicaid. Such an agreement also could be entered into between HEW and an organization designated by the state medical society.

The peer review function would include matters bearing on the reasonableness of charges, and the need and quality of services.

A state medical society or designated organization would appoint a five-member state PRO Commission, which in turn would set up local three-member review panels. Membership would be restricted to MDs and DOs.

Advisory councils composed of consumers, providers of health care, and Medicare Part B administrators, would be created (a nine-member council to advise the commission and seven-member councils to advise the panels).

Informal review meetings are stressed in the bill. In the event this fails, a local review panel would order hearings for the provider concerned and its recommendations would be submitted to the review commission, which would accept, reject, or modify them.

The commission would have the authority to terminate payments for services under federal health programs, such terminations not to exceed six months in the case of a first offense. In case of subsequent violations, permanent termination could be ordered.

The proposed National Peer Review Council would consist of 10 physicians "recommended to the secretary by national organizations of physicians," and the assistant HEW secretary for health. It would set administrative guidelines for peer review and the dissemination of information to the commissions and panels.

In the same issue, an article entitled, "One Last Chance for Peer Review" reiterated the AMA position—that review of physicians by nonphysicians was "abhorrent to the medical profession." The article described an AMA sponsored workshop on peer review which had been attended by 400 physicians. A note of urgency was present at the meeting, where practitioners of peer review had met to review mutual case histories. The attitude of those attending, and of the AMA specifically, was summed up by one attending physician: "I think the people here realize we have one last chance to do a job of peer review while it still remains actual peer review."

Footnotes

1. Louise T. Keelty, Mimi Law, Russell E. Phillips, Terrence M. Quirin, and Robert S. McCleery, *One Life—One Physician* (Washington, D.C.: Center for Study of Responsive Law), page 2.

2. Ibid., page 70.

3. Ibid., page 78.

4. George A. Woodhouse, "Relation of Grievance Committees and State Boards of Medical Examiners," *Federation Bulletin,* 49(4): 96-103, April 1962. Quoted in *One Life-One Physician,* page 81.

5. *One Life—One Physician,* pages 84-85.

6. Robert C. Derbyshire, *Medical Licensure and Discipline in the United States,* Johns Hopkins Press, Baltimore, 1969. Quoted in *One Life—One Physician,* page 80.

7. Forgatson, Rolney, and R.W. Newman, "Legal Regulation of Health Personnel in the United States," *Report of the National Advisory Commission on Health Manpower,* Vol. I, Washington, D.C., Government Printing Office, 1968, p. 309. Quoted in *One Life—One Physician,* pages 101-102.

8. Report of the Medical Disciplinary Committee to the Board of Trustees, American Medical Association, Chicago, 1961, p. 55. Quoted on page 104.

9. *One Life—One Physician,* pages 105-106.

10. Edwin J. Holman, "The Complex of Unprofessional Conduct," *Federation Bulletin,* 48(3): 58-69, March 1961. Quoted on pages 107-108.

11. "1969 Medical Disciplinary Report," *Journal of the American Medical Association,* 213:530, July 27, 1970. Quoted on page 131.

12. *One Life—One Physician,* page 132.

13. Avedis Donabedian, "Promoting Quality Through Evaluating the Process of Patient Care," *Medical Care,* VI:3, May-June, 1968. Quoted on page 145.

14. *One Life—One Physician*

15 Report of the Committee to Study the Operation of the Joint Commission on Accreditation of Hospitals, Adopted by the House of Delegates, American Medical Association, page 11, June 1963. Quoted on page 149.

16. John D. Porterfield. III, "The New JCAH Standards," *Journal of the American Hospital Association,* 43:71, October 16, 1969. Quoted on page 152.

17. Ibid., pages 153-154.

18. *One Life—One Physician,* pages 160-161.

19. Kerr L. White, "Research in Medical Care and Health Services Systems," *Medical Care,* VI:2 March-April 1969. Quoted on page 165.

20. *One Life—One Physician,* pages 193-194.

21. Ibid., pages 196-197.

22. Ibid., page 205.

23. Ibid., page 210.

24. Article on the Himler report appearing in the *Washington Post,* December 3, 1969. Quoted on page 212.

25. *One Life—One Physician,* page 220.

26. Ibid., pages 231-232.

27. Ibid., pages 233-235.

28. Ibid., page 241.

29. Ibid., pages 244-247.

30. *American Medical News,* October 12, 1970, page 10.

31. Ibid.

Note for Stephen Doyle (A) (B) (C) (D) (E)

Description

The "Stephen Doyle" series consists of five short cases which describe the use of behavior modification to effect on-the-job performance. The particular situation concerns a Director of Training at a large urban hospital who has been asked by the Director of Personnel to help solve a problem which has cost the institution a considerable loss of revenue.

The first case, Stephen Doyle (A), is a statement of the basic problem: inaccurate histories on Emergency Room reports have resulted in 30% of the bills sent in one week being returned because of incorrect addresses. Several alternatives are presented which involve the emergency room clerks who take the histories. An appropriate question which the instructor using this case might want to ask is, Which of the options sounds the most viable and why?

The second case, Stephen Doyle (B), focuses on Mr. Doyle's analysis of the problem. As a result of a test to determine the competence of the clerks, he discovers that their performance indicates further training is not necessary.

The third case, Stephen Doyle (C), describes Mr. Doyle's solution to the problem. He decides to institute a program of behavior modification that will rely on immediate feedback upon completion of the job, and appropriate awards for correct performance. The remainder of the case describes the technique Mr. Doyle employs, the personnel involved, and the cost of the program. An appropriate question in conjunction with this case might be: Do you think this strategy will work and why?

The fourth case, Stephen Doyle (D), describes the results of Mr. Doyle's application of behavioral systems analysis to the problem which has arisen in the emergency room and a similar attempt in the hospital's admitting and medical records departments. The case also refers to the hospital's reporting structure. An appropriate question suggested by the fact that Mr. Doyle leaves the hospital's employ approximately three months after the beginning of the ER program might be: What do you think happened after Mr. Doyle left?

The fifth case, Stephen Doyle (E), concludes the series. It presents the aftermath of Mr. Doyle's program and points out a few of the drawbacks of using behavior modification to change work performance. At this point, the instructor might want to elicit from the class their opinion of Mr. Doyle's evaluation and feeling about the implementation and usefulness of behavior modification to change work performance in a setting with high turnover like a hospital.

Teaching Objective

This case can be used as a basis for a discussion of different methods for handling worker motivation in general and in particular for the advantages and disadvantages of using the techniques of behavior modification.

The five cases have been designed so that the best way to use them might be to hand out Stephen Doyle (A) before the first class meeting with appropriate questions and then the subsequent cases during the course of the class in consecutive order with some discussion in between.

STEPHEN DOYLE (A)

In 1969, Stephen Doyle, Director of Training, was asked by the Director of Personnel at a medical center in Manhattan to assist with a serious and pressing problem in the hospital's accounting department. The Post Office was returning bills addressed to patients who had received treatment in the hospital's emergency room stamped "Unable to Deliver Because of Insufficient Address." An examination of returned bills for one week revealed that 145 bills, or 30% of those sent, had been returned. The cause was either incomplete or inaccurate histories on the Emergency Room reports which led to incorrent mailing addresses. Sometimes, the name which appeared on the report would be correct, but the street address incorrect; sometimes numbers were not transcribed carefully. The resulting loss to the hospital was estimated at a minimum of $1089.50 per week or $56,654 per year, assuming a minimum charge of $7.50 a visit.

The Directors of Training and Personnel were considering several options. Among these were (1) conduct a traditional training program that would (a) emphasize the importance of the report to the medical center and (b) teach the clerks how to fill out the report completely and accurately; (2) replace the clerks, who were union members earning approximately $106 per week and had been at the medical center on the average of two years; or (3) conduct a systems analysis that would indicate (a) why the clerks performance was below standard, and (b) develop an economical solution that would guarantee improved on-the-job performance and consequently reduce the number of uncollectables from Emergency Room card.

STEPHEN DOYLE (B)

Mr. Doyle's concern was to figure out how he could impact on the performance of the Emergency Room clerks. First, however, he wanted to make sure the problem was not one that could be corrected with further training. In order to do this, he had to determine how well the clerks could complete the patient report forms.

Under a test situation, each clerk was asked to complete an Emergency Room report for six hypothetical patients. To his surprise, the finished forms were 98% complete and correct. Further training was obviously not needed and Mr. Doyle decided to look at the job environment and the background of the clerks themselves. He found that the clerks were generally high school graduates. He then asked himself the following critical questions: Are the clerks aware of what they were supposed to accomplish; i.e., (a) were performance goals made clear and measurable? (b) were they receiving daily feedback on progress in relation to these goals? and (c) were they receiving adequate rewards for achieving these goals?

Further inquiry led Mr. Doyle to conclude that the Emergency Room clerks had little idea or interest in the accuracy of their completed tasks. When one of the clerks was asked if the reports she had completed the previous day were accurate, she replied: "I don't know . . . I think I did okay and no one has said anything to me. Have you heard of any problems?" Mr. Doyle concluded that the clerks assumed their performance was acceptable because they had received no indication to the contrary. Furthermore there was no incentive to improve performance because there was no reward system operating. As one clerk put it, "Sometimes I don't have a chance to complete the forms but it doesn't seem to make too much difference. Once in a great while one of us will get bawled out but no one tells us when we do a good job either." Mr. Doyle therefore concluded that from a clerk's point of view there were no significant differences in consequences if she did a job well or poorly. The rewards were nonexistent and the punishments consisted of an occasional bawling out.

STEPHEN DOYLE (C)

Mr. Doyle's strategy was to establish a program that would provide immediate feedback to the clerks and the appropriate rewards for correct completion of the Emergency Room reports. He was fortunate in that the Assistant Director of the hospital, Mrs. Sylvia Hale, supported Mr. Doyle completely throughout the program. The Emergency Room employees, clerks, and nurses reported directly to Mrs. Hale through their supervisors.

First Mr. Doyle designed a job aide to assist the clerks in evaluating the accuracy and completeness of their reports. Illustration 1 is a sample of the job aide. The second step was to provide feedback and self-measurement. On completion of a report, the clerk was to evaluate it for completeness and accuracy. Errors were to be corrected immediately on discovery. At the end of the shift, each clerk would compute the percent of reports filled out without error and submit the results to the supervisor on a Patient Information Feedback Report, Illustration 2. Third, a process of rewarding the clerks for completing the task accurately was initiated. Mr. Doyle taught the supervisors how to use positive reinforcement. The supervisors were to reinforce the clerks with praise, e.g., "Nice work, Hilda. Today you achieved 97%." Mrs. H. Hale similarly encouraged the nurses to reward the clerks with praise and gave positive reinforcement herself whenever possible. Weekly letters from the hospital's accounting department were forthcoming which said such things as "Congratualtions, girls! You have made your weekly target."

The entire cost for developing the program was $800. This amount covered the Training Department's cost for analyzing the cause of the problem, designing the job aide and feedback form, and time spent in instructing the supervisors how to use positive reinforcement.

Illustration 1

Job Aide — Patient Information Report

Did I fill in the following information:

— Patient's first, last and middle name?
— Apartment number, street?
— Borough, zip code, state?

Illustration 2

Patient Information Feedback Report

Hilda Jones   June 9, 1970

100   Number Reports Filled Out
97   Number Complete and Correct
97% Today's Performance

Standard = 95% filled out complete and correct

Did I meet standard today?   Yes   No

STEPHEN DOYLE (D)

The Director of Personnel was very pleased with the results of Mr. Doyle's application of behavioral systems analysis to the problem which had arisen in the Emergency Room. In one week's time, the percent of accurate and complete reports submitted by the Emergency Room clerks to their supervisors rose from 67 to 95%. The clerks for their part were experiencing increased job satisfaction. As one clerk put it, "I used to go home evenings wondering what I had done . . . now I look at my feedback report and can see what I have accomplished."

Because of the success of Mr. Doyle's program in the Emergency Room, a similar process was begun in Medical Records and Admitting. In the case of Medical Records, Mr. Doyle set up an interaction schedule by having the supervisor praise the good performance of the group that pulled the records from 12:00 to 8:00 A.M. A nightly evaluation of performance was recorded for the crew on a chit sheet. The evaluation was based on how many records were requested and how many were pulled. The change in work performance was almost immediate. In the case of Admitting, Mr. Doyle implemented a similar feedback and self-measurement system. Here, however, he was not as successful in providing positive reinforcement. The Admitting Department reported to the Accounting Office. Nobody in the Accounting Office would reward the Admitting personnel on a consistent basis and after a week, the program was dropped.

Three months after Mr. Doyle began the program in the Emergency Room, and two weeks after he began it in Medical Records and Admitting, he resigned his position at the medical center.

STEPHEN DOYLE (E)

When contacted some four years later, Mr. Doyle said that to his knowledge the programs had been discontinued. As he saw it, the major drawback in using behavior modification to change work performance is that without constant supervision to make sure the positive reinforcement is being given, the old work patterns will reemerge. When both Mr. Doyle and the casewriter tried to contact some of the administrative staff of the hospital to discuss the continuing effects of his program, they were unable to reach anyone who had been involved. Mr. Doyle said he had heard that the turnover rate of employees for that medical center in 1969 was 103%.

CHAPTER 3

ORGANIZATION: STRUCTURE AND OPERATING MECHANISMS

STRUCTURE: BASIC ELEMENTS

Any work organization is an open system which consists of the patterned activities of a number of individuals and which engages in transactions with the surrounding environment. The system has a boundary which separates it from its environment, and most organizations having several subunits also have a number of internal boundaries. The organization takes in inputs (patients) from the environment and executes transformation processes (medical care) which turn these inputs into outputs (healthy people). It also recruits employees, trains them, assigns them to jobs, and sooner or later exports them by resignation, retirement, or dismissal. It imports and consumes supplies and power. It also collects intelligence about its market (i.e., the population it serves) and its competitors (increasingly!), analyzes this information, makes decisions about the quality, quantity, and price of the service (or product), and issues communications of different kinds as a result of the decisions made (Miller and Rice, 1967).

The environment of the system (the community) is important in a number of ways. In the first place, it is the source of the inputs and the market for the outputs. Second, other organizations also exist in this environment which may well be competing with the organization under consideration (e.g., H.M.O.'s and private practitioners). Furthermore, the environment in general may influence the organization directly or indirectly, and in a way not connected with the major operating task of the organization, for example, the right of representation on the board of trustees of a community hospital of local community groups.

To summarize, the major inputs to the organization are (1) money, (2) material, and (3) men, and include also energy and information. The major task outputs are either products or services. In order to perform its task of conversion, an organization essentially engages in two types of processes: maintenance and task performing. The maintenance process is essentially those activities which the organization engages in to remain viable. It must build and maintain staff, plant, etc., in order to perform any task at all. The second set of processes are the actual activities by which raw materials are transformed into finished products, or services rendered. Finally, there are import and export processes across the organization boundary, as organization members gather resources and distribute products or services.

As an organization grows, efficacy requires that many activities which have to take place become divided, and the organization therefore develops subsystems. This process is called the division of labor, specialization, or task differentiation. Thus, personnel departments, purchasing departments, service departments, etc., evolve while production departments attend to the process itself, and advertising and sales departments (public relations, community education) attend to the delivery of the product or service to the customer. Although such specialization is efficient, as this specialization increases, it causes problems of coordination or integration. Control of the various components in the system and the subsystem, as well as their linking together, become major issues. A traditional method of control and coordination is that of the formal organization, with specific regulations and routines, and use of a management hierarchy. This formalized control is essentially a form of feedback. Feedback is the monitoring of output so that inputs can be changed to maintain a steady state in the system. Thus, if the performance of the task starts to deviate from acceptable limits, the supervisor may instruct the employee accordingly and rules may be enforced. More complex forms of feedback control include the development of specialized subsystems, (e.g., quality control, production control) to perform a similar function.

ORGANIZATIONAL INPUTS

Organizational inputs consist of two sets of variables—the formal organizational practices imposed from the system level and the management style of managers supervising the subsystem. Formal organizational variables are such factors as the following (Evan, 1963; Woodward, 1958; Burns and Stalker, 1961; Hall, 1962; Lawrence and Lorsch, 1967a):

Structure

Division of Work: the way work is divided among units and people within the unit. The work may be divided by product, by process, by time, or by geographic territory. Obviously such organizational choices are closely related to the nature of the task inputs for the subsystem. For example, they define whether persons will work on a small portion of the total task or the whole task. The psychological consequences may be different. Usually people working on a whole task get more satisfaction (Rice, 1963). Similarly, these organizational choices can determine whether people will work relatively independently or will have frequent contact with others.

Span of Control: the number of subordinates reporting to a common boss. In some subsystems the span of control may be very narrow with few subordinates reporting to each supervisor while in others the span of control may be wider with many subordinates reporting to each supervisor.

Hierarchy: this means the number of levels in the management hierarchy. As suggested above the principal function of the hierarchy is to provide a mechanism for coordinating the work of organization members. Through a network of common superiors, the work of individual members can be coordinated. In this process information can move both up and down the chain of command.

Operating Mechanisms

Rules and Procedures: this aspect of formal organization is concerned with the extent to which explicit rules and procedures about conduct (such as safety procedures) are imposed by higher management. In some situations rules and procedures can be so prolific and detailed as to cover every possible contingency. In others formalized rules and procedures are nonexistent. The only rules are those norms which develop within the subsystem itself.

Measurement and Evaluation Practices: these formal practices are concerned with the measurement and evaluation of performance, both for the subsystem as an entity and for individual members. Such practices can vary from those which have many detailed criteria for performance evaluation to those which have only a few general criteria. Similarly, measurement and evaluation of performance can take place at frequent intervals or only infrequently. It should be emphasized that these methods provide feedback to the individual, to the subsystem, and to upper management.

Compensation: financial remuneration has several parameters which can impact on behavior. First is the relative amount of compensation members are getting vis-à-vis other opportunities available to them. While recent research has indicated that high pay alone does not motivate people to work harder, it also suggests that people can become disenchanted with their situation if they feel their pay is inequitable given their level of self-esteem and their view of other opportunities (Meyers, 1964; Jaques, 1956). A second parameter is the basis on which payment is made. As already suggested, a group incentive plan can have one impact on people, while payment based on time or individual effort can have others. The third dimension of compenation which is important to consider is the range of payments within the subsystem. The distribution of pay can be one important determinant of status in the subsystem social structure.

Selection Criteria: these are the formally established criteria used to select new members for the subsystem. Characteristics such as skill, experience, age, psychological attributes (from tests) are frequently used to make selection decisions. While such criteria obviously will be affected by task requirements, if they are rigidly adhered to, they can have a significant effect on the individual inputs to the group. If these criteria are specific and many they will create a group with members who are homogeneous in many characteristics. If the criteria are few and more general they may lead to a more heterogeneous collection of members.

With the exception of division of labor and the type and amount of compensation, these organizational inputs can be arranged on a continuum from high formality to low (see Fig. 1). By formality is meant the extent to which the formal organization is intended to control behavior. Recent research suggests that within many subsystems these variables tend to move in the same direction (Lawrence and Lorsch, 1967a). Thus, a subsystem falls at some point along a continuum of formality of organizational inputs. The formality of these organizational inputs can affect the attitudes of subsystem members about the organization and partially determine the degree of autonomy they feel (see below). These inputs are also closely related to the task inputs of the subsystem. But before task inputs are discussed, the second major type of organizational input—management style—should be mentioned.

By style of management is meant the behavior pattern which is characteristic of the managers in the larger systems of which the subsystems are a part. Such behavior patterns have been characterized by different labels by a variety of theorists and researchers, but in essence most seem to be concerned with the extent to which managers are concerned with exercising unilateral control over subordinates versus the extent to which they foster a mutual influence process (Fiedler, 1967; Likert, 1967; Blake and Mouton, 1969). Since leadership is discussed in Chapter 6, the important points to be made here can be summarized briefly. First, management style obviously does interact with the other determinants of behavior to influence how a subsystem operates. Second, no one management style is appropriate for all situations. Which style of management will facilitate subsystem performance depends on the other inputs to the system as well as its social controls and social structure. Thus, consideration of management style must be concerned not only with what is comfortable, given the dynamics of any particular personality, but also with what fits the other variables in the relevant subsystem.

TASK INPUTS

Certain characteristics of tasks shall now be delineated which research has shown are related to individual and organizational inputs and behavior. In discussing these task characteristics, it is useful to remember that in a specialized subsystem efficiency dictates that members usually perform similar tasks.

The first task characteristic that is important is the relative certainty or uncertainty of the work. Several recent studies have amassed considerable evidence that there is a relationship between the certainty of a subsystem's task, its organizational inputs, and the effectiveness of the subsystem. When the task is highly certain and predict-

Figure 1

Formality of Organizational Inputs

	High Formality	**Low Formality**
Span of Control	Narrow	Wide
Hierarchical Levels	Many	Few
Rules and Procedures	Many and specific	Few and general
Measurement and Evaluation	Frequent and specific	General
Range of Compensation in the Sub-system	Wide	Narrow
Selection Criteria	Specific and many	Broad and few

able, the subsystem, if it is effective, will tend to have a highly formalized organization. Subsystems with more uncertain tasks (and again effective outputs) tend to have less formalized organizational inputs. An example of the latter situation might be found in a research laboratory.

The behavior of subsystem members also varies with the task. For example, in a research laboratory there is more autonomy of action among members and each member has more influence over his own work (see Chapter 2). In a manufacturing plant there is often less freedom of action for individual members, and the amount of influence over activities tends to correspond closely to the formal hierarchical level of the member. The reasons for the interdependence among this task characteristic, organizational inputs, and behavior are still being explored, but one of a number of possible explanations has to do with the fit between tasks and organizational variables. A good fit seems to have a motivational effect on subsystems members, providing them with a sense of mastery or competence in their work (Morse and Lorsch, 1970).

One problem with the concept of task certainty is that it is very broad and often difficult to apply to a specific task within a subsystem. A study by Turner and Lawrence (1965), which is closely connected to those referred to above, suggests six more specific task attributes which were also found to be linked to formality of organization in a number of manufacturing plants. These are (1) the amount of variety in prescribed activities; (2) the amount of discretion in job activities permitted and required of the job incumbent; (3) the frequency and diversity of interaction with others required by the job; (4) the amount of optional interaction possible; (5) the learning time required for job proficiency; and (6) the amount of responsibility assumed by incumbents as measured by the likelihood of serious error, the uncertainty about appropriate corrective action, and the length of time before feedback is received about the results of the work. When jobs were rated low on these dimensions (e.g., little variety, limited discretion, little required interaction, etc.), it was found that the organizational inputs in the plant were more formalized. The organizations were less formalized in those situations where tasks scored higher on these dimensions.

In addition to task certainty and the task attributes identified by Turner and Lawrence, there are other task characteristics which can also have an important impact on subsystem operations. One of these is the physical conditions in the work place. For example, high noise levels can block oral communication and lead to feelings of isolation unless group members can find some way to communicate in spite of this technological constraint. Poor working conditions such as extreme heat, odors, etc., can often contribute to subsystem members drawing together in a more cohesive group. By banding together they gain a sense of support in the face of this hostile environment. Such factors, often thought of as being relevant only in production settings and having a negative impact, may be present in other than production settings and can have a positive impact. Evidence of this is the fact that so much time and money is devoted to planning office environments so that they offer physical surroundings conductive to contemplative and problem-solving behavior.

Another important task input is the spatial arrangement of the work place. As suggested above, whether subsystems members are close together or apart can have an important bearing on the amount of contact they have and how the group functions. Recent research by Allen (1969) suggests, for example, that the spatial layout of research laboratories can be an important determinant in getting scientists to interact with certain colleagues who had a particular capacity to bring new technical information into the laboratory. Such interaction was important to the successful accomplishment of the laboratory's mission.

There is a final way in which task inputs affect subsystem operation, and it is perhaps the most obvious one. Since different tasks require different skills and interests they are likely to attract personnel who have particular individual characteristics even if formal selection criteria are minimal. The reasons individuals select particular job opportunities are complex and knowledge in this area is far from complete. Yet there is mounting evidence that persons with particular needs are attracted to different job opportunities (Dalton *et. al.*, 1968). The essential points at this juncture are to recognize that these and other task characteristics can and do vary among subsystems; that these task inputs are interdependent with the other inputs and social control and structure; and that together these variables produce the behavior which the executive has to try to understand and manage.

DIFFERENTIATION, INTEGRATION
AND THE MATRIX ORGANIZATION

Described above are the basic elements of any organization. How these are actually put together has been a matter of controversy for years. Organizations have veered from centralization to decentralization, from organizing by function to service, or geographic area (for example, utilization by geography in mental hospitals). Current theory essentially supports the contingency approach to organizational design: Organizational form depends on the particular task of the organization and the kinds of people in it, and so there is no one right way. The originators and foremost exponents of this approach are Lawrence and Lorsch (1967a,b). These authors have proposed some organizing principles known as differentiation and integration.

Differentiation is defined as the differences in cognitive and emotional orientation among managers in different functional departments and the differences in formal structure among these departments. The major dimensions of differentiation are (1) time, i.e., short or long run orientation; (2) formality of organization, i.e., highly formal and structured or informal and unstructured; (3) interpersonal orientation, i.e., task-oriented or person-oriented; (4) direction of interdependence, i.e., who initiates action; and (5) conflict management style. Two styles seem to be effective, namely, bargaining and confronting. Less effective forms of conflict resolution include unilateral decision-making and avoiding, smoothing, and forcing the issue.

Integration is the quality of the state of collaboration that exists among departments that is required to achieve unity of effort by the environment. The linking of differing functions places a great deal of emphasis on integrative mechanisms (e.g., task forces, committees) and the skills of the integrator (Lawrence and Lorsch, 1967b). The integrator is one who must achieve unity among functional specialties and resolve interdepartmental conflicts to facilitate decision-making. He must have a high degree of personal competence and a balanced orientation as well as skills in conflict resolution. Such integrators in the health care field include the unit manager, the leader of the patient care team, the "assistant to," etc. However, Charns (1974) points out in a recent paper that very often the unit manager is not an integrator but a glorified ward secretary.

There is an appropriate amount of differentiation and of integration suitable for each organization in its particular environment. This conceptual approach not only assists effective design, but as Morse and Lorsch (1970) point out, tailoring the organization to fit the task and the people leads to a higher sense of competence motivation.

It also becomes apparent that it is not always appropriate to organize entirely by function or by product (or service). The functional organization maximizes specialized interests but makes coordination difficult, while the product- or service-oriented organization speeds up coordination but diminishes the value of expertise (Great Lakes Clinic Foundation). Where multiple specialties (differentiated) have to work together (integrated) toward some set of products or services as for example in the aerospace industry form of project management, the matrix organization has become popular as a solution to the dilemma. The matrix organization proposes that people may belong for certain purposes to a functional group, but for others to a service group and they may therefore have two or more bosses. For those unfamiliar with this concept, the idea of two bosses and the potential conflict therein may seem strange, but since the conflict is appropriate and inevitable, it is only a question of how to force it into the open.

Lawrence, in a large study of several medical schools including Canton State, points out that education, research, and health care are all important but require different kinds of professional behavior and therefore must result in conflict. But since health professionals wear multiple hats and work autonomously in multiple roles (unlike industry where things are simpler and researchers are researchers only), there tends to be under-differentiation in the usual form of health organization; the conflict lies within as much as between people, and so does not get expressed clearly or well (e.g., the Canton State A case). To render the conflict of different purposes open, useful, and creative requires structures and processes to strengthen the necessary differences, but also to help them get worked through and then linked together in a common purpose, and this may be best achieved by the matrix organization [e.g., Canton State University Academic Medical Center (B)]. The matrix organization in health care is structurally a mixed model of organization in which both departments and programs exist and there is a balance of influence between departmental chairmen and program heads.

While few managers may have the luxury, as in the University of Missouri Medical School at Kansas City, of designing the objectives and structure of their organization, most have the opportunity afforded the Dean of Canton State—reviewing and initiating change. The difficulties of this latter process are only too evident in the Canton State (C) and (D) cases, and are discussed in Chapter 5.

OPERATING MECHANISMS: CONTROL AND INCENTIVE SYSTEMS

One of the frequent headaches of organizational consultants is that senior managers in organizations, when confronted by problems, have a tendency first to request a management training program, and second, help in restructuring their organization. The former may, if successful, provide executives with additional skills but does not necessarily help solve the problems of the organization. The latter simply puts people in sets of different boxes, but the boxes, however carefully sculptured, do not of themselves necessarily produce any change in behavior. What produces change in behavior is change in those operating mechanisms that measure certain kinds of behavior and reward or punish it. The behavioral consequences of control and incentive systems are profound as the most cursory inspection of the effect of reimbursement mechanisms on behavior in the health care system would demonstrate. The lack of reimbursement for outpatient care led, until recently, to an overemphasis on high cost hospital treatment, the consequences of which are still being suffered.

Anthony (1965) distinguishes among strategic planning, management control, and operational control. Strategic planning is "the process of deciding on objectives of the organization, on changes in these objectives, on the resources used to attain these objectives, and on the policies that are to govern the acquisition, use, and disposition of these resources." Management control is "the process by which managers assure that resources are obtained and used effectively and efficiently in the accomplishments of the organization's objectives." Operational control is "the process of assuring that specific tasks are carried out effectively and efficiently." The first determination is a program of committing what resources to what programs. Budgeting is the process of deciding who will spend what, when, how, and for what in the future. Accounting tells you who did spend what and how well in the past.

The purpose of a management control system is to take the objectives of the organization as given and to enable the managers of the organization to control it. It is a regular process in which key measures of organizational input and output are compared so that they may be influenced in time and so that the manager can have an influence and make a difference. This means being able to attribute some kind of management and performance responsibility. It is a cybernetic process in the sense of comparing actual and intended, inputs and outputs. What is compared may be a forecast, a norm, a limit, or a target. The problems with control systems in the health field are that good measures are hard to come by, especially on a regular basis and not as a result of special research studies. The usual health statistics are far too intermittent and delayed to be of any value as part of a management information system. Nor is there consensus even about the units of measurement, e.g., patient visit, patient illness, illness episode, or physician hour!

There is a great temptation because of the difficulties of measurement to build a system around what can easily be measured such as the volume of service or the cost of service or the cost of staff time. This, though not unreasonable, can result in absurdities. A cost accounting system for a clinic can measure the amount of time spent on doing a chest x-ray or a physical examination. It is therefore possible and feasible to develop standard times for doing these procedures and to obtain productivity rates. By pushing more patients through the system, one can increase productivity. By using less expensive staff time than that of physicians, one can reduce cost per unit of production. But this method of measurement cannot so easily be applied to disciplines like psychiatry or community medicine. When these measures are applied to such disciplines, they are very obviously not cost effective. These results lend spurious support to those who would regard this as less than surprising and consider that expenditures on such functions should indeed be reduced. Moreover, there is a considerable difficulty in such systems in determining how overhead should be allocated and charged off because the form of allocation, while easily made arbitrarily, will produce behavioral results such that it may diminish the use of a central service when the goal is to increase its use.

A control system has to provide information. It is only as good as the speed, quality, and reliability of that information and whether or not it provides feedback about critical aspects of the task in a way that is useful to the recipient manager and to the provider of information. If it does not do this, it will be garbage in, garbage out. Physicians especially, and health workers in general, loathe filling in forms, especially if the product is invisible or inimical to them. (The Harvard Community

Health Plan's early attempts to build a management information system were bedeviled by this.) If the system is useful to them as well as to the manager, the quality and value of the system will improve immeasurable. This is merely an application of motivational theory: Involvement is a motivator.

This feedback will usually be about variation from a standard or over a limit. In peer review as practiced in the Foundation for Health Care Evaluation or as described in the Peer Review problem case (or in PSRO's), feedback is usually variation from standard patterns of practice. (As a solution to the problem of cost escalation, one must wonder about this. The development of alternatives to high cost hospitalization and the incentives to use these are fine. But the cost of monitoring deviations is often higher than the savings discovered by doing so and the real crunch in cost reduction may be to change the standards themselves.)

There is no manager in the system in peer review, but the physician obtains feedback from some group supposedly like himself which periodically monitors some aspect of his behavior, usually his billing, and adherence to quality standards. While the evaluative monitoring process is done by the peer group, they do not usually have any great degree of power over the physician and will rarely invoke sanctions. It is true that information alone can help (Irish general practitioners learning of the true cost of their prescriptions to the health service were shocked and subsequently more modest) and that the disapproval of one's peers as a normative form of control is not insignificant. But sanctions more severe than disapproval will rarely take the form of recommending additional education or providing a degree of supervision and almost never take the form of removing the license of the physician. Moreover, one wonders about the perceived legitimacy of quality standards set up by others. More direct and regular incentives or disincentives may come from the third party, namely, the insurer who may pay or refuse to pay the physicians bills. Thus, the measurement mechanism is not linked directly and systematically to an incentive system. Of course, one might well say in despair what does it matter how well designed a system is when no one wants constructive criticism for it is all that they can do to cope with constructive praise.

An additional problem is that the valued incentives in many health institutions lie outside patient care. In teaching hospitals, physicians are primarily concerned with teaching students and doing research, and their careers lie in the medical school departmental hierarchy rather than the hospital. Moreover, the ability to obtain research grants from outside foundations insulates them to some degree even from medical school sanctions. Thus, the hospital may have relatively little power over many of the physicians providing the patient care within its walls, for it cannot provide valued rewards either in the form of salary or promotion. Where then are the real incentives to reduce the costs of patients care? Especially when prevailing (though slowly changing) reimbursement mechanisms pass on the cost of anything and everything to the consumer. Even if it is possible for a physician or a hospital to find some way to increase productivity and reduce costs, what incentive is there for the individual physician or nurse to do this? None of the savings (or kudos) accrue to the institution or individual, except rarely in some Blue Cross experiments. Moreover, it is uncommon for measurement systems to be able to keep track of current productivity so that the effect of improvements can be detected!

The University of Missouri-Kansas City (B) case describes a control system based on the problem-oriented medical record invented by Weed (1970). It allows patient care units to determine regularly the efficiency of their performance. Who the manager is in the system, what incentives are available to him, and what he can in fact influence (and how) are questions for pondering. In the Department of HEW cases one may also wonder about the possibility of influence on the progress of programs, even though measures of this progress exist.

Key questions about any control system are who has what responsibility for what, and what is being measured? Is the result of the measurement system (and any incentives attached to it) to do the same cheaper, do more of the same, or to do something different? Is there in fact any linkage between what is being measured and any kind of incentive? Is the nature of the feedback involved regular, or only on exceptions? Is the nature of this feedback timely in the sense that it is received rapidly enough and in a way which is likely to have some impact on behavior? Or is there some kind of lag or delay in the system sure that is unlikely to produce change?

In conclusion, any management control system is intended by its development to focus the manager's attention on what is being done, what ought to be done, what the difference is, and how much is being expended. Cost is only a convenient form of data, of measurement, for the one important purpose of such a system is that it encourages and discourages health care behavior.

MANAGEMENT BY OBJECTIVES

A form of control system which has successfully been applied in the health field as well as in industry is management by objectives M.B.O. (Brady, 1973), and the form by which it is known at HEW, the operational planning system (O.P.S.). This is not so much a management control system in Anthony's terms, as an operational control system as well as a device for insuring the implementation of planning and the motivation of individuals in an organization. This latter is extremely important, for many traditional motivational systems meausre individual managers or patient care staff against some set of standards, or against each other, rather than against the objectives which they collaboratively, with the organization, set for themselves to attain.

Levinson (1970) has specifically criticized M.B.O., not so much in concept as in application. It is intended to be a method of defining and reconciling people's objectives with those of organizations, appraising progress toward the attainment of those objectives, and rewarding that progress. As a process it is meant to assist the measurement and judgment of performance and the relation of individual performance to organizational goals. It is intended to clarify the job, the expectations of accomplishment, to foster competence and growth, to enhance communication, and to serve as a basis for judgments about promotion and salary. Thus, it is both a stimulus of motivation and a device for organizational control. The sequence of events is that the individual discusses his objectives with those of his superior, who establishes targets, checks progress through a series of checkpoints and then determines the results.

However, Levinson points out that it is often difficult to pin down objectives. Frequently these may be interdependent, yet the individual does not have control over those others who may influence his success, so emphasis should be on the system and on counseling. Often because time is short, peers do not get together. The superior may find it difficult to evaluate progress because this may be experienced as a hostile act. This evaluation process is always subjective and because of this may lead to a spurious focus on supposedly objective goals with a neglect of vague goals. Often personal objectives are left out, and there is a very real question as to whose objectives are being served. While the process should be mutual, it often is not.

O.P.S. is a particular application of management by objectives and the Department of HEW cases describe how the system is supposed to work and how it has been received in a number of different Departments of Health, Education, and Welfare. In a civil service system, there are few incentives to those who are successful and negligible disincentives to those who fail, for promotion is more heavily tied to seniority than it is to performance. Thus, the system may be less than effective in a federal bureaucracy in motivating individuals toward the attainment of objectives than it is in providing a tracking system for top management of what is being done. One wonders how long it might take to discover whether things are off track, and when things are off track, and if that might be too late. Brady (1973) feels that the system can work effectively in the public sector, where objectives are complex and require much coordination. But the objectives may take the form of interim results rather than ends.

La Framboise has castigated the wave of alphabet soup of management techniques (M.B.O., D.P.B., O.D., etc.) which inundated the Canadian government and especially its health services over the last decade. He pointed out that while each was to some degree valid, management techniques tend to be associated with individual enthusiasts, and when applied in large numbers and with little sense of the real intent, become a succession of games which bureaucrats learn to play. A danger is that any technique has, in addition to its stated reason for being, latent intentions and/or effects. O.P.S. can be experienced as an attempt to reduce the autonomy of top HEW managers by feeding control information to the secretary rather than assisting them in their jobs. If so, they will play the game of meeting their superior's expectations for data, but it will have little mening. Techniques are not ends, they are means. A manager has to do certain things and get others to do them also as efficiently and effectively as possible. All management techniques are intended to help him think through this process clearly and carry it out well. If this is not the real purpose, and is not seen to be so, no technique will work.

Note for "The Great Lakes Clinic Foundation (A) (B) (C)"

Description of the Cases

These three cases deal with the decision to restructure nursing services of the hospital division of the Great Lakes Clinic Foundation (GLCF), implementation of the decision and implications of the new structure for GLCF. GLCF is a large multi-specialty group practice (over 200 physicians) with clinic, hospital, education, and research divisions. GLCF is best known for open-heart surgery and other highly specialized or complex medical procedures.

The (A) case is set in 1971. At this time GLCF had an annual budget of $40 million; 1000 patients per day were treated at the clinic; the 600-bed hospital was running at close to 100% occupancy. The nursing structure was traditional (Director and Assistant Director of Nursing), with responsibility to one of three administrative directors of the hospital. (The use of three rather than one administrator was new in GLCF.) The nursing department was felt by the physicians to be unwieldy, not responsive to change, and generally difficult to deal with. At the end of the (A) case, a decision must be made by the Executive Vice-Chairman of the Board of Governors regarding possible restructuring of nursing services.

The (B) case, also set in 1971, describes in general terms the major restructuring which took place. The Director and Assistant Director of Nursing had resigned. In their place were seven clinical Directors of Nursing who reported to the Administrative Director to whom the Director of Nursing had reported previously. The seven women were drawn primarily from supervisors and head nurses within the hospital. The case issues concern the workability of such a system in light of certain early problems which were developing.

The (C) case, set in 1973, describes the Clinical Director system as it developed and focuses on the points of view of the Clinical Directors, the Administrative Director over them, and the Executive Vice-Chairman of the Board of Governors. The latter is considering impact of the arrangement on GLCF, the Administrative Director, and the Clinical Directors.

Methodology

This series could be used most effectively by distributing the (A) case before class, discussing it in class, and distributing the (B) and (C) cases in class, allowing time for discussion of each since both present a set of "solutions" but also raise new problem issues.

Teaching issues include organization redesign as a means of changing internal relationships, resistance to change and means of dealing or not dealing with it, and the use of groups rather than individuals in management roles.

GREAT LAKES CLINIC FOUNDATION (A)

In September 1971, Dr. Paul Mueller, Chairman of the Board of Governors of the Great Lakes Clinic Foundation (GLCF), and Dr. David King, Executive Vice-Chairman of the Board, were meeting in Dr. Mueller's office to discuss the latest problems between physicians and nurses in the Great Lakes' 600 bed hospital.

"I had another visit from one of the surgeons," said Dr. Mueller. "He said he was both desperate and angry. After the Board of Governors agreed with him that there was a need for more intensive care beds for post-operative patients he started negotiating the various arrangements. He found the space and the money. But when he talked to the Director of Nursing, she told him that it was impossible to get enough nurses to staff another ICU. He tried to argue with her but she continued to say it was impossible so he came to me for support. I'm at the end of my rope with that woman, too. Dave, we must make some changes in the nursing service and we must do it now!"

A Brief History of GLCF

In 1912, five established private physicians in a large midwestern industrial city, decided to enter into joint medical practice. They built a clinic building over the next two years and in 1914 formally incorporated as the Great Lakes Clinic Foundation, a not-for-profit corporation. The Foundation was directed by a Board of Trustees and all physicians employed were salaried. Besides providing direct medical care on a referral basis in the clinic and hospital, GLCF included research and teaching divisions.

When the clinic opened in 1914, the staff consisted of thirteen physicians. By 1917, their practice had expanded sufficiently to necessitate the addition of a 237 bed hospital to the facilities. In the 1920's, a tornado destroyed substantial sections of the clinic facilities and resulted in the loss of over 100 lives. The clinic began to rebuild but efforts were restrained by the financial crises of the country throughout the 1930's. The 1940's saw substantial growth of the patient population and GLCF facilities and increasing specialization by the medical staff. In order to cope with the changing needs and goals of GLCF, a Board of Governors composed of nine members of the professional staff with responsibility for operations of the clinic and hospital was established in 1950. By this time there were 100 members of the medical staff, 150,000 patient visits per year, and 440 hospital beds in use.

GLCF in 1971

Substantial growth of GLCF continued through the 1960's. By 1971, GLCF had a staff of 165 physicians, 225 nurses, 275 interns and fellows and 2,000 ancillary employees. Approximately, 1,000 patients per day were treated at the clinic and the 600 bed hospital was running at close to 100% occupancy.

Since the creation of the Board of Governors 20 years before, this group had gradually been given a greater role in the control of the resources and activities of GLCF by the

Trustees. Under the chairmanship of Dr. Mueller, who was both a physician and an experienced businessman, the Board began working very closely with the Executive Committee of the Board of Trustees to create a closer relationship between the business and professional activities of the Foundation and to develop plans for long-range expansion, which was anticipated as substantial.

In the 60 years since the establishment of GLCF, the physicians in the group practice had continued to be active and interested in the operations of the Foundation. Because GLCF was a group practice in which physicians received a salary rather than fees for service, they were interested in how funds were generated and utilized, especially in the hospital. The physicians in general and the Board of Governors in particular became deeply involved in the hospital's operation and when the hospital director, who had held his post for 18 years, resigned in 1971, he was not replaced. Instead, three administrative directors were appointed. Each of these directors was responsible for a set of people and activities throughout all divisions of the Foundation (i.e., clinic, hospital, research and education). Because the responsibilities of the administrative directors were thus rather diffused, the Board of Governors felt they would have more control over the actual workings of the Foundation under this system.

The three administrative directors had the following title and responsibilities:

Administrative Director for Patient Care: responsible for all medical personnel who had patient contact with the exception of the physicians, e.g., social services, pharmacy, physical therapy, nursing.

Administrative Director for Administrative Services: responsible for the areas which did not have direct patient contact such as maintenance, security, purchasing, housekeeping.

Administrative Director for Management Services: responsible for areas concerned with patient logistics such as communications, admissions, reception, secretarial.

These three directors reported directly to the Executive Vice Chairman of the Board of Governors, who in 1971 was Dr. King. (See Exhibit 1 for organization chart.)

The Nursing Area

GLCF nursing services in 1971 followed the traditional lines of organization. There was a Director of Nursing, an Assistant Director of Nursing, supervisors, head nurses and staff nurses. The Director and Assistant Director were both middle-aged women whom nurses and physicians alike considered to be members of the "old guard."

As the GLCF facilities expanded and the physicians assumed more control over operations, a number of problems had arisen in the nursing area and between nurses and physicians.

First, a number of physicians had repeatedly experienced problems in dealing with the nursing administration. One physician, the director of the cardiovascular area, had simply refused to accept the authority of the Director of Nursing. The nurses in his area were responsible directly to him and operated outside of the nursing hierarchy. Other physicians had taken less drastic action but there had been a number of complaints directed to Dr. Mueller that the nursing area was unresponsive to physicians' needs and goals. The physicians felt that the nursing administration was particularly reluctant to become involved in any innovative programs or to allow nursing services to be used in any but the most traditional ways.

The hospital administration (first the Hospital Administrator and then the Administrative Director for Patient Care) felt that the Director and Assistant Director of Nursing acted as a barrier between hospital administration and the nurses providing direct patient care. The nurses themselves were not allowed to participate in decision-making nor were the wishes of the administration relayed to them.

There were also some indications that the staff nurses were dissatisfied with the nursing administration. Specific complaints included lack of nurse contact with the Director and Assistant Director, even at the head nurse level. The Director had begun by making occasional rounds on the units but the administrative demands of her position had apparently led to increasingly greater distance from the floor nurses. In addition, there was an extremely high turnover of nurses: 1969-70 turnover was 65-70%, compared to the national average of 45-50%.

Finally, there was a problem which directly affected nurses, physicians, administration and patients. Recruitment of nurses to replace those leaving was extremely difficult, with positions left unfilled at times. The Director of Nursing, who handled all recruiting, felt that it was impossible to recruit enough competent nurses to staff any additional units and consequently, new units such as intensive care units were not being opened even when they were clearly needed.

Dr. King's Decision

With these problems in mind, Dr. King returned to his office. His conversation with Dr. Mueller was not the first on the topic of nursing services. He realized that he had to make a decision and recommend action very quickly. The pressures from the professional staff were growing stronger and no purpose would be served by letting the situation continue as it was.

GREAT LAKES CLINIC FOUNDATION (B)

In October 1971, the nurses of the Great Lakes Clinic Foundation(GLCF) were informed of several major administrative changes in the organization of the clinic hospital. First, they received word that effective immediately the Director and Assistant Director of Nursing had resigned. Although there had been some rumors circulating in the hospital concerning problems with nursing administration, the actual resignations came as a great surprise to most of the nurses. A substantial amount of anxiety arose, especially at the supervisor and head nurse levels as these nurses began asking themselves and one another if they were in danger of being fired as part of a management shakeup.

Some of the anxiety abated over the next few days as several supervisors were asked to meet with top management of the hospital to discuss nursing structure and their roles in a new organization. After several weeks, the staff nurses were informed that no new Director and Associate Director of Nursing would be appointed. Rather, there would be seven Clinical Directors of Nursing, each directly responsible for certain units in the hospital and each reporting to the Administrative Director of Patient Care Services. Of the seven Clinical Directors, five were supervisors in the hospital, one was a head nurse and one came from another hospital where a somewhat similar organizational structure existed.

Exhibit 1

Great Lakes Clinic Foundation (A)
Partial Organization Chart, 1971

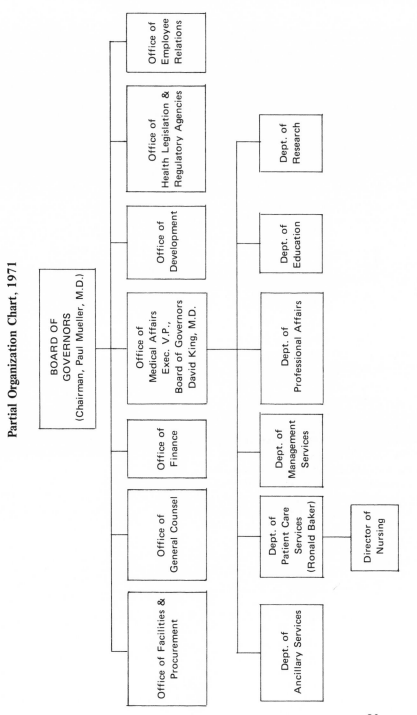

The seven new Clinical Directors, whose ages averaged approximately 35, began meeting as a group and with other management units to determine specific areas of responsibility for each CD and for themselves as a group. They were given no formal job descriptions and only general ideas of what they should do. In a meeting with the Board of Governors in November, the Clinical Directors were reminded that the bi-yearly visit of the Joint Commission of Hospial Accreditation would take place in December and they should be prepared for scrutiny by team members who were usually quite conservative. At the same meeting, one of the Clinical Directors informed the Board that she had been approached by the president of the City Nurses Association who expressed the concern of that group about the changes in nursing structure in the hospital.

After this meeting and in view of the issues introduced there, Dr. King wondered if he should take some further action related to the changes, and if so, what he should do.

GREAT LAKES CLINIC FOUNDATION (C)

In November 1973, two years after the major restructuring of nursing administration in the Great Lakes Clinic Foundation (GLCF) Hospital, the nursing administration, which consisted of a group of six Clinical Directors (CDs) of Nursing, met a major challenge to nursing in the hospital. In that month the hospital expanded from 644 beds to 982 beds with consequent increases in nurisng staff and patient population. Three months later, it was clear that the expansion had gone smoothly and that the Clinical Directors were a strong and effective unit in the hospital administration.

Development of the CD Group

As described in the Great Lakes Clinic Foundation (B) case, the top administration of GLCF had restructured the Division of Nursing in 1971, replacing the traditional nursing hierarchy with a group of nurses who were given the titles, Clinical Directors of Nursing. The original group of nurses had consisted of seven women, most of whom were drawn from the supervisory level with the hospital. At the time they became CDs, these nurses had little idea of what was expected of them. One CD, however, had been hired specifically for this position and had come to GLCF from another hospital which had a decentralized nursing organization. This nurse felt she understood the requirements of the position.

During the first few months of the new organizational structure, two CDs resigned. They were replaced by two women who were head nurses in the hospital. After the change, the group remained stable for over a year until the oldest CD, who was then 62, retired. The other six CDs decided that they would divide her areas of responsibility among themselves rather than attempt to find a new CD and top management agreed to this plan.

After the November 1973 expansion, each CD had responsibility for coordinating the work of 150-200 nursing and auxilliary employees covering four to eight units with a total of 100-200 beds. (See Exhibit 1 for areas of responsibility.) Specific duties of the CDs are described in Exhibit 2, a job description written by them. Basically, each CD coordinated the work of her units with the administration of the hospital and with the other CDs; provided supervision of the nurses including professional counselling to supervisors, head nurses and staff nurses; acted as administrative director of the staff on her units, e.g., handled hiring, firing and promotion; and participated in the hospital administration by preparing budgets, sitting on policy committees, etc.

The Clinical Directors' Point of View

The six CDs saw themselves as a closely knit group which had evolved over two years through constant interaction and internal negotiation. Each CD had an office on one of the units for which she was responsible. In addition, all six shared a set of offices adjacent to the hospital administration offices. In the shared offices, the CDs frequently met both formally and informally to discuss problems and coordinate policy decisions.

Almost every day most of the CDs had lunch together. Because the group had strong informal channels of communication, they were well aware of what happened on all units. Furthermore, a policy of encouraging staff to move from one unit to another rather than leave the hospital altogether meant that each CD knew not only all the nurses on her units but also many of the nurses on other units, so in-depth discussions of staff and their needs were frequent.

All of the CDs felt that they worked well together. Disagreements were always settled within the group by discussing issues until concensus was reached. Each woman had her own style of leadership and her own set of priorities for managing. These differences were appreciated but did not hinder the action of the group as a unit.

The six women felt that the success of the system was in part due to the fact that they had all become CDs at about the same time; they all had found it necessary to define their own jobs since top administration had provided only general guidelines; they all had similar backgrounds and experiences before becoming CDs; and they all were fairly close in age, ranging from early to late thirties. The feeling that their growth together made them a successful group had been reflected in their decision not to replace the retiring CD.

All of the CDs were pleased with and committed to the Clinical Director structure. One advantage to this system was that nursing employees on the floors were able to have much closer contact with nursing administration than they had formerly. Problems could be solved more quickly with less red tape; more individualized counselling could take place; nursing staff members could easily be moved from one unit to another if they desired; more authority could be delegated to head nurses because they had close backup from the CDs; there was more flexibility in decision-making and more opportunity for change.

Another advantage of the structure was that nurses, through the Clinical Directors, had improved communications inter- and intra-departmentally. In certain situations, the CDs made recommendations which affected the whole hospital. One instance of this had occurred when the additional beds were added to the hospital in November, 1973. The CDs had submitted a plan for physical reorganization of units to the physicians and administrators who had approved the plan with some modifications. As a result, patients, equipment and person-nel for entire units had been relocated to meet departmentalized objectives.

Finally, the CDs were pleased with the existing organization because it gave each of the six women a chance to continue to have patient contact and involvement in clinical decision-making and care rather than isolating them as administrators who would rarely visit a floor, talk to a patient, or counsel a floor nurse.

As the roles of the CDs had evolved, their relationship with the Administrative Director for Patient Care Services, Mr. Ronald Baker, had also evolved. By 1974, they felt that although he had final authority over policy decisions, more immediate administrative decisions concerning nursing were made by the CDs who kept Mr. Baker informed of their actions informally.

The Administrative Director's Point of View

Shortly after the nursing area was reorganized, the original Administrative Director for Patient Care Services resigned and was replaced by Mr. Baker. Like the CDs, Mr. Baker was pleased with the reorganized structure of nurisng services.

He saw the CDs as basically responsible for clinical care while he was responsible for actual administration on all units. He described himself as the person who provided motivational and administrative leadership, who saw to it that the policies and procedures of GLCF were adhered to. He felt that he was very supportive of the CDs and of the nursing employees of the hospital.

Mr. Baker was especially pleased that recruitment of nurses was going well (in 1974 this was handled by a specific personnel area entitled Nurse Recruitment) and that attrition had dropped well below the national average (45-50%) to 27% for RNs and 10% for LPNs in 1973 for a staff of 365 RNs and 412 LPNs.

Dr. King's Point of View

Dr. Mueller, Dr. King and the other members of the Board of Governors felt they had attained the goals they envisioned when they reorganized both the top hospital administration and the Department of Nursing in 1971. By 1974, a delicate balance between the Administrative Director for Patient Care Services and the six Clinical Directors had been reached. Mr. Baker was dependent on the CDs for technical expertise and clinical care decisions; the CDs depended on Mr. Baker for management know-how and administrative support. Despite his overall satisfaction with the arrangements, however, Dr. King was concerned about the long-range effect of the recent major expansion on the administrative structure of the hospital.

The greatest pressures of the expansion seemed to be on Mr. Baker. Because of his extensive responsibilities in the area of patient care, it was possible that Mr. Baker could not continue to work as closely with the Clinical Directors of Nursing, and to critically review their requests and activities with them as he had been doing. Would Mr. Baker become overextended and cease to play an integrating role by virtue of his removed but involved position? If Mr. Baker no longer played this role, would the nursing services run as smoothly?

Another aspect of this question concerned the future of the six CDs. Would they find that their responsibilities in the expanded facility were too great to allow them to have the close nurse contact they valued? Would it be necessary to find a new CD, and could an outsider be successfully integrated into the group. Or perhaps one of the CDs would gradually find her work less challenging and move to another hospital or into teaching.

These were questions about what would happen in the next six months or so. More interesting, perhaps, Dr. King thought, and more difficult, were questions about longer range situations. GLCF had been at the forefront of administrative changes in the health delivery organizations. But would the present organizational structure continue to be appropriate, in light of the growing need to manage costs and the continuing desire of the physicians to be involved in management? This question was hard to answer but Dr. King felt strongly that it should be considered so that if changes became necessary, GLCF administration would not be caught unprepared.

Great Lakes Clinic Foundation

Exhibit 1

Hospital Nursing – Division of Patient Care Services

Area	Clinical Director	Division	Type of Unit	Head Nurse	Clinical Director Relief Assignment
I	Ms. Merry (Margaret)	7 N	Hypertension-Research	Ms. Gloris	Ms. Jones
		7 U	Pediatrics	Ms. Kiser	"
		7 E	Pediatrics	Ms. Charnes	"
		6 N	General Med/Surg	Ms. McGinnis	Ms. Friedlander
		6 S	Musculoskeletal	Ms. Turner	Ms. Siar
		6 Q	Musculoskeletal	Ms. Harris	"
II	Ms. Mrozinski (Sue)	CVU	Cardiovascular Intensive Care	Ms. Lifson	Ms. Moran
		CIC	Coronary Intensive Care	Ms. Harper	"
		2 S	Surgical Intensive Care	Ms. Scorpius	Ms. Merry
		Rec. Room	Recovery Room	Ms. Hull	"
		7 S	Cardiovascular	Ms. Eaton	Ms. Jones
		7 Q	Cardiovascular	Ms. Richards	"
		MIC	Medical Intensive Care	Ms. Copp	Ms. Moran
III	Ms. Siar (Patricia)	IV Nurses		Ms. Nesmitt	Ms. Moran
		4 W	Private Med/Surg	Ms. Files	"
		4 N	Eye-ENT-Plastic	Ms. Coolidge	Ms. Friedlander
		5 S	GU-GYN-Renal	Ms. Synge	"
		5 Q	GU-GYN-Renal	Ms. Lee	
		Float Assignments: 7-3:30 p.m. 3-11 p.m. 11-7 a.m.			

		Unit	Specialty		
IV	Ms. Moran (Barbara)	7 W	Psychiatry	Ms. Chernefsky	Ms. Merry
		4 E	Hematology-Med-Oncology	Ms. May	Ms. Moran
		3 W	GI Med/Surg-Gen Surg	Ms. Cassidy	"
		3 N	GI Med/Surg-Gen Surg	Ms. Roberts	Ms. Siar
		3 E	GI Med/Surg-Gen Surg	Ms. Modeste	Ms. Jones
V	Ms. Freidlander (Alma)	8 W	Gen Med/Surg	Ms. Brown	Ms. Friedlander
		5 W	Neurosurgery	Mr. Bentley	"
		5 N	Neurology	Ms. Coolidge	Ms. Merry
		5 E	Peripheral Vasc-Endocrine	Ms. Sharp	"
		Emergency Room		Ms. Lincoln (AHN)	Ms. Siar
VI	Ms. Jones (Donna)	8 S	Cardiovascular	Ms. Chung	Ms. Friedlander
		8 Q	Cardiovascular	Ms. Martins	"
		6 W	Gen Med/Surg	Ms. Patterson	Ms. Merry
		6 D	Hemodialysis		"
		4 A	Pre-op Cardiovascular	Ms. Lightbody	Ms. Siar
		4 B	Dermatology-Ambulatory	Ms. Smith (LOA)	"
		3 A	Pre-op Cardiovascular	Ms. Lardner	Ms. Friedlander
		3 B	Pre-op Cardiovascular	Ms. Nobel	"
		Private Duty Nurses			Ms. Siar

Evening Supervisors: Ms. D. Whele – Ms. V. Dans
(3-11 Float Assignments)
Rotating Supervisors: Ms. E. Barrett – Ms. N. Vale – Ms. D. McCann

Night Supervisors: Ms. G. Faux – Ms. E. Bourke – Ms. E. Christenson

Staff Development Instructors: Ms. E. Gershwin – Ms. P. Waters – Ms. S. McMay – Ms. K. Olan – Ms. S. Berrigan

Clinical Coordinator: Ms. V. Marimekko
Secretarial Team Leader: Ms. K. Lundquist

Nurse Clinician: Ms. B. Clark
Nurse Epidemiologist: Ms. J. Fischer

GREAT LAKES CLINIC FOUNDATION

Exhibit 2

Division of Patient Care Services

Director of Clinical Nursing

Position Description

General Responsibilities

Organizes and administers the Department of Nursing in conjunction with other Directors of Clinical Nursing. Assumes total authority and responsibility for nursing service on a designated number of nursing divisions.

Position Duties

1. Implements administrative policies established by the governing authority.
2. Establishes lines of authority and delegates responsibility in the Nursing Department.
3. Defines the duties of nursing service personnel, consistent with good administrative techniques, to assure that department objectives are accomplished.
4. Selects and recommends promotions of qualified nursing staff.
5. Participates in and sometimes initiates conferences and discussions with administrative and nursing staff to encourage participation in formulating departmental policies and procedures, promote initiative, solve problems, and interpret new policies and procedures.
6. Coordinates activities of various nursing units, promoting and maintaining harmonious inter and intra-departmental relationships.
7. Promotes and maintains good public relations.
8. Analyzes nursing and auxillary services to improve quality of patient care and to obtain maximum utilization of nursing staff time and abilities.
9. Approves programs of continuing education and training at all levels of nursing service for purposes of improving and updating patient care.
10. Encourage participation of all levels of nursing staff in continuing education programs for professional growth.
11. Meets with Medical Staff through proper committee structures to plan and establish effective procedures for optimum care of patients, suggesting and recommending improved nursing practices and procedures where medical care aspects are involved.
12. Works in conjunction with Recruitment Department and the Employment Department in the hiring and placement of all nursing personnel.
13. Disciplines and discharges persons for the purpose of maintaining an organized and competent staff.

14. Performs duties such as reviewing evaluations for nursing staff and subsequent salary adjustments, authorizing leaves of absence, and approving time and vacation schedules.
15. Assists in preparing and administering budgets for the Nursing Department. Prepares reports as required and performs other duties delegated by the Director of Patient Care Services.

Position Qualifications

1. Education, training, and experience:
   a. Graduation from an accredited school of nursing with a Bachelor's Degree preferred and a Master's Degree desirable.
   b. Current licensure by the State Board of Nursing is required.
   c. Five years or more nursing experience, including satisfactory experience as Head Nurse, Supervisor, or Assistant Director with demonstrated administrative ability and leadership skills.
2. Aptitudes:
   a. Administrative skills required to plan and control all activities of the Nursing Service Department and to confer and cooperate with other department heads.
   b. Human relations skills necessary to establish good relationships with all people.
   c. Communicative skills required to effectively present oral and written ideas and views to superiors and subordinates.
   d. Numerical skills necessary in order to review and evaluate reports and statistical data and to make various computations in planning departmental operations and budgets.
3. Personal Characteristics:
   a. Possesses intelligence, integrity, initiative, self-discipline, and leadership ability.
   b. Good mental and physical health.

Job Relationships

1. Workers supervised: Supervisory staff and all professional and ancillary nursing staff
2. Supervised by: Director of Patient Care Services
3. Promotion from: Supervisor or Head Nurse
4. Promotion to: No formal line of promotion

Professional Affiliations

Professional affiliations are desirable with local, state, and national nursing associations.

Note for Canton State University
Academic Medical Center (A), (B), (C), (D)

Description

The series of four cases describes one medical school dean's attempts to take a critical look at the organization of his school in relation to its changing tasks and the needs of people, with the help of an outside academic research team. In the A case the medical school is described, its programs detailed and its organization commented on by a variety of people involved in it. The B case reports the results of NIH-financed organizational study and details the major recommendations of the study group. These are based on current organizational contingency theory. In the C (Chapter 5) case the earlier approaches to implementing the recommended changes are laid out and the early change process described graphically through the comments of many of the people involved. The D case (Chapter 5) presents the situation of the dean's resignation and the dilemmas of the continuing change process.

Teaching Objective

The case series has two major objectives, namely the application of organizational theory to the design of medical school organization and an illustration of the organizational change process. The cases are best handled sequentially in which the reader should consider the dilemmas posed successively at the end of each case. Thus the first case raises questions about what should be done in the light of some obvious problems of organization as evidenced by the experiences of medical school personnel. The second case lays out the academic answer and describes the application of the matrix organizational design to the medical school. The reader may consider whether this is entirely applicable. The latter two cases deal with the change process and describe one particluar method of implementation. Whether this is the best or how it could be improved is an open question.

CANTON STATE UNIVERSITY
ACADEMIC MEDICAL CENTER (A)

In August, 1971 Dr. John Gray, Dean of the School of Medicine and Vice President of Health Sciences at Canton State University (CSU), was wondering what actions he could take to improve the organization of the Academic Medical Center. In performing its missions in the areas of medical research, education, and delivery of health care, the Medical Center faced a diverse, complex, and changing environment. Medical science was increasing in complexity at an increasing rate, placing demands on the medical profession for greater specialization. Patients and government were demanding more comprehensive and better coordinated care. In response both to those demands and to financial incentives, medical schools across the country were attempting to increase class sizes and train more physicians for both specialized and primary care.

Simon Hunt, M.D., Director of the Regional Medical Program at CSU, commented on the environment of American medicine:

> I think the problems with medical schools, hospitals, even doctors' offices is that they are static institutions. They have planted their flag in a fixed location and wait for people to come to them . . .

> Organized medicine is voluntary with small staff and is just not equipped to deal with the overall problems of health care delivery. The physician . . . being an individualist and tending to be of a conservative persuasion and not being a good team member, can't do very much either as an individual or through voluntary organizations.

Dr. Gray considered the complexity of the tasks and environment of the Medical Center and the characteristics of the professionals who comprised the faculty of the Medical School and the medical staff of the teaching hospitals. As he analyzed the organizational arrangements of the Medical Center, he questioned the effectiveness of its structure and reporting relationships, promotion and reward systems, and organizational climate for achieving the Center's goals.

Canton State University

Canton State University was located in a sparsely populated, relatively poor, and predominantly rural state. A large number of the state's residents were members of ethnic minorities in the United States, and many could not speak English. In many parts of the state no physicians were immediately available.

The CSU Medical School was the only one in the state. It was heavily dependent upon the state legislature for funding, and it could not estimate funding levels accurately from year to year. The legislature had initially approved construction of the Medical School, hoping to increase the number of physicians practicing in the state. Preference for admission to the School was given to state residents.

The School of Medicine was less than ten years old. Its full-time faculty numbered about 250, and there were approximately 50 students in each year of the four-year M.D. Program, as well as a number of M.S. and Ph.D. candidates. The faculty represented several basic science disciplines in addition to numerous clinical specialties and sub-specialties. Together with its affiliated hospitals the School sponsored internships and fully accredited residencies in over ten specialties.

CSU was located in Canton, the largest metropolitan area in the state. The Medical School and the Canton City Hospital, its major teaching hospital, were within a few blocks from the center of the University campus. Other schools of the health professions at CSU were not physically proximate to the School of Medicine. However, plans had been made to construct new facilities for all these schools near the School of Medicine. Dr. Gray felt it was important to train physicians and other health professionals in a common setting, saying:

> I think we should teach more human biology to everybody, especially to nurses, pharmacists, and dentists. Anybody going into the medical professions should have a common educational experience . . . The physician will always be at the apex, but he will have a higher regard for his co-workers who are not physicians when they have a better basic education . . . We can't

continue to educate them in different boxes and expect them to talk the same language. We need to pull together these educational experiences.

The Academic Medical Center

The Academic Medical Center was an affiliation of the School of Medicine and several teaching hospitals. There was no single legally recognized entity called the "Academic Medical Center." (In some centers such an entity did exist.) The School of Medicine was a part of CSU. It was formally separate, had identifiable assets and employees, and had separate management for each of the hospitals. The hospitals were each legally separate organizations formally linked to the Medical School through affiliation agreements. Medical School faculty comprised most of the medical staff in each of the affiliated teaching hospitals. Other personnel, such as secretaries, technicians, nurses, dieticians, and administrators, were generally employees of only the Medical School or only one of the hospitals.

The hospitals provided the Medical School with settings for clinical education and research. The hospitals hoped to deliver a higher quality of patient care through their affiliations with the Medical School than they could without such affiliations. The Medical School and its affiliated hospitals were very dependent upon each other for successful accomplishment of their individual goals. Effective organization of the Medical Center was important to all of the member institutions.

Hospital Affiliations

The Canton City Hospital (CCH) and the Canton Veterans' Administration Hospital (CVAH) were the major teaching affiliates of the School. CCH was a 200-bed city general hospital with a large outpatient service. Through the School of Medicine CCH was managed by the University under contract from the city. CCH had its own board of trustees and was funded from the city budget. All physicians on the CCH staff were members of the faculty of the School of Medicine.

The CVAH was a 550-bed general medicine and surgery hospital located a few miles from the University. Most but not all of the physicians on the staff were Medical School faculty. A very significant portion of the clinical teaching programs of the School was conducted at the CVAH. Most internships and residencies included a period of rotation at the CVAH as well as at the CCH.

The Canton Mental Health Center (CMHC) was also a city facility. Located among the cluster of Medical School buildings, its professional staff were members of the School's Department of Psychiatry. Its primary focus was upon outpatient and community-oriented programs, although it did have a small inpatient service.

In addition to the major teaching hospital affiliations mentioned above, the School also had affiliations with a number of other hospitals in Canton and in other parts of the state, and participated in several programs to deliver health care in remote parts of the state. While providing expertise for these programs, the Medical School utilized them as clinical settings for teaching and for research in health care delivery.

Organization of the Academic Medical Center

The Academic Medical Center was composed of the School of Medicine and its major teaching hospital affiliates. Although this super-organization did not have an independent legal status as an organization, there were great interdependencies among the component organizations. Clinical research and education were often performed by the same individuals and at the same time as direct patient care. The specific directions of the Medical School programs highly influenced those of the hospitals, and vice versa, making it difficult to consider organizational issues in one member organization of the Medical Center without considering those of the others.

Dr. John Gray was both Dean of the School of Medicine and Vice President of Health Sciences. He reported directly to the University President. The deans of the schools of the health professions and the Medical Director of CCH reported to Dr. Gray in his position as vice president. The chairmen of the Medical School departments and several assistant deans and Medical School administrators reported to him in his position as dean. (These portions of the organization of the School of Medicine are shown in Exhibit 1, and the organization of CCH is shown in Exhibit 2.)

As shown in Exhibit 1, the organization of the CSU School of Medicine reflected the departmental structure typical of most medical schools in the United States. Faculty, grouped by specialty, reported to a department chairman, who was responsible to the Dean. Some had joint appointments as members of two or more departments. The norms of academic freedom of faculty and individual autonomy for physicians supported a rather "loose" organizational structure.

Faculty in basic science departments had offices located in a building of classrooms, laboratories, and faculty and administrative offices. Some full-time clinical faculty were also located in this "basic sciences building," but most had offices in the CCH, CMHC, or CVAH. Part-time faculty participated in Medical School programs very infrequently and did not have offices in the Medical Center complex.

Each faculty member performed some combination of the tasks of education, research, patient care, and administration. Very few faculty performed only one of these tasks. Within a department, the faculty member was formally responsible to his chairman for all of his tasks. In some departments the chairman had delegated responsibility for parts of the department's activities to an associate chairman.

Tim O'Malley, Director of Administration in the Medical School, commented on the position of the Dean: "The relations between the Dean and the faculty chairmen were something I had to learn. This is a guy in office (the Dean) by the sufferance of those he's supposed to administer."

George Campden, M.D., Medical Director of the CCH, said: "Department chairmen are selected on the basis of scientific excellence. Suddenly thrust into a job that's primarily administrative, they are not prepared."

Andy Light, Medical School Comptroller, said of the School's environment and of his position: "This place changes every other day, not every other year . . . I have responsibility without authority in a lot of areas, and I don't like that situation at all, but I don't know what to do about it."

"Service Chiefs" (or "Directors") were formally responsible for patient care in each of the specialty services in each hospital. Chairmen of the Medical School clinical departments all were chiefs of the corresponding services in the CCH. For example, the chairman of the Department of Surgery was also Chief of the Surgery Service in CCH, and the chairman of the Department of Pediatrics was also chief of the Pediatrics Service in CCH. Chiefs of sub-specialties were not necessarily department chairmen. Except for temporary assignments as "acting department chairmen," none of the service chiefs at the CVAH were department chairmen. Some were designated as "associate chairmen" in their departments.

Following the national pattern in Veterans' Administration hospitals, service chiefs at the CVAH reported to a "Chief of Staff" for their activities at the Hospital. The CVAH Chief of Staff, a member of the School's Department of Psychiatry, held no administrative position in the Medical School.

As shown in Exhibit 2, there was no line of responsibility from most of the directors or chiefs of service to the hospital administration. However, the Chief of Anesthesiology, a member of the Department of Surgery, was responsible to an assistant administrator in CCH, and the Director of Clinical Laboratories, a member of the Pathology Department, was responsible to the Hospital Administrator. The Director of Radiology was also Medical Director of CCH. He was shown as being responsibile to himself, then to Dr. Gray in the CCH organization. No other service chiefs were shown on the CCH organization chart as it appeared in the Fall of 1971.

The Director of the CMHC was responsible to both the Board of Trustees of the Center and the Chairman of Psychiatry. Psychiatry faculty provided consultation services at the CCH, and CCH physicians provided consultation to CMHC inpatients when requested.

Several faculty and administrators commented on the affiliations between the School of Medicine and the hospitals and on the relationships among patient care (the primary goal of the hospitals) and education and research (the primary goals of the Medical School). Allen Blake, Administrator of CVAH said:

> As the Dean has expressed it many times, "We're not affiliated, we're married."
>
> Education to me is rather bothersome at times because of certain individuals. Our primary mission is patient care. Some physicians think education is the priority . . . They even say things in front of the patient that they shouldn't. The hell with the patient. The disease is interesting [to them].
>
> Sometimes they at the University make a decision that we can't accept. The chairmen make a unilateral decision without consulting us. For example, the chairmen determined that the house staff could have a three week vacation. The VA can't live up to that because they allow only 12 or 14 vacation days a year. We cannot take our proportional share when the house staff rotates through here.

Philip Kraft, M.B.A., Administrator of CCH, commented on the missions and environment of the Hospital and on its relations with the Medical School:

> My most important community is the patient. If we can't please them, I might as well get out of the business.
>
> Patient care, education, research and community service . . . The problem is if we are going to have education [at the Hospital], it should be paid out of education money. The problem comes when somebody tries to put education above patient care, and that's to the detriment of the patient.
>
> It is important that we keep communicating with the Dean, so that we don't become as inefficient as most teaching hospitals are.
>
> There's the whole business of coordination of all of the hospitals in the Center . . . Like the satellite clinics. [The clinic director] reports to no one.

George Campden, M.D., CCH Medical Director, commented:

> They're [the medical staff] no different than any other medical staff. They're a bunch of goddam individualists, and they don't like to abide by rules.

There certainly are some [conflicts among patient care, research and teaching]. There are several clinical departments that put patient care first. That doesn't regress teaching too far because they can go on together. But others don't care much about patient care, but are interested in research.

[Conflicts between the Hospital and Medical School] are not a problem because the Hospital is run by the Medical School. The problem is the Hospital meeting the expectations of the Medical School . . . especially with money and adequate personnel.

Dr. Simon Hunt noted: "It's a problem for medical schools that in the clinical years they use the apprenticeship system. They [faculty] don't have time to prepare their lectures. They treat their students as they were treated. They don't organize their life because patients organize their life for them. If some patient becomes ill, they miss a class."

Faculty Contracts, Compensation, and Promotion

In general, faculty were recruited by their department chairmen. All full-time faculty received a salary agreed upon by the faculty member and chairmen, and approved by the Dean. Full-time clinical faculty professional fees were collected by the Medical School and put into a "Faculty of Medicine Fund" (FMF). Allocation of FMF monies was made by the Dean to budgets of both basic science and clinical departments. FMF monies were not paid directly back to the individual physician. While high earning departments (such as Pathology and Radiology) had a bargaining position based upon their contribution to the FMF, budgeting of FMF monies was not strictly proportional to departmental earning capacity.

Research grants and project funding were formally awarded to the School, but the principal investigator usually controlled the majority of these funds. Salary was included in research and project funding, but the award of a grant from a source outside the School did not mean an automatic salary increase for the principal investigator.

Other than by assuming administrative positions, physicians had few opportunities for formal promotion in the hospitals, and there were few administrative positions at all attractive to physicians. Assuming one of these positions meant reducing the physician's patient care activity or increasing his total workload. Within the Medical School, faculty sought academic promotion from starting positions of Instructor or Assistant Professor to tenured positions of Full Professor. Such promotion and tenure decisions in the Medical School were made by a faculty committee. The committee considered the candidate's academic performance, which could be displayed best through research accomplishment. In addition to receiving recommendations of the department chairman and other faculty, the committee often solicited comments from colleagues outside the School in the candidate's field.

Lee Hall, M.D., Assistant Dean for Student Affairs, commented on the career dilemma of Medical School administrators: "Your promotions come from your department. I'm constantly apprehensive. I don't think either of my bosses [the Dean or the Chairman of the Department] fully understands what I do."

The Educational Programs

The CSU School of Medicine had three major educational programs: 1) post-graduate education, training interns and residents, 2) graduate degree education, leading to a Ph.D. or M.S. degree, and 3) under-graduate medical education, leading to an M.D. degree.

Post-graduate and graduate degree education were to a great extent responsibilities of individual clinical and basic science departments, respectively. Graduate students took courses outside of their major department and outside of the Medical School, but the program for any one student focussed heavily upon a single discipline, and he worked closely with faculty in his department on research projects.

Internships could involve a single specialty, e.g., Medicine or Pediatrics, or could be rotating internships, in which the intern spent time in several specialties. Residencies were offered in individual specialties, and the several years of residency training were successfully completed upon receipt of specialty board certification. While house officers (interns and residents) were students in the post-graduate educational program, they also provided the bulk of patient care in the hospital and played an important role in teaching M.D. candidates. House officer salaries were paid by the hospitals, and for those specialties in both the CVAH and the CCH, each hospital provided a portion of the house officer's salary.

The undergraduate education program at CSU was structured along innovative lines. Rather than following the traditional curriculum structure reflecting academic disciplines, the first two years of the four-year program included interdisciplinary study of biological principles and human organ systems. Courses were the responsibility not of departments, but of committees composed of faculty from several departments who were actually teaching the course. For example, a physiologist, pharmacologist, cardiac surgeon, cardiologist, pediatrician, pathologist, and anatomist constituted the Cardiovascular Committee. Sometimes several members of a committee attended laboratory and classroom periods together. Dean Gray stated an objective of this form of curriculum organization, ". . . This permits correlation in examining situations in which . . . interrelationships among traditionally separate disciplines can be emphasized. . . ."

Clinical material and student contact with patients were introduced in the first week of the program and integrated throughout the first two years, as well as in the traditionally clinically oriented third and fourth years. The third and fourth years of the program included required and elective courses and clerkships in the clinical specialties (learning experiences as rotations in clinical settings where the student was given a well-prescribed and supervised patient responsibility). These clerkships were the responsibility of individual departments.

In addition to and apart from the department structure shown in Exhibit 1, the Curriculum Committee of the faculty was responsible to the faculty for undergraduate medical education. This committee was composed of some members appointed by the Dean and some elected by the faculty. It had two sub-committees, Steering Committees I and II, responsible for the first and last two years of the program, respectively. The members of the steering committees were chairmen of the various course committees. The Assistant Dean for Education was an *ex officio* member of the Curriculum Committee. He was a young faculty member, recently appointed to the assistant dean position. Faculty were not formally responsible to him for their educational or other activities.

Lester March, M.D., Assistant Dean for Undergraduate Education, spoke of his new job and of the educational program:

> The job has several components . . . One, it's a vehicle for enhancing the effectiveness of the curriculum committees. Providing an office in which things can be implemented . . . Coordinating . . . To a lesser extent it's a way for me to contribute to these committees.

> There is difficulty in implementing programs that they [the curriculum committees] favor . . . Getting things through the faculty as a whole is a block . . . I perceive a lot of power lying with the department chairmen, especially in the third and fourth years. They carry the prestige and

weight. In implementation of any curriculum, you're dependent upon these people to provide space and people. I'm sure Dr. A. [department chairman] and others don't see me as anything but [a subordinate to] him in a relationship. This exists for me, and for the curriculum committees as well.

One structural change that I perceive is to let the departments exist to do research and provide clinical service. Let the departments contribute or sell teaching capacity. Let the teaching body have the leverage in terms of money to implement what it sees . . . It would be difficult to get through, but it would greatly strengthen the teaching programs. In [Department Q] teaching is considered a chore and referred to by that name . . . People may or may not do what they're asked to. In an institution that has its primary purpose as teaching physicians, things are upside down. While there's been lip service to that effect, there is no consideration that teaching will lead to promotion. I would like to pull this from the department chairmen. People say that teaching, research, and service [patient care] blend together. I think they should be better delineated, so we can deal with these functions separately.

Lee Hall commented on the curriculum and on the Dean's office:

Steering Committee II is totally unsuccessful in coming up with any innovations in the third and fourth years. I blame the Administration. The Curriculum Committee does not have authority. The Dean has sided with the department chairman. He has kept the Curriculum Committee emasculated . . . Our very best faculty have been on the Curriculum Committee but have not had the authority to do anything. Recently the Dean appointed Lester March as Assistant Dean of Undergraduate Education. Hopefully he will get us off the dime, but he's relatively inexperienced. It's like being thrown into a lion's den.

Tom Evans, M.D., Chairman of the Department of Pediatrics, commented: "To my way of thinking the single problem with the curriculum is we do not have specific leadership. We need an associate dean for academic affairs . . . We appointed a guy who probably doesn't have enough clout."

Scott Richard, Ph.D., Chairman of the Department of Physiology, said: "50% of my time is in research, 50% in administration, and 65% in teaching . . . That's right. It adds to more than 100%. The curriculum requires a lot of faculty time. There are lots of meetings."

Dan Spring, M.D., Acting Chairman of the Department of Psychiatry, said: "The [integrated teaching] committees are a good idea, but the mechanisms are difficult. It's hard to evaluate if it's better than if it were taught by departments."

Ed Goodman, M.D., Acting Chairman of the Department of Pathology, commented: "The teaching committee I'm on is totally ineffectual. It's totally dominated by one group , . . From the basic science end, the basic scientists have not been interested in fighting for their rights . . . I think it's got potential."

John Gray said of the curriculum: "The undergraduate curriculum is the property of the entire faculty, not the chairmen and not the Dean. It's kind of a self-controlled anarchy, in which everybody is responsible."

The Organizational Climate

Many people at the CSU Academic Medical Center felt that they had an organizational climate somewhat unique in academic medicine. For example, Scott Richard ommented:

The major thing that makes the School unique is there is a lot of interdepartmental communication that we wouldn't have without the integrated curriculum. It creates a social, casual atmosphere.

This is not the place for a guy who wants to retire. It's for a guy who wants to build something. There's a lot of flexibility in the system. The bad side is there's a lot of chaos.

It's so much fun to walk into the Department of Medicine and have people know your name. At [School V] it was so different. No one knew what anyone else was doing, and if they did, it was to screw them.

In the early days everybody had to cooperate to get the job done, and it has carried through.

Ed Goodman said: "We have considerably less interdepartmental bickering than most medical schools. It doesn't mean we don't fight like cats and dogs—but there still is a spirit of cooperating."

Several people mentioned the processes of decision-making and budgeting, and a number commented on the management style of the Dean. Allen Blake of CVAH said: "We could be arbitrary in the allocation of money, but we don't feel it's the way to do it. The Chief of Staff gets all the chiefs together, and they decide."

Andy Light noted: "Dr. Gray is a very democratic man. There's a lot of politics in the budget because of the differing abilities of departments to earn money."

Ed Goodman did not agree: "Gray is very much an autocrat. I'm for it or he won't survive . . . When decisions have to be made, he makes them. He makes committees up of people so he gets what he wants . . . At least that's my gut feel."

Tom Evans commented: ". . . Fights—Every Tuesday afternoon I lose an hour and a half over how money earned in the School of Medicine is to be distributed among departments. That's done in sub-committees appointed by the Dean. There's an awful lot of administrative activity to get money for the department . . ."

George Campden stated: "My opinion is that there's probably too much openness. I think Gray wastes a lot of our time with committees, trying to be democratic. I personally would be willing to accept an autocratic decision."

The CSU Strategy and Organizational Structure

Dr. Gray felt that the Center had moved beyond the initial stages of its development and needed a way of setting priorities. He said:

Our environment is infinitely elastic. There's so much to do that it doesn't matter what we do first . . . But I think we're coming to the end of this period in our development . . . Now we will begin to need objectives and strategy. Up until now I think we would have had less fun and grown less quickly if we had a game plan and tried to follow it . . . But I think we are past that period now.

He thought the CSU Medical Center should not put its major emphasis on research, but rather it should try to balance education, research, and patient care in an effort to improve the health care in the state. He felt the present organization held the Center back in its pursuit of these missions, but he was not sure what organizational changes to make.

Exhibit 1

**Organization of the School of Medicine
Canton State University**

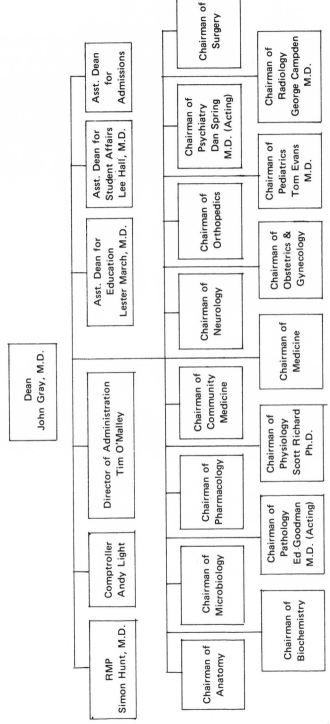

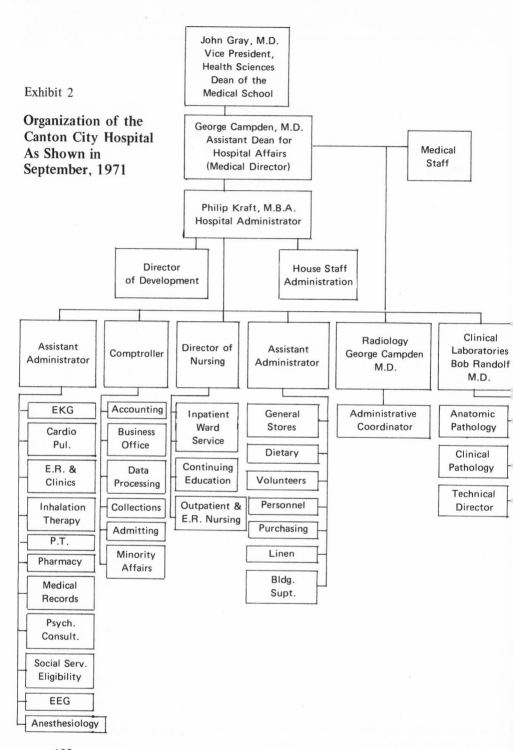

Exhibit 2

Organization of the Canton City Hospital As Shown in September, 1971

John Gray, M.D.
Vice President,
Health Sciences
Dean of the
Medical School

George Campden, M.D.
Assistant Dean for
Hospital Affairs
(Medical Director)

Medical Staff

Philip Kraft, M.B.A.
Hospital Administrator

Director of Development

House Staff Administration

Assistant Administrator

Comptroller

Director of Nursing

Assistant Administrator

Radiology
George Campden
M.D.

Clinical Laboratories
Bob Randolf
M.D.

EKG

Cardio Pul.

E.R. & Clinics

Inhalation Therapy

P.T.

Pharmacy

Medical Records

Psych. Consult.

Social Serv. Eligibility

EEG

Anesthesiology

Accounting

Business Office

Data Processing

Collections

Admitting

Minority Affairs

Inpatient Ward Service

Continuing Education

Outpatient & E.R. Nursing

General Stores

Dietary

Volunteers

Personnel

Purchasing

Linen

Bldg. Supt.

Administrative Coordinator

Anatomic Pathology

Clinical Pathology

Technical Director

CANTON STATE UNIVERSITY
ACADEMIC MEDICAL CENTER (B)

In February, 1972 Dr. John Gray, Dean of the School of Medicine and Vice President of Health Sciences at Canton State University (CSU), was considering recommendations for reorganization of the Academic Medical Center. (See Canton State University (A) for details on the organization of the Medical Center). In late 1971 the CSU Medical Center participated in the Study of Organization and Management of Academic Medical Centers. In February of 1972 the Study Team presented their findings at a meeting of representatives of the four centers that participated in the Study. Dr. Gray wondered whether these recommendations applied to the CSU organization, and if any of them were applicable, what steps he should take to implement organizational changes.

The Study of Organization and Management

The Study of Organization and Management of Academic Medical Centers was financed by the National Institutes of Health (NIH) and was conducted by a group of four organizational theorists and consultants, seeking to apply concepts developed originally in management of industrial organizations to problems of medical school and hospital organizations. The Study focussed heavily on application of contingency theories of organization.

Contingency theories of organization[1] state that there is no one best way to structure all organizations, but that organizational arrangements are contingent on task and environmental characteristics. The most successful organizations are those that achieve a good fit among task and environmental requirements, types of individuals in the organization, and organizational arrangements.

The Study looked at the organization of four academic medical centers (medical schools and their affiliated hospitals, sometimes but not always formally designed as "medical center"). One pair of sites, A and B, were private medical schools, each with both private and municipal hospitals. Both were located in the same large urban area. Site D was similar to Site C (CSU). It was located in a different but similar state, was relatively new, state-owned, and had a similar set of hospital affiliations.

Data collection for the Study included interviews, observations of medical school and hospital activities, inspection and analysis of documents such as by-laws and affiliation agreements, and analysis of responses to a questionnaire sent to faculty and administration. All department chairmen, members of the Dean's office, administrators in each hospital, chairmen of key committees, and a sample of faculty in each site were interviewed by the Study Team. A sample of approximately half of the faculty and administration were then sent a comprehensive questionnaire developed by the Team. Sixty percent of the questionnaires were returned directly by the respondents to the Study Team.

Presentation of the Findings

In February, 1972 the Study Team presented its findings to representatives of the four sites, at a meeting held at the National Institutes of Health. The major points presented were as follows:

1. Each of the missions of the academic medical center (education, research, and patient care) has independent value in our society.

[1] See Lawrence, Paul R. and Jay W. Lorsch, *Organization and Environment* (Homewood, Ill.: Richard D. Irwin, Inc., 1967).

2. Each has its own identifiable sub-environment and tasks which require different organizational arrangements and different orientations of the professionals performing these different tasks.

3. In the medical center—in contrast to industry—the key individuals in the organization perform multiple tasks. These multiple task professionals (MTP's) tend not to recognize the differences among their tasks to be as great as they actually are.

4. The organization must help MTP's differentiate among tasks. It can do this by separating responsibilities for the different programs at administrative levels. For example, it can separate the roles of clinical department chairman and chief of service, and can have different individuals at the dean's office level responsible for education, research, clinical programs, and administration.

5. The different scientific disciplines and clinical specialties also represent significant sub-environments of the medical center. The traditional departmental organization reflects response to these sub-environments.

6. To meet the demands of both types of sub-environments, a mixed model[1] of organization is required. In this organization (Exhibit 1) a faculty member is responsible both to the chairman of his department and to directors of each program in which he participates. Thus, for different tasks such as teaching a course to medical students, providing patient care, or doing research, a faculty member would be responsible to different people.

7. While the mixed model of organization might appear complex, it is a reflection of the complexities of the tasks and environments of the academic medical center.

8. If effectively implemented, the mixed model would result in more manifest conflict in the organization. This conflict is inherent in the differences among the tasks themselves. Effective conflict management, as shown from research in industrial settings, requires open acknowledgement of conflict, rather than avoiding issues or smoothing them over and attributing them to personality problems.

Reaction to the Presentation

The Dean from Site A agreed with the findings that MTP's tend to blur distinctions among tasks. He said, "What we have is a bunch of switch-hitters, and they're batting only about .150 from either side of the plate." Of the four sites, the greatest separation of the roles of chief and chairmen was at A. In site A different associate deans were responsible for each of undergraduate medical education, clinical affairs, scientific affairs, and administration. Respondents to the questionnaire in site A also reported the greatest distinction in characteristics among tasks, and the most conflict among pairs of tasks. The average quality of relations among departments was also perceived by respondents as being the lowest of the four sites in site A.

Dr. Gray thought about the points made by the Study Team and wondered whether they applied to CSU. The mixed model of organization had several features that were quite different from traditional organization of academic medical centers. While he felt strong pressure to improve the present organization, Dr. Gray was not sure of the specific steps he should take to implement changes. He also wondered what specific considerations were necessitated by the fact that the key individuals in the organization were professionals, and most physicians.

[1] The mixed model is similar in structure to the "matrix organization" occasionally found in industrial organizations.

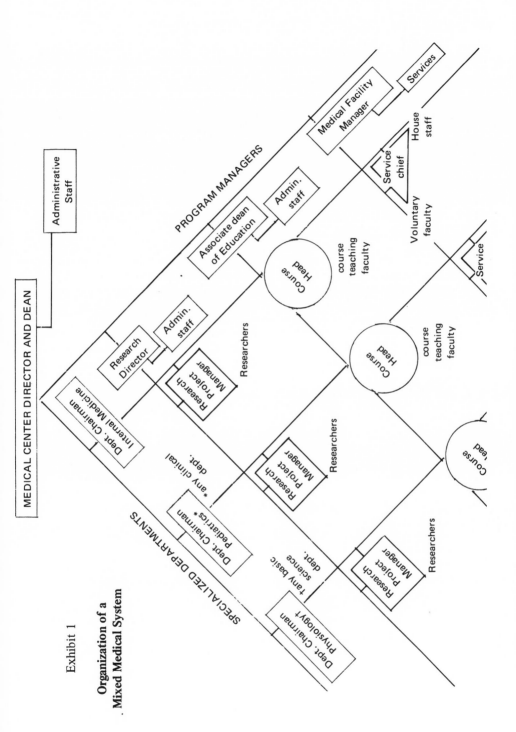

Exhibit 1

Organization of a
Mixed Medical System

MEDICAL CENTER DIRECTOR AND DEAN

Administrative Staff

PROGRAM MANAGERS

SPECIALIZED DEPARTMENTS

Medical Facility Manager

Services

Service chief

House staff

Voluntary faculty

Associate dean of Education

Admin. staff

course teaching faculty

Course Head

Service

Research Director

Admin. staff

Research Project Manager

Researchers

Course Head

course teaching faculty

Dept. Chairman Internal Medicine

Dept. Chairman Pediatrics*

*any clinical dept.

Research Project Manager

Researchers

Course Head

Dept. Chairman Physiology†

†any basic science dept.

Research Project Manager

Researchers

105

Note for University of Missouri
Kansas City Medical School (A), (B)

Description

The A case describes the history, objectives, organization, and curriculum of a highly unusual and innovative medical school. In the B case a unique control system is described, which was developed for this organization and based on the problem-oriented medical record. The control system allows the three medical care organizational units to receive weekly accounts of their performance.

Teaching Objectives

The A case essentially provides the reader with an opportunity to consider the relationship of organizational design to organizational purpose and objectives. Using current organizational theory the reader may consider whether or not the unusual organizational design will further the designated purpose of the medical school and what problems are likely to be experienced both within the medical school and between it and its affiliated hospitals. The B case which can be read alone or which may be prefaced by the A case as background, describes an unusual control system more like that found in industry than that usually found in health institutions. However, whether this control system will enable measurement of achievement of the objectives of the institution to be made, and if it does that, whether it will allow for timely intervention in programs, is a question the reader should consider. What exactly, for example, does the administrator receiving the control data have any influence over? How will this system work? How could it be improved?

UNIVERSITY OF MISSOURI
—KANSAS CITY MEDICAL SCHOOL (A)

Drs. E. Grey Dimond, Provost for the Health Sciences of the University of Missouri—Kansas City, and Richardson K. Noback, Dean of the medical school, were preparing for the annual consultation visit by the Liaison Committee of the Association of American Medical Colleges and the American Medical Association. The school had been in operation for approximately one year, since August 1971. Drs. Dimond and Noback planned to review the history, goals and objectives of the new school with members of the committee. The Liaison Committee had been closely following developments at the new school because of the unique nature of its program.

Embodied in the organization structure of the new school were a particular set of innovative associations and affiliations for the purpose of educating students and delivering health care. In view of the fact that over the years Kansas City had established no less than eleven medical schools, none of which was operating, the two physician-administrators tried to anticipate the kinds of questions that might be asked by their colleagues on the Liaison Committee who were accustomed to a more traditional type of medical school. They felt the central question was, "How effectively was the school structured to achieve its goals in the light of the unique philosophy of education and the delivery of patient care?"

Arrangements were made for members of the Liaison Committee to speak to several medical school administrators, Docents, students, and community leaders. In addition, they received outlines of the academic plan for the school and access to any material that might be useful in piecing together background information about its origin.

The first thing committee members did was try to find out about the community forces which were instrumental in getting the medical school started.

The Community

Kansas City, Missouri, located in the westernmost part of the state on the Missouri River, is a large urban center of close to a million-and-a-half residents.[1] Approximately 617,000 people live in Kansas City, Missouri, and 181,500 to the west of the state line in Kansas City, Kansas. The greater metropolitan area sprawls over six counties and two states. The city's economy was built around agriculture and livestock. In recent years, it has changed to industrial, manufacturing, and service industries.

Hospital Hill, the site of the new medical school and many of its affiliated teaching institutions* is located in the downtown area which falls in the southeastern part of the quadrant in what was once a run-down and blighted area. This area is serviced by both the Office of Economic Opportunity Neighborhood Health Center and the Model Cities Programs. In the fall of 1972, relations between the Hospital Hill institutions and the community health centers were still being worked out, and it was hoped that medical students would soon be assigned regular rotations at them. Much of the section had been razed in the course of various redevelopment programs. The most outstanding of these was the Crown Center project consisting of 25 city blocks, undertaken by Hallmark Cards, Inc., which was headquartered in Kansas City. When completed in 1983, this center would include apartment units, office space, a hotel, two motor inns, two retail areas, an entertainment center, an audio-visual and graphic communication center, and parking facilities.

The area immediately adjacent to Hospital Hill on the other three sides contained many three family dwellings and some small businesses. There was some evidence that the increasing number of students was having an impact. A few new pubs catering to a youthful lunchtime clientele opened, and there was talk of building student housing.

Civic Leaders

The first local group to become actively involved in health care delivery in the area was the Kansas City Association of Trusts and Foundation incorporated in 1949. The president of the Association since inception was Mr. Homer Wadsworth. In this role, he had been one of the key personages in the development of health care locally and on a national level. Mr. Wadsworth's philosophy of civic activism was expressed by him in a paper written in 1972.

> The country is crying out for leadership at all levels of our society, and especially in our public affairs. I think it is wise to consider systematic ways of building such leadership, and drawing people for such services from every level of our society. It is particularly fortunate that a sizable number of such people now exist in Kansas City, perhaps on the order of about 200 or so, with about 50 being persons long acquainted with conditions and long accustomed to joint effort.

*These institutions include Kansas City General Hospital Medical Center, the Children's Mercy Hospital, the Western Missouri Mental Health Center of the State Division of Mental Diseases, the Brothers of Mercy Extended Care Facility.

As early as 1961, Mr. Wadsworth was pursuing the objective of establishing a new medical school in Kansas City. The following is an excerpt from a letter he wrote to the then City Manager, Mr. Robert A. Weatherford, Jr., in regard to the nonprofit corporation that would take over General Hospital.

> We have here at General Hospital the second largest body of clinical resources in this country not now fully utilized for both undergraduate and graduate instruction in medicine. This leads to an obvious conclusion: If we can create a stable, properly financed, and efficient operation of the General Hospital, and if we can assure medical school levels of training through affiliation with the University of Missouri, it is quite inevitable that a new medical school will arise from this effort. I would not hesitate to guess that this could be accomplished in less than five years.

A fellow hospital board member remarked of Mr. Wadsworth to a Liaison Committee member, "Homer Wadsworth has the ability to take the hospital out of politics into education. He can realize a dream for the future if anyone can."

Mr. Nathan Stark, Chairman of the Board of Crown Center Corporation; Senior Vice President of Hallmark Cards, Inc.; and Chairman of the Kansas City General Hospital and Medical Center Corporation, was another civic leader who was committed to the establishment of the Medical School.

Mr. Stark was also a member of the American Medical Association Committee on Undergraduate Medical Education, and the Liaison Committee of the AMA-AAMC, and was formerly Chairman of the American Hospital Association Committee on Hospital Governing Boards, and Vice Chairman of the Health Insurance Benefits Advisory Council of the U.S. Department of Health, Education and Welfare. He explained his involvement in the genesis of the new medical school to the committee.

> In 1946, a study was made to find why blacks weren't accepted as patients or physicians in Kansas City's hospitals, and to make recommendations for changing the situation. At the time, I was Chairman of the Area Hospital Association Health Facilities Planning Council. We tried to put some heat on the hospitals to cease and desist in this practice of discrimination, but got nowhere. Under the leadership of the Archbishop of the Kansas City-St. Joseph Diocese, we finally raised funds to convert an all-white maternity hospital into a fully integrated General Hospital. As a result, we provided a good place for black doctors to practice and a place where people could go regardless of race. This was the spark the community needed to integrate other hospitals.

In the 1950's Homer Wadsworth developed the idea of starting the Mental Health Foundation, which in turn built and staffed with federal, state, and local funds an intensive care psychiatric hospital.

By 1961, the Psychiatric Receiving Institute had gained national recognition as a first-class institution. At this time, the General Hospital, a city operation, was going downhill for the same reason most county and city hospitals were travelling the same course—lack of funds. The hospital was now at the point of being disaccredited, which meant it would no longer be able to attract house staff—the lifeblood of that hospital. On a county level, we tried to get a special taxing authority set up, but necessary state legislation failed.

It was during this time that our city was undergoing a very traumatic situation in which we had at least ten city managers. Homer Wadsworth finally captured the imagination of one of these more responsible city managers and sent him a letter outlining a plan for taking over the operation of the city's hospitals (General Number One for whites; General Number Two for blacks). The plan Homer Wadsworth outlined was very similar to that used in developing the prior successful Psychiatric Receiving Institute.

The city manager bought the plan and with our assistance sold it to the City Council. We formed our corporation—fifteen members—covering the entire spectrum of socio-economic life in Kansas City; entered into a contract with the City of Kansas City, Missouri to operate the hospitals on a fixed-fee basis; and with the Board of Curators of the University of Missouri to be responsible for all educational programs within the hsopital. This was a tri-party agreement in which General Hospital turned over all of its pediatrics to Children's Mercy Hospital for a fixed fee.

In trying to plan for the future, an Assistant Surgeon General advised us to call a meeting of national figures in architecture, government, medicine, and education. The Assistant Surgeon General agreed to chair the meeting. In order to insure frankness, we held a closed session for the first day of the meeting, and on the second day opened it to the public. The conclusions of these meetings were that we wanted both a medical center and a medical school.

For brevity's sake, let me now say that the next turning point occurred the day of the dedication of the new out-patient wing of the Menorah Medical Center in Kansas City where Dr. E. Grey Dimond was introduced to me. Homer Wadsworth, Grey Dimond, and I went back to my home and spent most of the afternoon talking about our plans and aspirations. Dr. Dimond said that if we were planning a traditional medical school, his advice was to forget the whole project. He outlined his imaginative thoughts about a new kind of medical education which captured both Homer and me.

Previously Homer Wadsworth had "twisted" the Dean of the University of Missouri School of Medicine into agreeing that he would take on the educational programs for General Hospital. Now, we went to see Vernon Wilson, the Dean of the Medical School in Columbia, and asked him if he could help us get Dr. Dimond to join us in Kansas City. This plan was delayed for some time; however, at about this time, Michigan State began to think about a two-year medical school. It seems they were in competition with the University of Michigan for state funds and were, therefore, looking outside their state for some help. General Hospital seemed to be the most compatible of hospitals available to provide the last two clinical years for them. Dr. Noback, who was then Executive Administrator of General Hospital,was in touch with the Michigan State people and worked out a deal. This would have put us well ahead of schedule in getting our medical school into Kansas City, but plans fell through when Michigan State decided to go the four-year school route.

Homer Wadsworth and I decided that if we were to get the medical school really underway, we would need a strong, imaginative person to head the school. Again, we sought the help of Dr. Wilson, who was now the Executive Vice President of the University of Missouri. The three of us had the same thought in mind: to bring Dr. Dimond back to the area. Dr. Wilson decided to opt for a Chair for Dr. Dimond at the University of Missouri in Columbia, giving him complete freedom to work with us in Kansas City. Dr. Dimond agreed but stated his desire to live as well as work in Kansas City. He pushed us to a commitment of at least $250,000 to support his ideas for getting the medical school launched.

A late evening meeting was held with Dr. Wilson, Dr. McCoy (then Chairman of the Medical Staff at General Hospital), Dr. Olson (Chancellor of the University of Missouri at Kansas City), and me. We came up with a commitment of $100,000 from the Medical Staff Fund of General Hospital; $100,000 committed previously by Homer Wadsworth and the Association of Trusts and Foundations, and a pledge on the past of Dr. Wilson that he would guarantee raising $50,000 toward this goal.

Dr. Wilson then called Dr. Dimond who agreed to accept a position as Vice Provost for Health Affairs at the University of Missouri at Kansas City.

Now we needed legislation to approve a new medical school and to get not only planning money—which was quite minimal at that time—but also matching funds to build the medical school. Every step of the way was fraught with problems.

When this part of our program was over, we had 100% support from every legislator in this entire area. This had never been accomplished before, and I know of no proposition in the immediate future that will do it again.

In 1963, Dean Noback was approached by the University of Missouri to be its agent for graduate medical education in Kansas City. He assumed the role of Executive Director of Kansas City General Hospital and Medical Center (KCGHMC) and then became acting Dean of the medical school in 1969 until the state contributed the operational dollars to the new school.

In Kansas City the general feeling was that the officials at the state medical school in Columbia regarded the idea of a new medical school as a political issue. According to Pat Brady, Associate Director of Kansas City General Hospital and Medical Center:

> It was civic initiative that brought about the medical school. The university wouldn't deal with the city in part because of municipal politics. This area had been trying to get a medical school for years. We had one at the turn of the century, but it was phased out during World War I.
>
> Some years ago the Board of Curators of the university decided to put their medical school in Columbia despite the fact that a contingent from the western part of the state went down to Jefferson City to fight for a school out here in Kansas City. When the corporation took over the operation of General Hospital in 1962, its goal was a medical school in ten years. The University of Missouri didn't want the responsibility of the deficit financing of indigent care. In the late 1960's, Dr. Olson prepared a report which was reviewed by a national body of health experts. The report examined the health needs of the entire state and concluded that another medical school was needed.[2] The choices for a site were Kansas City, St. Louis, and expansion at Columbia. The possibility that was offered the state and the university was that the county would build the new teaching hospital on city property and the current board of the hospital would continue to manage it.

The Missouri Commission on Higher Education passed two motions in September 1968 urging that 1) the Board of Curators of the University of Missouri proceed with the establishment of a medical school in Kansas City with a developmental objective of an entering class size of 100 students; and that 2) sufficient additional funds for this item should be requested in the regular budgetary process. The commission also recommended that the University carefully obtain adequate guarantees for the sharing of costs before committing itself to the opening of such a school.

Frank P. Sebree, President of the Board of KCGHMC, corroborated this belief: "The legislature was faced with a tremendous drain from the University of Missouri Medical School at Columbia which had an extremely high annual operating budget. They wanted it made clear that the state wouldn't have to pay for our patients at KCGHMC. Vernon Wilson wanted to know if we .at KCGHMC would progress fast enough. Everyone felt that we couldn't be innovative enough." Mr. Sebree further explained that as the agreement was finally worked out, it was determined that the city would continue to pay the cost of caring for the indigent ill after moving to the new hospital. The medical school would have the responsibility for undergraduate medical education at the hospital. The medical school would reimburse the hospital for teaching time on a quarterly basis.

In 1965, the voters of Kansas City approved two bond proposals that provided funds for: 1) an urban renewal project including 135 acres for the Medical-Dental Center, and 2) funds for the acquisition of land for the first stage of building and for the construction of the first portion of the core building to house common facilities. In 1967, the voters of Jackson County approved general obligation bonds to finance the replacement of the existing Kansas City General Hospital and Medical Center with a new teaching hospital. In addition to the bond money, as of September 1972, approval was received for federal grant and subsidized loans at a 3% guaranteed interest rate. Kansas City General Hospital Medical Center had applied for $1 million in Hill-Burton money. The entire projected cost of the new hospital was $29 million. The medical school building was expected to cost $13 million.

Capital costs for the medical school building in Kansas City were estimated at $13 million of which the university's share would be $4 million. It was expected that federal matching would provide approximately $8 million and other resources, the remainder. When projecting the budget, expenditures for support services for faculty were also projected. These included the cost of educational resources and supplies, secretarial and clerical assistance, library operations, maintenance and utilities. Exhibit 2 summarizes an early projected yearly budget of income and expenditures for the medical school. It is based on calculations common to other schools. According to Dr. Cross, Vice Provost for Health Science at UMKC, the projected cost of undergraduate medical education would be $3,700 per year in 1968 dollars.

When he made his proposal to the Board of Curators of the University of Missouri, Dr. Dimond promised to graduate 100 students per year for a $2 million annual budget at the 1968 dollar value Dr. Dimond told the committee that he had promised 1) to pay the affiliated institutions for their teaching time, 2) that the medical school would pay only for under-graduate education, and 3) that the faculty from the University of Missouri-Kansas City campus and the community would be utilized. A formula was eventually to be worked out for reimbursing the hospitals according to the amount of teaching time involved. "Several hospitals wanted students faster than we were geared up for. Our budget the first year was $560,000. This was a purely operational budget. For the first two years' development costs, the state legislature appropriated $2 million. Other money was contributed by local groups. Three hundred doctors volunteered time for teaching. Altogether, the 11 community hospitals that our students have access to have a budget of over $90 million including capital investments."

Goals and Objectives

Dr. Dimond wanted the committee to have a full understanding of his philosophy of medical education. It had guided the formulation of the goals and objectives of the new school. The main objective of the school was to produce what Dr. Dimond called "a safe physician." He defined what was meant by the phrase. Next he explained how the curriculum of a medical school could be developed:

"Safe" in this sense means several things. It means a sufficient fund of facts, e.g., to know that a normal blood pressure is approximately 120/80 mm. Hg. It means sufficient concepts, e.g., the physician knows how the blood pressure varies from right to left arm, and what is the range of meaning of a high or low systolic pressure compared to a high or low diastolic pressure.

In every area—fact, skill, or concept—safeness means that the physician applies this range of knowledge to the patient's welfare and that he will not deviate or lessen this standard of application if he is alone, or tired, or hurried: he is capable of monitoring the quality of his own performance, worth of licensure by the board, and worthy of public trust, i.e., a "safe physician."

He must be more than a collection of facts, skills, and concepts who can pass a test at a moment in time; he must also be a morally responsible problem-solver for people in difficulty.

A new type of medical school could be based on a single question: "What is a safe physician?" One could extend this question to all of the specialists of medicine: dermatologists, plastic surgeons, ear, nose, and throat specialists, hematologists, cardiologists, etc. All the physicians in a given community who identify themselves as "specialists" could come together and reduce to paper those facts, skills, and concepts that they would consider essential for a physician upon his graduation. Then those men in general practice should be asked to do the same, and take 12 to 18 months to finish the project; one would accomplish a great deal more than initially anticipated.

The result would be a large pharmacopoeia of facts, skills, and concepts. One would also have, perhaps for the first time in their lives, been faced with defining just what education is required to become a physician.[3]

Dr. Edward Cross, University of Missouri Vice Provost for Health Sciences, also met with the committee members. Dr. Cross came to the new medical school with a background of 21 years in the Public Health Service. During a period of that time, he had served as Assistant Surgeon General. In addition to his role as Vice Provost of the medical school, Dr. Cross was President of the Health Resources Institute, a nonprofit corporation dedicated to the development and integration of local health care systems in the community. As a result, a good deal of his time was spent acting as liaison between the community and the school.

Dr. Cross outlined the goals for the new medical school, as he saw them, to committee members:

My feeling is that education and service can't be separated. For too long, we haven't addressed ourselves to preparing a physician for his life's work. Dental schools have done a lot more in this direction. It has traditionally been six years from the end of high school before a med-student sees his first patient. We feel we want our students to appreciate all the different ways health care is delivered. We want them to think in terms of the whole person, not just illness. They should have the feeling that all of us are incomplete human beings. We also believe that the multidisciplinary team is the best way to achieve this and that peer relationships are the best way to deliver health care. We don't want our students to think in terms of whether it is a good teaching case or not. It is unrealistic to prepare people in a crisis-oriented situation, and then they are bored when they see regular cases. We want to emphasize the ordinary clinical setting. We're not training GPs but people who won't be merely disease oriented. We want our students to have an understanding of comprehensive health care. We want them to be safe doctors and know when they should seek the help of others. In the traditional system, the students tends to be seduced into a specialty. We want to let the student see the whole spectrum. I feel that a lot of our students will go into family practice and internal medicine.

Both Dr. Dimond and Dr. Cross referred the committee to the school's "Academic Plan" which they felt best expressed the goals and purpose envisioned by the key people responsible for the medical school's existence. The following goals are listed in the Academic Plan.[54]

A. To individualize the educational process for medical students by providing continuing contact between scholars at all levels and by facilitating the access of those scholars to all necessary sources of information.

B. To expedite and maximize the use of precious educational hours.

C. To educate the student in a prototye setting of his future office and practice relationships.

D. To develop a model of university-community cooperation, where each component provides those programs of special concern and interest to it.

E. To provide the student with a relevant clinician or basic science model with which he can identify and to which he can aspire.

While these goals did not differ markedly from the traditional medical school orientation, the emphasis on producing primary care physicians, with clinical specialties learned in affiliated community hospitals, was somewhat unique. Other distinctive aspects of the Kansas City approach were the emphasis on automation for conveying information and the encouragement of students to advance at their own pace. The Academic Plan explained these assumptions as follows:

A. That the core educational program should be designed and controlled by: 1) Individuals *primarily* concerned with the education of the student candidate for the M.D. degree, and 2) physicians who have limited, primary, and realistic patient care responsibilities for a representative population of patients. The care which they provide will extend into the community and home.

B. That patient problems as seen by the primary physician will provide the core content of the curriculum, thus providing an education which will be problem centered. 1) Basic sciences will be available from all university disciplines with few, if any, new departments created. 2) The clinical specialty disciplines as such will be available in the affiliate hospitals but their departmental organization will be responsive to that hospital rather than the curriculum per se.

C. That the professional of the future will depend heavily upon automated resources for needed factual data and for complex analytical solutions to problems.

D. That the best professional education will take place in the most realistic setting, and that the span of time required can be reduced through individualized approaches to the particular intellectual needs of each student and his particular background.

E. That by use of didactors and appropriate challenge examinations (compared with required national board examinations), the "threshold" recommended for basic factual information can be acquiared at a rate and in a manner responsive to the student's interest and capabilities, utilizing agreed-upon standards developed by all disciplines involved but screened by a senior scholar or Docent who has the student as his first responsibility.

The Docent Unit

The central philosophy of the school was embodied in the key organizing entity—the Docent Unit. The Docent Unit functioned three ways, as 1) a multidisciplinary health team; 2) an organizational framework; 3) a physical facility, and 4) an educational team. The head of a Docent Unit was a senior Docent who served as a clinician-scholar, student ombudsman, program planner counselor. Each senior Docent would be responsible for approximately 50 medical students as well as a Docent Unit Team consisting of physicians, students, house officers, nurses, chemical, medical, librarians, pharmacists, and clinical technicians. When the medical school enrollment reached 400, it was anticipated that there would be eight Docent Units. Together the eight senior Docents would make up the hospital's Department of

Medicine; yet each senior Docent would himself function like a department head or dean of a medical school. Medical students customarily spent 12 weeks per year on the Docent Unit. At any given 12-week period, 12 students, three from each of the last four years of the program, would be assigned to a unit. Three other Docents would be assigned to each Docent Unit, for a total of 32 Docents.

In addition to the Docents on each team, clinical faculty for the most part, were in private practice and either taught in addition to their patient load or participated in a visiting teacher-learner program. The basic strategy of the University of Missouri was to offer faculty appointments to teaching physicians without the commensurate salary and without tenure that accompany regular full-time appointments. This system had enabled the medical school to build up a full roster of clinical specialists at lower than usual cost. The value in terms of such a structure for quality control of teaching was that teachers who did not measure up could readily be replaced without the worry of a tenure system. The only members of the medical school community who were tenured were the Provost, the Vice Provost, and the Dean. They were on full-time salary from the university. Docents were full-time salaried teachers; however, half of their salary was paid by Kansas City General Hospital Medical Center and half by the medical school. The Docent was accountable to the Committee on Evaluation for his performance as an academician. Faculty selection, however, was to be made through the Council on Selection.

According to students interviewed by the committee the quality of teaching had been excellent except for some instances when foreign house officers demonstrated deficient training. With regard to Docent-student relationships in the few cases where these had proved unsatisfactory, there had been little difficulty in switching Docents.

The Council System

Docents participated in formulating school policy with respect to education, through their representation in the council system. The council system replaced the administrative and department structure of a traditional medical school.

There were five councils which recommended policy and educational decisions for the medical school: the Council of Docents, the Council on Curriculum, the Council on Selection, the Council on Evaluation, and the Council on Health Programs. There was a Coordinating Committee with representatives from all five councils.

The Council of Docents met with the Dean once a week to discuss matters of philosophy, procedure, and policy. It would eventually consist of 8 Docents as well as one representative from the Office of Medical Education, and one representative from the Dean's Office. According to the Academic Plan for the School of Medicine, "the Council of Docents represents the senior individuals who will have the responsibility for implementing the programs made available through the Council on Curriculum . . . The Docents, although represented on the Council on Curriculum, do not prepare the curriculum, but, function by coordinating it, advertising and preparing the students, act as ombudsmen for the students, and demonstrate the art and science of medicine."

The Council on Curriculum was composed of the following elected members: one Docent, one Basic Arts and Science professor, two basic scientists, two clinical scientists, two students. Permanent members included a representative from the Office of Medical Education and a representative from the Dean's Office. Its function had been defined in "The Academic Plan" as having "the responsibility to define a core of knowledge needed by anyone granted the M.D. degree; the elective experiences and the individuals prepared to offer this information; the time and location for certain subjects; the assumed antecedent information base of the student. This Council will function through numerous work committees formed from throughout the region who will be charged with specific subunits of curriculum development." The functioning of the Council on Curriculum was somewhat unique in that the classic academic departments were abolished in the new medical school. The development of the curriculum was carried out over a two-year period by physicians who practiced in the metropolitan Kansas City area. These physicians were requested to list the specific competencies in their respective subspecialties which would be required material for the students to master. This list was further refined by another group of physicians representing the major specialties, and final refinement was carried out by the Council on Curriculum.

Another function of the Council on Curriculum was to make modifications and changes in curriculum offerings based on interaction with the Docents, the Council on Evaluation, and the student body. As well, the Council on Curriculum had the responsibility to define the types of elective experiences that were necessary to fit the specific needs of students.

The Council on Selection was composed of the same members as the Council on Curriculum except that the number of students was limited to one. Its chief responsibility was the admission of students and faculty members to the medical faculty. At the end of the first two years, a student was evaluated by the Council on Selection before she or he could move into Year Three. In addition, the Council on Selection sought, interviewed and recommended new members of the staff.

The Council on Evaluation had a similar make-up to the latter two. Its responsibility was evaluating performance on all levels of the medical school, including both students and faculty. With regard to the evaluation of student progress, this was covered longitudinally as the student progressed toward graduation. The student's individual progress through the series of exams helped establish standards for the school as a whole. In the case of faculty, it is the responsibility of the Council on Evaluation to recommend promotions.

The final council was the Council on Health Programs. Its members included the Executive Director of Kansas City General Hospital as well as the administrators of all the affiliated teaching hospitals and health centers. Also represented were the Office of Medical Education and the Dean's Office. According to the "Academic Plan," it was "charged with considering systems of delivering health care and keeping the medical school faculty advised as to changes and improvements in health care delivery and services. Through its membership, it provided a forum for the administration of each of the teaching institutions involved in the medical school activities whether hospital, health clinic, or health center, to discuss matters of mutual interest and concern."

The Coordinating Committee was composed of two elected members from each of the four medical school councils each serving a 2½ year term with staggered elections. The Executive Director of Kansas City General Hospital Medical Center was a permanent representative; and the chairman of the committee was the Dean of the medical school. Its duties were outlined in the Academic Plan as follows:

> The Coordinating Committee has responsibility for review and endorsement of all academic programs and faculty matters forwarded by the Councils. Research grant applications involving new space or personnel require review by this committee prior to endorsement by the Dean. Task force or working committee membership does not require approval of the Coordinating Com-

mittee . . . In these matters (budget and funding) the Coordinating Committee has advisory capacity (to the Dean). The Coordinating Committee has the right to place on the agenda any matter relating to the life of the medical school and express their opinion. The Coordinating Committee bears the additional advisory capacity to the Provost for Health Sciences and shall meet with him on a regular basis.

Curriculum

Appendix A taken from the Academic Plan outlines the basic curriculum of the new medical school. The curriculum was geared to allow students entry directly from high school. During the first two years as an undergraduate, the student would be actively enrolled and identified by the medical school. The purpose of this provisional label in the first two years was twofold: a) to be sure a student measured up, and b) to let the student know that changing his mind is an honorable decision. By special counseling and appropriate examinations, those who seemed particularly fitted for medicine would be allowed to move in that direction at their individual rate of speed. Entry into the formal medical education system would be a threshold phenomenon based upon certain required examinations and willingness of the Evaluation Council to admit them to the group. It was possible for students to enter the program at any level. For example, a Ph.D. in a relevant discipline could transfer into the school and obtain the M.D. degree in approximately two years. A premedical student from another campus could enter at any level appropriate for his ability.*

Exhibits 3 and 4 show the proportions of time devoted to different disciplines in the six-year program compared to the traditional four-year medical school curriculum. The course of study was to provide students with 15 weeks less than a 4 plus 4 program and 17 weeks more than a 3 plus 4 program.

Initially, research in both basic and clinical sciences would be restricted to special grants and research projects of individual faculty members. With the full student complement, it was anticipated that full scale research programs would be undertaken. Epidemiological and operations research might be contracted from such independent organizations as the Health Resources Institute (HRI), a private nonprofit corporation. The focus of HRI's programs was the integration of health agencies and institutions in Kansas City.

The academic plan of the medical school was built around the concept of the Kansas City General Hospital and Medical Center, as the primary adult teaching hospital with all of the Docent Units based there. When students were not spending time on the Docent Unit learning general medicine (see Exhibits 3 and 4), they either took courses at the University of Missouri-Kansas City campus or learned clinical specialties and subspecialties at several other affiliated teaching hospitals, located on Hospital Hill or elsewhere in Kansas City. In order to use the resources of the community and to implement the philosophy of a community of scholars, there was no intention of building a university-owned teaching hospital.

---

*The first group of students, 94 in number, to begin studies in August 1971, were placed in years I to V of the medical school program. Forty of the 94, all Missouri residents, went into year I with a high school background. This group was selected from 128 premedical students accepted at the University of Missouri, on the basis of academic performance in high school, pre-admission college test scores, interviews, etc. Of the group, five were first-year students funded through a $50,000 grant from the Kansas City Association of Trusts and Foundations which sought high school students of disadvantaged background who showed academic potential. Eighteen students went into year II, and the other 36 either into year III or Advanced Standing. The Advanced Standing students included four Ph.D.'s, one dentist, and five Master's degrees.

An initial problem during the school's first year of operation was the need to interpret a new program and to overcome both student and faculty anxiety about the new program. For example, one student cited the instance of being sent to spend some time in a large community blood bank which was not fully prepared to integrate a medical student into its daily operations.

Another student experienced some difficulty when he arrived at a hospital for a month's rotation to discover the staff's expectations from him were unrealistic. "When I got to hospital X and told them I was a fourth-year medical student, they had no idea it was in a six-year program. As a result, their expectations of what I could do were somewhat off." It was the general belief of the students, however, that these problems would right themselves in time. It was also hoped that a system of evaluation could be worked out to determine which affiliated institutions provided the best teaching experiences. In the meantime, as one student put it, "Someone is going to have to be a guinea pig and try a place out first."

Educational Affiliations

The new medical school was designed to function as a part of the University of Missouri - Volker campus in Kansas City and thus as a part of the four-campus state university system. The result was the opportunity for a sharing of courses, faculty and services within the university framework. The medical school anticipated participation from other colleges and faculties such as the College of Arts and Sciences, the School of Dentistry, and the School of Pharmacy in providing instruction in the basic sciences and the behavioral sciences. Similarly, the medical school anticipated cooperative programs with the School of Education in matters of educational psychology and evaluation of educational programs. The existing medical school at the University of Missouri in Columbia had strong affiliations and cooperative programs with industrial engineering, electrical engineering, journalism, library science, education, veterinary medicine, and law. Similar programs were anticipated for the medical school in Kansas City since the two medical schools had parallel interests in intercollege and interdepartmental cooperation to advance fundamental knowledge and to develop program improvements. Examples of such areas of cooperation included: assistance for the medical school in information storage, retrieval, and use; computer simulation of various systems operations in health care delivery; bio-engineering programs for the development of improved investigative, diagnostic, monitoring, and therapeutic procedures; and help from the School of Journalism to increase the effectiveness of informing the general public about health matters.[5]

In particular the development of a six-year program necessitated very close cooperation between the College of Arts and Sciences located at the Volker campus a few miles away in Kansas City and the medical school. Faculty members at the undergraduate campus were to join medical school faculty to design the six-year curriculum. During the last four years approximately 25% of the students' time was to be available for course work on the University of Missouri-Kansas City campus. This arrangement of a split campus had been questioned, however, in the 1968 Olson Report written for the Missouri Commission on Higher Education:

> The split campus—Volker Campus of the University of Missouri and Hospital Hill—makes it difficult to visualize the development of a highly integrated university medical center. That a split campus arrangement will work is not in question because far less advantageous arrangements have been made to work in other communities. What is questioned is the lack of determination to

develop a fully adequate plan, especially so when both institutions—the University and the Medical Center—are at the earliest stages of their development. The university campus is scarcely large enough for its proper growth and Hospital Hill with the 135 acres formally committed to the Medical Center is just barely large enough for its existing plans.

In actuality no significant problems arose during the first two years, because students were accustomed to the idea of an urban commuter campus. In 1970 there were seven nursing schools and two medical schools in the greater metropolitan area. By 1972, General Hospital hoped to phase out its nursing school with the opening of the Penn Valley campus. The new 30 acre Penn Valley campus of the Metropolitan Junior College System was located 1¼ miles from Hospital Hill. Upon completion it would serve 3,500 students, providing the nucleus for an Allied Health Professions program to be operated in conjunction with the new medical school. The two existent medical schools were the Kansas City College of Osteopathy and Surgery located three miles to the northeast of Hospital Hill in Missouri, and the University of Kansas Medical School in Kansas, three miles to the southwest. Both institutions offered medical and house officers' programs. While individual patients from the Missouri side of the state line were using the services of the University of Kansas Medical Center, the nature of the school's support by the State of Kansas dictated serving the people of that state first.

Three clinical programs in Kansas City had contractual affiliations with the Board of Curators for between five and seven years. These were the Kansas City General Hospital and Medical Center (KCGHMC), the Children's Mercy Hospital, and the Western Mental Health Center of the State Division of Mental Diseases. Educational programs were defined as those in which a collegiate degree of nationally recognized certification was involved. These progams included internships, residencies, nursing education, physical therapy, medical technology, X-ray technology, and other such programs falling in the above definition.

Such programs could fall in one of three categories at the option of the university and hospital: a) integrated, in which certification and recognition of the program was vested directly in the university, b) coordinated, in which case two parallel programs were operated with an active exchange of students or trainees, based upon individual arrangements, and c) independent, in which case each institution was to operate its own training program subject to rules and standards which were mutually established and agreed upon.

In all such programs, the university had the right, subject to rules and standards mutually agreed upon by the hospital and the university, to develop affiliations at a rate deemed appropriate by the university with the ultimate objective of having all programs integrated or coordinated.

Standards for performance in educational programs were established by the respective disciplines in the organization of the university and administered through the Director of Medical Education of the hospital. These standards related to selection of candidates accepted, number and qualifications of the teaching staff, duration of training program, and minimum teaching facilities available.

Kansas City General Hospital (KCGH), founded in 1860, is a voluntary nonprofit corporation with public accountability, and functions as the primary adult teaching facility for the school. It was licensed for 310 beds; however, only 227 were in operation, excluding 40 bassinets. Up until 1960, KCGH was segregated. Hospital #1, the present structure, served the indigent White community, and General Hospital #2, the indigent Black community. The physical structure of General Hospital #2 became the Western Missouri Mental Health Center. According to the Associate Director of the hospital, only 19 beds in the present antiquated structure of KCGH were up to state standards, yet it was operated at a 79-80%

capacity. Of the patients, 89% came from within a 3-mile radius of the hospital. After several years of financial difficulty, with the city underwriting a deficit budget several civil leaders approached the City Manager with the offer to establish a nonprofit corporation which would operate KCGH under the new name Kansas City General Hospital and Medical Center (KCGHMC).

The affiliation agreement between the University of Missouri and Kansas City General Hospital Medical Center for the clinical and academic programs was in effect since July 7, 1962. The agreement specified the areas that were the responsibility of the Medical Center, of the university, or shared. The Medical Center was responsible for direct administrative, legal and fiscal aspects of health care. The university administered all educational programs, including the academic appointments of the Medical Center. The affiliation provided that the Dean of the School of Medicine annually designated a member of the full-time staff at the Medical Center, of appropriate academic and professional status, as Director of Medical Education. The Executive Director of the Medical Center had this designation and was responsible for coordinating, supervising, and implementing educational training programs of the medical school and university.

Because the medical school had no teaching hospital of its own, it purchased services from KCGHMC as well as other hospitals in the community. During the fiscal year 1972, $100,000 was allocated by the medical school for the purchase of services from KCGHMC with an increase to $398,000 for the following fiscal year. According to KCGHMC's annual report, the funds were not on-line budget allocations, but were used at the discretion of the hospital for time sent by any health care providers in the education of undergraduate medical students. As well as providing training for students from the medical school, a new clinical pharmacy program initiated by the School of Pharmacy was introduced at the hospital. As part of the new curriculum, doctors of pharmacy acted as part of the Docent Team.

In the area of patient costs, an attempt was made to sequester the costs of education from patient care dollars. The first step in this direction was the transfer of nursing costs through the affiliation and merger of Penn Valley Community College and KCGHMC's School of Nursing. It was also hoped that in the near future the same transfer of costs would occur with other Allied Health Professions: Radiological Technology, and Inhalation Therapy.

From 1970 on, KCGHMC's interaction with the community it served increased considerably. This interface was a result in part of programs which developed because of the new medical school and its use of the hospital as a primary teaching resource and in part because of the long-standing philosophy at the hospital. Two neighborhood health centers lay within the population area served by the hospital, the Wayne Miner Neighborhood Health Center and the Model Cities Neighborhood Health Center. In August, 1970, direct admitting privileges to the Blue Docent Team located at KCGHMC were extended to the primary physicians of the Wayne Miner Neighborhood Health Center. Through the aid of the Health Resources Institute (HRI), a systems development program allowing for admissions to and discharges from this unit back to the neighborhood health center was instituted. As well, public health nurses from Wayne Miner were encouraged to go on regular patient rounds. KCGHMC continued to supply emergency and night call clinic services to residents of the Wayne Miner Neighborhood Health Center.

Unfortunately, relations between the hospital and Wayne Miner were not without some strain. There was a feeling on the part of the staff and administration of the hospital that the neighborhood health centers, which had full-time paid staff, needed more staff. From the point of view of the health center, they desired more access to the hospital.

According to a report filed by an on-site team sent by the Carnegie Foundation to examine the HRI and its programs, both Black and White patients were treated with equal courtesy at Wayne Miner. The Wayne Miner Clinic began by serving a population that was 99% Black. By 1972, its patients were 50% Black and 50% White.

Dr. Densen, Director of the Harvard Center for Community Health and Medical Care, and a member of the on-site team, indicated that he saw a major problem with the current arrangement. The Docents responsible for their team's medical care of patients referred from neighborhood health centers were not trained in community medicine and epidemiology. Dr. Densen speculated that the Docents, who came from backgrounds of general medicine, might not be fully prepared to teach students how to manage referrals from the health centers.

KCGHMC's relations with the Model Cities Neighborhood Health Center included direct admitting privileges for its primary physicians to the Red Docent Team. Upon completion of its new hospital, KCGHMC was to provide the backup gynecological and obstetric services for the Model Cities Health Center.

Further liaison between KCGHMC and the medical school was established in 1972 when the 15-man hospital board was expanded to 40 members. Exhibits 5, 6, and 7 show the breakdown of representation on the reorganized board, the makeup of the Executive Committee, and the organizational design of the hospital. Representation included three municipal officials: the City Manager, the Chairman of the City Finance Committee, the Presiding Officer of the County Court. Other new members included the Executive Director of the hospital, the Provost of the Health Sciences, a hospital paymaster representing the nonhealth professionals, a nurse, a citizen and consumer representatives, an elected member from each of the hospital's four divisions, the Council of Docents, Clinical Services, Pathology Labs, and X-ray, and physicians-at-large.

Exhibit 8 diagrams the complex of educational and health care relationships the medical school established with other institutions in the community.

Footnotes

1. "Estimates and Projections, 1969," *Metropolitan Planning Commission, Kansas City Region Planning Bulletin No. 2,* February 1969.
2. Stanley W. Olson, M.D., *A Survey of Physician Manpower in Missouri for the Missouri Commission on Higher Education.*
3. *Archives of Internal Medicine,* Vol. 129, Jan. 1972.
4. "The Open Medical School: A Community of Scholars; The Academic Plan for the School of Medicine, University of Missouri-Kansas City."
5. "Long-Range Planning, University of Missouri, 1968."

Exhibit 2

University of Missouri–Kansas City Medical School (A)

Projected Yearly Income and Expenditures for Education
of 100 Additional Medical Students*

Total Income for Medical School Programs:		$5,460,000/yr.
Medical Student Education	$1,665,000	
Internships, Residencies, Clinical Fellowships, Continuing Medical Education in Affiliated Hospitals	1,308,000	
Sponsored research	1,245,000	
Medical service plan	600,000	
Graduate & general campus programs	170,000	
Self-supporting programs – Postgraduate education, other educational programs, community and public health services	472,000	
	$5,460,000	
Total Expenditures for Medical School Programs:**		$5,460,000/yr.
Direct Costs:		
188 Faculty members	$3,196,000***	
Supporting personnel and services	2,264,000	
	$5,460,000	

* 1968 current dollars.
** All costs are based on operating expenses of medical school at Columbia, Missouri.
*** This estimate is based on 141 full time teaching equivalents directly involved in the medical school program and a minimum of 47 full time equivalents in the programs of internship residency, continuing education carried on by the affiliated hospitals and located in them. All figures are based on experience at Columbia.

121

Exhibit 3

University of Missouri-Kansas City Medical School (A)

Pre Health Sciences Curriculum

YEAR 1	YEAR 2	MEDICAL SCHOOL CURRICULUM
		Docent Team
		Specialty Electives
		Community Health Facilities
		Liberal Arts

Information Basic to Health Sciences: Mathematics, physics, chemistry, biology; general human biology including substantial portions of medical basic sciences such as introductory anatomy, biochemistry, and physiology; human growth and development; and medical sociology. Selection varies with the student and his plans.

Structure of Health Care System: Consumers of care; providers of care; community; regional, national, international considerations; consideration of factors in policy decisions.

Field Experience: Two assignments to prototype health care institutions for 12 weeks during the two years. Provides orientation, experience, and improved basis for student and faculty judgment about career choices.

General Education Courses: Selected by student and advisors according to his background, interests, and plans.

Exhibit 4

University of Missouri–Kansas City Medical School (A)

Curriculum

	Year 1	Year 2	Year 3	Year 4
DOCENT TEAM 25% of time				

Responses to Illness: The social and psychological response of the individual; the types of responses of society to different health problems; consideration of optimal responses and how they might be attained.

Fundamental Understandings: Structure, organization, metabolism, integrating mechanisms, reproduction, development, vulnerabilities, responses to injury of cells, organs, and individuals.

Clinical Requirements: Interviewing skills, physical and laboratory examining ability, types manifestation of diseases, logic of clinical reasoning, major forms of therapy, personal discipline of the M.D.

Experience: In General Hospital, Children's Mercy Hospital, Psychiatric Hospital, other affiliated institutions.

SPECIALTY ELECTIVES 25% of time

Emphasis: Fundamental understandings and clinical requirements as they are basic to the physician's care of any patient. Understanding and increased competence with the operational attitude and major methods of specialties.

Special Features: Arranged in consultation with Docent to meet the student's interests and needs.

COMMUNITY HEALTH FACILITIES 25% of time

Experience: In community facilities such as an OEO Health Center, community hospital preceptorship, or Indian Hospital.

Emphases: Epidemiology, environmental health, care of disadvantaged, infectious diseases control, public policy for health, urban health hazards, organization for health care.

LIBERAL ARTS 25% of time

Experience: On the campus of the University of Missouri – Kansas City.

Objectives: Acquire a continuing liberal education. Take courses that the student's evolving career finds missing.

Examples: Statistics, public speaking, techniques of teaching, language, philosophy, psychology.

Exhibit 5

University of Missouri–Kansas City Medical School (A)

Board of KCGHMC

Reorganization of the Board

a. Eight new public Directors − 40 Members

1. A Senior Docent of the Medical School of the University of Missouri at Kansas City nominated by the Senior Docents.
2. A physician or dentist nominated by the Clinical Staff of the Medical Center.
3. A physician nominated by the Clinical Support Departments of the Medical Center.
4. A physician or dentist nominated by the entire Medical Staff of the Medical Center.
5. A health professional of the Medical Center who is not a physician or dentist nominated by his peers.
6. The Executive Director of the Medical Center.
7. The Provost of Health Sciences of UMKC or a representative designated by him.
8. An employee of the Medical Center who is not a physician, dentist or health professional nominated by his peers.

b. Executive Committee of the Board

1. Chairman of the Board of Directors of the Corporation.
2. President of the Corporation.
3. Three members of the Board of Directors designated by the President.
4. Chairman of the Finance Committee of the Board.
5. Chairman of the Finance Committee of the City Council of Kansas City, Missouri.
6. Presiding Judge of the County Court of Jackson County, Missouri, or designate appointed by him.
7. Executive Director of the Corporation.
8. Lay member of the Board of Directors assigned to the Senior Docents as referred to below.
9. Lay member of the Board of Directors assigned to the Clinical Services as referred to below.
10. Lay member of the Board of Directors assigned to the Clinical Support Departments as referred to below.
11. Provost for Health Sciences of UMKC or a representative designated by him.

Exhibit 6

University of Missouri–Kansas City Medical School (A)

Policy and Decision Making KCGHMC

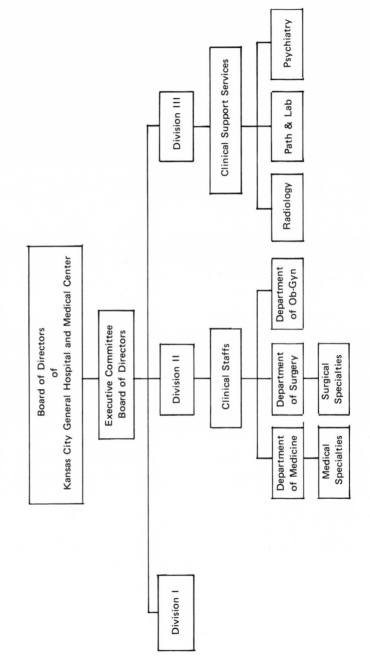

Exhibit 7

University of Missouri–Kansas City Medical School (A)

Administrative Relationship of KCGHMC and UMKC

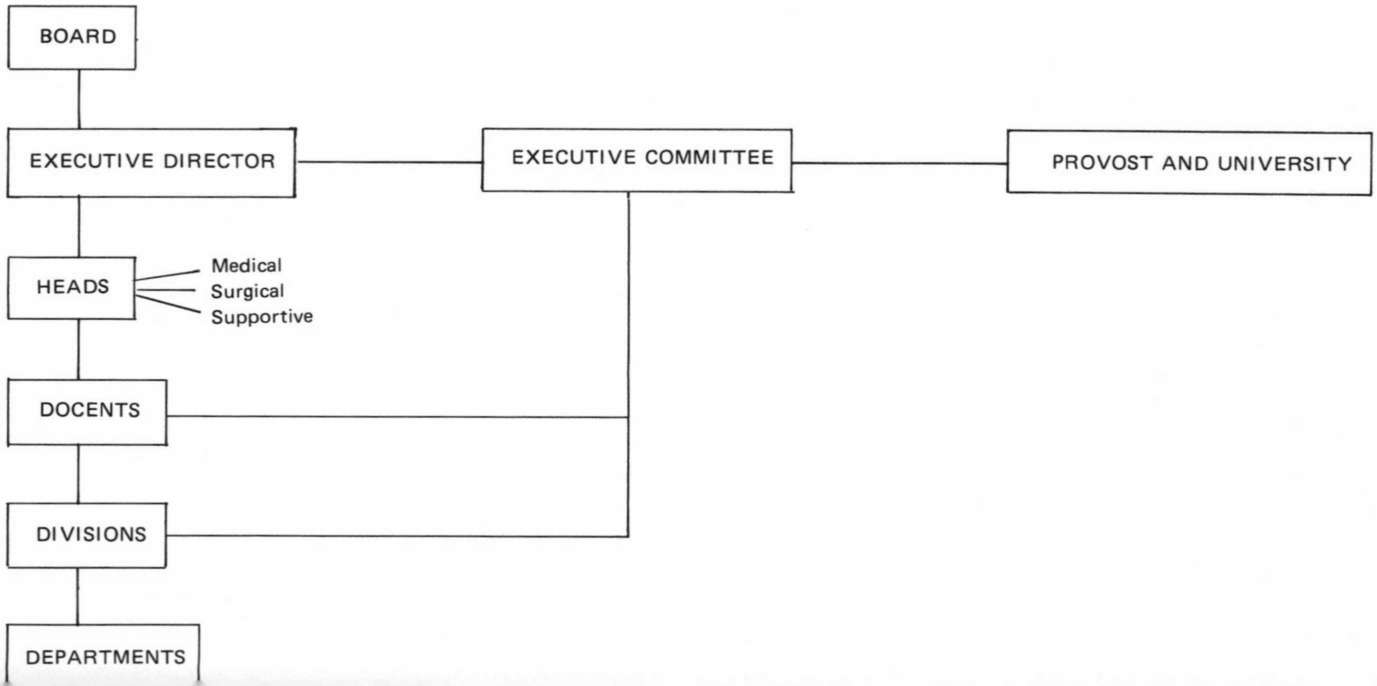

University of Missouri–Kansas City Medical School

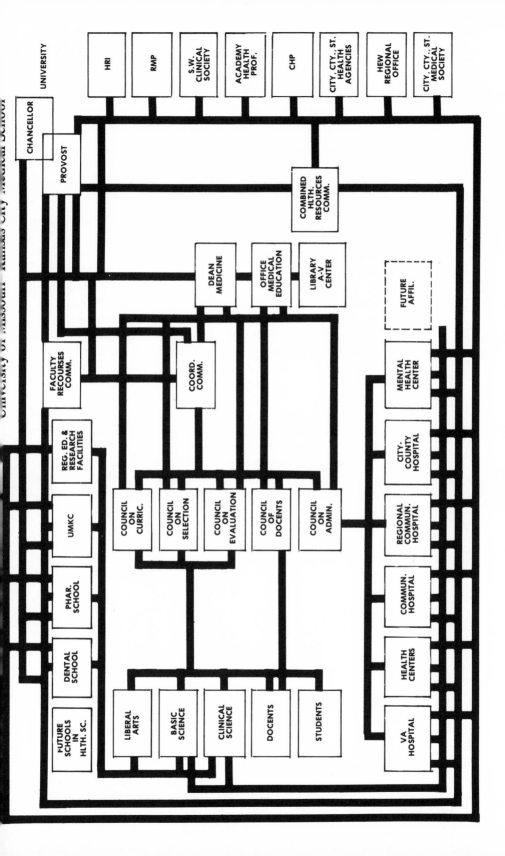

Appendix A

University of Missouri–Kansas City Medical School (A)

Six-year program coordinating two pre-medical and four medical years. M.D. degree six years out of high school.

1. The first two years of the six-year curriculum are divided into nine months of arts and sciences (liberal arts) and three months of pre-health science education each year (Figure 1). This latter program will be administered through an academic dean, coordinating community hospitals, health centers, private physicians, and regional liberal arts institutions. This academic dean will require a dual appointment: as associate dean in the Medical School and also as associate dean in the College of Arts and Sciences. The participant will be offered a planned curriculum giving exposure to units of information in the fields of behavioral sciences, medical ethics, medical history, anatomy, physiology, biochemistry, and pathology (Figure 2). Carefully controlled tasks, for example at the orderly level, will be assigned. Practicing physicians will be assigned as counselors to the pre-health science students. Adequate additional counseling will be provided to offer the student an alternate source of guidance. This program will be designed so the participant may elect to go on and finish his liberal arts degree prior to medical school, may elect to go to medical school and acquire his liberal arts degree simultaneously, or enter pharmacy school, dentistry school, nursing school, to take a Ph.D., et cetera. This will not be the only route of entrance to the medical school (or health science careers) during the initial trial years and students will be actively encouraged to transfer in from other pre-medical education backgrounds. If possible, however, the six-year program will offer a double degree upon completion: a Bachelor's and a Doctorate.

2. Curriculum will be forty-eight weeks each year for five years; thirty-six weeks for a sixth year.

3. Basic trunk of the four-year medical school curriculum will be the general medical service, under guidance of a docent team. This general medical experience will be based on twelve-week service of daily ward rounds, each year, with the same docent team. During the remainder of each year the student will continue to maintain outpatient responsibility for the patients met during the twelve-week general medical service. He

will schedule these appointments and maintain "office hours" as needed to give professional advice to his "practice" and to see the family complex surrounding the patient (Figure 3). His "practice" will be under the continuing supervision of the docent staff.

4. This patient experience will serve as the case history data base for the individual student. Extensions from this case history base will provide the guidelines for the student's needed information in the basic sciences and sub-specialties, and approximately seventy-five percent of his time will be devoted to acquiring this basic information, over a four-year period. The docent bears the responsibility of completing the basic science base of the student's medical education. This base knowledge, begun in high school, added to in years one and two, will, of course, not be taught solely by the docents, but by members of his team and by any faculty resource as defined by the Council on Curriculum. This instruction will be not only in the quarter of time assigned to general medicine but throughout the other quarters.

5. Throughout the four years, the student will have approximately twenty-five percent of his time available for continuing his liberal arts education. An equal amount of experience in the specialties of medicine will be electively available under docent counsel. Community health activity will be considered a specialty.

6. Where possible, learning will be accomplished in the student–docent area; the teaching will come to the student. Liberal arts credit experience will be arranged when possible as small group seminars, in the student-docent area. However, it is appreciated that the student will have classroom experience on the main University campus throughout the four medical years, year three, four, five, and six.

7. Each twelve-student docent unit will be composed of an equal mixture of students from each of the classes. Thus the twelve-man team will have three students from each year sharing the twelve-week general medical experience, throughout the four years.

8. A docent team consists of the docent, associate docents, visiting docent, outpatient physicians, residents, related nursing, pharmacy, and ancillary personnel, related research and clinical laboratories, approximately twenty inpatient beds, and outpatient facilities for general medicine patients, and four teams, twelve each, of students and their personal offices, discussion room, and laboratory. Figures 4 through 10 illustrate in detail the docent concept.

9. A student will have his own office, open to him twenty-four hours a day for the full four years. It will provide privacy, security for possessions,

personal telephone, individual television and viewing and audio apparatus, potential for microfiche use, computer linkage, and a place for personal memorabilia (Figure 8).

10. The medical school and hospital will be so constructed that students, their offices, their personal docents, their related inpatient and outpatient services are all on the same horizontal level (Figures 9 and 10). Within reason, all admissions to the hospital will be through the general medical service. The hospital will therefore be divided approximately equally between general medical service and the other services required by a general hospital. General medicine will be construed to include practically all initial admissions to the hospital that are not obvious special problems: labor and fracture are obvious exceptions. The definition of the general medical services would be a responsibility of the professional staff of the General Hospital but it would be the expressed and requested desire of the medical school that this definition be encompassing and bring to the general medical service a very broad and undifferentiated patient care responsibility.

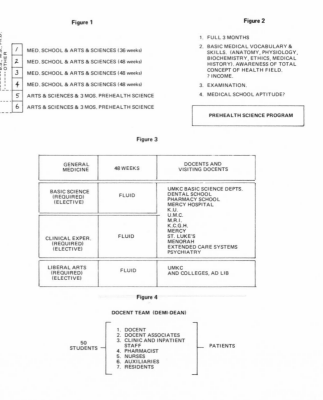

Figure 1

D.D.S.
B.S. (PHARM.)
B.S., M.S., Ph.D.
OTHER

1	MED. SCHOOL & ARTS & SCIENCES (36 weeks)
2	MED. SCHOOL & ARTS & SCIENCES (48 weeks)
3	MED. SCHOOL & ARTS & SCIENCES (48 weeks)
4	MED. SCHOOL & ARTS & SCIENCES (48 weeks)
5	ARTS & SCIENCES & 3 MOS. PREHEALTH SCIENCE
6	ARTS & SCIENCES & 3 MOS. PREHEALTH SCIENCE

Figure 2

1. FULL 3 MONTHS

2. BASIC MEDICAL VOCABULARY & SKILLS. (ANATOMY, PHYSIOLOGY, BIOCHEMISTRY, ETHICS, MEDICAL HISTORY). AWARENESS OF TOTAL CONCEPT OF HEALTH FIELD. ? INCOME.

3. EXAMINATION.

4. MEDICAL SCHOOL APTITUDE?

PREHEALTH SCIENCE PROGRAM

Figure 3

GENERAL MEDICINE	48 WEEKS	DOCENTS AND VISITING DOCENTS
BASIC SCIENCE (REQUIRED) (ELECTIVE)	FLUID	UMKC BASIC SCIENCE DEPTS. DENTAL SCHOOL PHARMACY SCHOOL MERCY HOSPITAL K.U.
CLINICAL EXPER. (REQUIRED) (ELECTIVE)	FLUID	U.M.C. M.R.I. K.C.G.H. MERCY ST. LUKE'S MENORAH EXTENDED CARE SYSTEMS PSYCHIATRY
LIBERAL ARTS (REQUIRED) (ELECTIVE)	FLUID	UMKC AND COLLEGES, AD LIB

Figure 4

DOCENT TEAM (DEMI-DEAN)

50 STUDENTS —
1. DOCENT
2. DOCENT ASSOCIATES
3. CLINIC AND INPATIENT STAFF
4. PHARMACIST
5. NURSES
6. AUXILIARIES
7. RESIDENTS
— PATIENTS

Figure 5

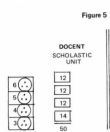

DOCENT	DOCENT
SCHOLASTIC UNIT	PATERNAL FIGURE
	DEMONSTRATE PRACTICE
	OF MEDICINE (TEAM)
	COUNSELOR
	PROGRAM PLANNER
	(P_x WRITING)
	OMBUDSMAN
	TEACHER
	ADMINISTRATOR

Figure 6

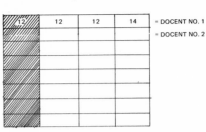

☐ = DOCENT NO. 1
☐ = DOCENT NO. 2

GENERAL MEDICINE = 12 WEEKS, EACH
YEAR FOR 4 YEARS, SAME DOCENT,
SAME STUDENTS

Figure 7

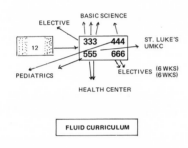

FLUID CURRICULUM

Figure 8

STUDENT'S OFFICE	
FOUR YEARS	VIEWER
TAPE RECORDER	MICROFICHE
TV	BOOKS
PHONE	TERMINAL

Figure 9

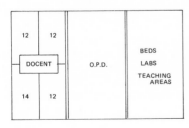

Figure 10

Office	Office	DISCUSSION		
Office	Office	ROOMS	GROUP	
Office	Office		LAB	
Office	Office			
Office	Office	Computer Terminal & Testing	PATIENT INTERVIEW ROOMS	
Office	Office		1	2

131

UNIVERSITY OF MISSOURI-KANSAS CITY
MEDICAL SCHOOL: CONTROL SYSTEM (B)

Both the administration of Kansas City General Hospital Medical Center (KCGHMC) and of the University of Missouri-Kansas City Medical School shared common concerns over the following: 1) providing student education in a real setting; 2) monitoring the quality of care given the patients; 3) controlling for the cost of that care; 4) delivering patient care from a common philosophic base.

From the conception of the new medical school through the first two years of its operation, a reporting and control system had developed around patient care practices at the school's primary affiliated teaching hospital KCGHMC. The elements of the control system included the Monthly Docent Unit quality of care audit. Together, both institutions had worked out a team approach, although the primary concern of each administration differed somewhat.

As Dr. E. Grey Dimond, Provost for Health Sciences, University of Missouri, reviewed the Monthly Docent Unit Reports for July 1972, he contemplated how the reports, the school's use of Weed's POMR, and the soon-to-be implemented quality of care audit would mesh. He was particularly interested in how these reporting systems could be made more useful to the senior Docents responsible for both education and patient care.

While sharing the above interests, the administration of KCGHMC for their part wanted to concentrate on what effect the Docent Unit Concept would have on the cost of running a hospital floor and on the quality of patient care delivered.

Description of the Medical School

In September 1971, the University of Missouri-Kansas City Medical School admitted its first group of 94 students. This group was dispersed among years I through V of the six-year program. What attracted the bulk of these students to the new school was its innovative approach to medical education under the guidance of Dr. E. Grey Dimond, Provost for Health Sciences. The primary objective of the school was to produce what Dr. Dimond had called a "safe physician." The school's emphasis was to be on the training of sound clinicians who were especially well-equipped to practice general and family medicine although a full range of experience in the sub-specialties was available to all students. Basic sciences would be learned as an integrated part of total patient care. There would be a relatively small amount of basic science research and clinical research among the first years of the school's operation; later, the amount would be appreciable. Education and patient care in general medicine would be carried on under the tutelage of an experienced clinician-scholar called a Docent. All patient care would take place in several community hospitals which would be affiliated with the medical school rather than owned by it. Students would have the opportunity to enter the medical school from high school on a provisional basis. After two years of a pre-health curriculum and electives at the University of Missouri-Kansas City campus, if a student's academic performance was sound he could choose to continue in the program. The measure of academic success during the last four years would involve a thorough assessment of performance and a series of challenge exams on questions by nation-

*The Problem-Oriented Medical Record, developed by Dr. Lawrence L. Weed, is a method of organizing a patient's chart according to a precise format based on a problem list.
*It was his hope that the students, through their participation on the Docent Unit, would be able to stimulate the entire medical community.

ally known practitioners. By the end of the six-year program, a student was expected to have acquired enough medical knowledge and experience to help him become a "safe clinician." It was anticipated that the student would demonstrate both on National Medical Boards and in internship and residency a comparable competence to those students with a more traditional medical education.

The integrative unit around which the curriculum for the new medical school revolved was the Docent Unit. The Docent Unit formed the nucleus not only for training and educating medical students and allied health personnel but also for providing all health care (ambulatory and inpatient) for a group of patients at Kansas City General Hospital Medical Center. As an educational and health care unit, the Docent team represented: 1) an organizational framework, 2) a physical facility, and 3) a multidisciplinary health team. Furthermore, it had the potential to operate as a separate cost unit. The method employed by the medical school and Kansas City General Hospital for recording data pertaining to the function of the Docent Unit on a daily basis was the POMR. In addition, a monthly summary of Docent Unit activities was compiled and distributed to the senior Docents and medical school and hospital administration.

Docent Unit as an Organizational Framework

By 1971, the first group of students enrolled in the medical school was divided into three Docent teams. The Docent teams comprised the Department of Medicine of the medical school and of Kansas City General Hospital Medical Center. It was hoped that eventually with the full complement of 100 students in each class, there would be eight Docent teams under the supervision of eight senior Docents and 24 Docent associates. Each team would consist of twelve students, three from each of the last four years of medical school. The Senior Docent was considered the team leader and was responsible for the selection of the remainder of the Docent team. A typical team might consist of a Senior Docent, Docent Associate, Clinic and Inpatient staff, a clinical pharmacist, nurses, auxiliaries, dietician, Master of Social Work, residents and students (see Figure 4, Appendix A).* The main responsibility of the Docent was the teaching of General Medicine to medical students as well as the house staff officers at KCGHMC. Each student spent twelve rigorous weeks per year gaining daily ward round experience with his team, with the average team having 48-50 students for the year. The result would be a small or demi-medical school clustered around a Docent figure who acted as ombudsman, counselor, program planner-evaluator, teacher and administrator for the student and the program in clinical medicine. Ideally, the student was expected to get from 30-50% of his total clinical experience directly in the health care delivery system under the supervision of a Docent. The remainder of his time was spent on elective and specialty services (see Figures 3 and 6, Appendix A).*

Docent Unit as a Physical Facility

One goal of the Board of KCGHMC was to take an old city hospital catering to the disappearing indigent charity patients and to turn it into a hospital serving a community. In order to do this, continuing comprehensive health care delivered by a continuing comprehensive health team in a physical location analogous to a clinic was their solution. The entire Kansas City General Hospital Medical Center (KCGHMC) was utilized as a facility for the medical school's integrated education-patient-care curriculum based on the Docent team

*p. 127

concept. A similar arrangement was to be carried over to the new Truman Medical Center upon its completion in 1974. Exhibit 1 is a floor plan showing the layout of the Docent Units in the new medical complex. When the Medical Center was completed, each Docent Unit would be housed in a self-contained physical space in the hospital for patient care and in the medical school for office study and laboratory space. All bed units, office suites and lab facilities were to be color coded in order to give patients, staff and students a sense of belonging in one unit. Figure 9, Appendix A provides a magnified overview of each Unit, while Figure 10, Appendix A shows the position of each of the student offices in relation to the computer terminals, discussion room, group lab and patient interview lab. Each student would be assigned his own office with the Docent Unit containing the software listed in Figure 8, Appendix A.

One method for controlling utilization of hospital facilities in the new medical center was the required listing of demands that would be imposed on all spaces like conference rooms in each setting. As a result, each team would have the flexibility to schedule patient care education meetings to suit its own needs. Exhibit 2 is a chart which illustrates the demands on teaching space in the inpatient and ambulatory care setting.

Docent Unit as a
Multidisciplinary Health Team

The Docent Units were designed to operate and to be staffed from a central administrative control center so that maximum utilization of personnel could be achieved.

As regards the inpatient 20 bed unit, during the peak hours (7:00 A.M. to 3:00 P.M.), each 20-bed unit was to be fully staffed. The 3:00 to 11:00 P.M. shift and the 11:00 P.M. to 7:00 A.M. shifts were to share clinical supervision and other support personnel. This was possible due to the design and sharing mode of the administrative control center.

The Truman Medical Center's senior and principal clinical nurse would be expected to follow a designated census of stabilized outpatients and to have the proficiency to follow patients into the outreach setting. Staffing patterns, therefore, were to be uniquely different from the conventional hospital or medical center. In a tandem team with the clinical pharmacist, the principal clinical nurse was in a prime position to negate frequent and often avoidable hospitalization for chronic illnesses.

It was anticipated that the following categories of personnel would utilize the administrative control center: Docents and attending physicians, resident physicians, medical students, principal clinical nurses, senior clinical nurses and clinical nurses, clinical pharmacists, nurse coordinator unit manager, ART (Accredited Record Technician), dietician, Master of Social Work, and other students.

The following representative staff and numbers were calculated:

Docent	1
Resident Physicians	4
Medical Students	12
Clinical Pharmacists	1
Clinical Pharmacy Students	4
Nurse Coordinator	1
ART (Accredited Record Technician)	1
Unit Manager	1

If correlated with the traditional time shift, the following staffing pattern would cover inpatient, outpatient, and home care:

Time Shift	7–3	3–11	11–7	Total
Registered nurse	6	3	3	12
L.P.N.	3	2	3	8
Nurse aid	3	3	3	9
Ward clerk	2	–	–	2
Social worker	1	–	–	1
Dietician	1	–	–	1
Unit manager	1	–	–	1

This time shift scheduling did not take into account the rotations and night call scheduling of the Docents, resident physicians, medical students, and clinical pharmacy students, as well as nursing students.

Physician input was to be derived from the following areas: full-time physicians, clinicians in all areas, part-time physicians and community volunteers. Community physicians in specialties of Radiology, Obstetrics, Gynecology, Pathology, and Surgery were to continue to contribute to the patient care programs of Kansas City General Hospital and Medical Center.

The School of Pharmacy contributed faculty which helped with the staffing, supervision and maintenance of quality control of the central hospital pharmacy. They functioned in the following areas: a Clinical Pharmacist to man a currently operational Drug Information Center; a Clinical Pharmacist to staff the currently operational Medications Advisory Profile System Center,* and a Clinical Pharmacist and an Associate Dean of the School of Pharmacy to supervise patient care and ongoing clinical pharmacy programs.

Faculty Costs and Teaching Time

Faculty were divided into three categories: full-time, part-time, and volunteer. In an analysis done at the medical school in Columbia, 22.4% of the faculty effort was devoted to the education of medical students. The balance of faculty time was spent on research programs, graduate education, continuing medical education programs, and the provision of direct patient care.

The cost of support services for faculty was based on the operating experience of the existing medical school at Columbia. Fifty-eight per cent of the faculty salaries represented the expenditures required for secretarial and clerical assistance, teaching supplies and equipment, library operations, maintenance, and utilities.*

*A study conducted by the UMKC School of Pharmacy revealed that the indigent patients received multiple prescribing from more than one health care institution. The objective of the program was to reduce the cost of patient prescriptions by establishing a central collating agency for collation and sequestration of prescription carbon copies.

*No allocation was shown for faculty members in affiliated hospitals which provide their own secretarial and office support for full-time faculty members or for direct care of patients and sponsored research activities.

The medical school's staffing patterns included 14 full-time equivalents in the medical school programs, and a minimum of 47 full-time equivalents in the programs of internship, residency, continuing education, etc., conducted in the affiliated hospitals. For purposes of projecting faculty requirements as related to income sources, the term "full-time equivalents" was employed. If a faculty member was full-time, he or she was counted as a full-time equivalent; two faculty members employed on a half-time basis together are considered one full-time equivalent.

At the time of a 1968 study done for the Missouri Commission on Higher Education, projected salaries were based on those of the medical school at Columbia and were comparable with both the national average and the AAMC salary summary. The range was as follows: instructor, $10,000 to $12,000; assistant professor, $12,000 to $14,000; associate professor, $14,000 to $18,000; professor, $18,000 to $22,000; department chairman, $23,000 to $24,000.* Faculty vacancies were scheduled to be filled on a sequential basis as the number of students increased. It was the policy of the school, whenever possible, to offer university titles and appointments to physicians in the community without the appropriate salary and the possibility of tenure. In this manner, the school was able to enlist teachers in all the clinical specialties in accordance with the effort they could provide. The major exceptions were the Provost, Vice-Provost, and Dean, who were on full-time salary from the university and were tenured; Docents were full-time salaried teachers but untenured. Their salaries were paid half by KCGHMC and half by the medical school.

Docent Reports and Auditing
of the Docent Unit

Since early 1971, each of the Docent Units—Red, Blue and Green—was required to submit a monthly summary and activity report. The data contained in the reports were obtained from the following sources: charging systems and unit managers' record. From the three reports a composite was made which provided significant standards for comparison which could be assessed simultaneously with a medical audit. Appendix B is a reproduction of the July 1972 monthly composite summary.* It includes data for inpatient stays, outpatient

---

*Clinicians can augment their salaries by approximately one-third through the Missouri Medical Service and Research Plan. A 5% annual increase was assumed.

*Appendix B is summarized as follows: Table 1 shows that the total inpatient days, average length of stay and % rate of occupancy are considerably higher for the Red Team, 522, 12.20, 76.54, respectively, than the Blue with 399, 6.67, 53.63, and the Green falls somewhere in between with 412, 8.92, 60.41. Other obvious differences are the number of Social Worker cases opened, 17 for the Red Team as opposed to 4 for the Blue Team; R.N. hours: 1280 for the Red Team, 773 for the Blue; L.P.N. hours: 850 for the Red, 1024 for the Blue. Table 2 shows the number of lab tests per admission as well as the charges for lab tests and medication per admission which were considerably lower for the Blue Team than for the Red or Green. In the case of the outpatient summaries, Table 3, the Blue Team outpaced the Red in number of Social Worker cases opened, 10 versus 1, and Dietician instructions, 84 versus 41. From Table 4, it is apparent that the number of bacteriology tests, 69, and the charges for total lab tests for the Red Team exceed those of the other two teams.

Table 10 gives the budget variances for the three teams for July. In all cases, the inpatient deviations were under budget for the month, although the % deviations from May 1972 to the end of July showed that the Red Team was 3% over and the Green 23% under. Outpatient figures showed that the Blue Team was 17.0% over its budget for the month of July and 4.0% over for the three-month period May to July while the other two teams were under.

visits, and cost comparisons. Although each Docent Unit was structured comparably, its performance profile was varied. The unit giving the most care for the health dollar could be readily identified.

Administrators at both the medical school and KCGHMC explained that their first priority would be to insure the reliability of the figures appearing in the monthly Docent Unit Report. A major difficulty was finding the right people to prepare accurate data collection whether automated or manual. Experience had shown that it was particularly difficult to get accurate lab information. It was felt that an imperfect reporting and recording system may have accounted for large discrepancies in such items in the July 1972 reports as number of social work cases opened.

During the first year of the school's operation use of the Monthly Docent Unit Reports was somewhat experimental. Dr. Dimond adopted what he referred to as the "behavioral scientist approach." His ultimate goal was to stimulate an entire medical community through the students who would have access to the data in the Docent Unit Reports. His strategy was to prepare the data and release it without comment to the Senior Docents, hospital and medical school administration, and the student body through the student newspaper. Following release, Dr. Dimond sent cautious letters to the Senior Docents reviewing the information contained within the reports. There was no attempt at drawing conclusions. Dr. Dimond felt that ultimately the usefulness of the monthly reports would increase with an increase in the Docent census. Student feedback was to take the form of weekly seminars run by students where they would review the data compiled in the monthly report.

It was anticipated that after a year or so, a determination would be made as to what data should permanently be contained in the report. After this point such items as patient volume, death rate, length of stay could be further examined. While there was some feeling that the reports might be useful tools for controlling costs and establishing standards of care, it was conceded that their usefulness would come in the future and that in the meantime, they should be circulated internally with minimal discussion.

One of the Senior Docents felt even broader control mechanisms than the Docent Unit reports were needed. He envisioned a chart review committee that would look at the following items: record, audit, transfusion, infection, vital signs, tissue, with the objective of 1) conserving physician's time, and 2) quality assessment. The Docent considered the monthly Docent reports "just fun and games" which should be replaced by a system utilizing algorithms, thus obviating the need for judgment decisions.

Dean Noback, on the other hand, saw the Docent Unit Reports as an attempt to provide a data base and throw light on what was happening in terms of patient care. On the issue of whether standards should be established based on the data, he felt that there was no right answer to such problems as the correct number of diagnostic tests necessary for treating a disease entity.

The Problem-Oriented Medical Record, Chart Review, and Quality of Care Audit

In November 1970, General Hospital's medical patient census was divided into three color-coded groups: red, blue, and green, each group related to a Docent team which was also color-coded. The outpatients' clinics were decentralized, color-coded, and located geographically adjacent to a defined inpatient unit of 20-24 beds. As a result the Docent team of health professionals began following its own patient census, both on an outpatient and inpatient basis.

When a patient was discharged from a Docent inpatient unit, his master record was sequestered into two sections. The outpatient section included outpatient progress notes (SOAP) and an updated problem list, enumerating current drugs prescribed for each problem. The outpatient record also received copies of the discharge summaries and clinically pertinent flow sheets.

Accredited Record Technicians were assigned to each Docent team. Their function was to assist each health professional maintain current documentation of health services rendered to the patient whether the consumer be ambulatory or hospitalized. The ART on each Docent Unit functioned in both settings, inpatient and outpatient. Their prime responsibility was to maintain current problem lists, current charts, gather statistics, implement utilization review, and assist in medical audit of health services rendered.

To expedite the transfer of patient data, the use of Weed's Problem-Oriented Medical Record was subsequently implemented. (The POMR consists of a numbered problem list which serves as a "table of contents" and an "index" combined. After the problem list is completely formulated so as to include all the patient's problems, past and present, social, psychiatric and medical, a careful analysis and follow through on each problem is presented in the form of program notes. One primary advantage, attributed to the POMR was that it lent itself readily to both microfiche and computerization, thus facilitating storage and retrieval.) All health care personnel entered their comments in regard to patient care and services rendered on the same program sheet according to title, number, and problem.

A quality of care audit to monitor patient care at KCGHMC was in the developmental stage. Its goal was to audit one service of Docent Care Unit per month and the results would be integrated with the Docent Unit Monthly Report. Dr. Twin, Administrator of KCGHMC, further envisioned taking the format of the POMR and using the problem-oriented approach for administrative problems at the hospital.

Exhibit 2

University of Missouri–Kansas City Medical School (B)

Example of Demand Scheduling on Conference and Classroom
Space in Inpatient and Ambulatory Setting of the Proposed Truman Medical Center

USER	SUBJECT	DENSITY	FREQUENCY
1. Docent Unit	Business of unit	All members 15 – 20	1 hour weekly
2. Docent and his medical students	Teaching rounds and patient care, inpatient care	13	2 hours daily
3. Docent, and his medical students	Work rounds and patient care, inpatient care	13	2 hours daily
4. Residents and medical students	Teaching rounds, patient care	14 – 20	1 hour daily
5. Clinical pharmacist, residents and medical students	Teaching rounds and patient care	14 – 20	1 hour daily
6. Clinical nurse and medical students	Teaching rounds and patient care	14	1 – 2 hours, weekly
7. Docent and clinical nurses	Work rounds and patient care, inpatient and outpatient	4	3 hours weekly
8. Clinical pharmacist and clinical nurses	Work rounds and patient care, mostly outpatient	4	1 hour daily
9. Clinical nurses and nurse students	Teaching rounds and patient care, inpatient and outpatient	20 – 25	1 hour daily

Exhibit 3

University of Missouri–Kansas City Medical School (B)

Analysis on Terms of Full-Time Equivalents (FTE's)

42	FTE's from Medical Education Support
49	FTE's from Sponsored Research Programs
24	FTE's from Missouri Service and Research Plan
7	FTE's from Graduate Education
19	FTE's from Self-Supporting Programs
141	FTE's in Programs of School Included Above
47	FTE's in Programs of Internship, Residency, Continued Education Carried on by Affiliated Hospitals
188	FTE's Available for School's Programs in toto

Exhibit 4

University of Missouri–Kansas City Medical School (B)

Discipline			FTE's Available from Affiliated Hospitals	Totals
Anatomy	6		—	6
Biochemistry	7		—	7
Microbiology	6		—	6
Pathology	8		6	14
Pharmacology	6		—	6
Physiology	9		—	9
Behavioral Science	9		—	9
Anaesthesiology	4		4	8
Medicine Docents	32		8	40
Neurology	4		2	6
Obstetrics–Gynecology	6		3	9
Pediatrics	4		15	19
Physical Medicine and Rehabilitation	4		—	4
Psychiatry	6		20	26
Community Health and Medical Practice	7		—	7
Radiology	7		4	11
Surgery Surgical Specialties	9		8	17
Research in Medical Education	7		—	7
	141		70*	201

*This total is greater than the 47 FTE's shown on an earlier page. 47 FTE's represents a deliberately conservative estimate. In showing the distribution of FTE's, a less conservative estimate is used.

University of Missouri–Kansas City Medical School

DOCENT UNITS ACTIVITY REPORT

MONTHLY SUMMARY

Kansas City General Hospital and Medical Center

Affiliated with the School of Medicine
University of Missouri – Kansas City

JULY, 1972

Appendix (continued)
University of Missouri–Kansas City Medical School
Table 1

INPATIENT DATA SUMMARY COMPARISON

Subject	All Teams	Blue Team	Red Team	Green Team	Yellow Team
Basic Data					
Number of Beds	68	24	22	22	
Bed Days Available	2108	744	682	682	
Total Admissions	142	49	48	45	
Total Inpatient Days	1333	399	522	412	
Average Length of Stay	9.26	6.67	12.20	8.92	
Rate of Occupancy %	63.53	53.63	76.54	60.41	
Deaths	15	8	2	5	
Autopsies	5	3	1	1	
Referrals					
Social Worker Cases Opened	30	4	17	9	
Dietician Instructions	40	13	16	11	
Nursing Personnel					
Total Nursing Hours	10877	3309	4042	3526	
RN Hours	3251	773	1280	1198	
LPN Hours	2546	1024	850	672	
Aide Hours	5080	1512	1912	1656	
Nursing Hours per Patient Day	8.1	8.2	7.7	8.6	
RN Hours per Patient Day	2.3	1.9	2.3	2.9	

University of Missouri—Kansas City Medical School

Table 2

INPATIENT COMPARATIVE DATA SELECTED ITEMS

Subject	All Teams	Blue Team	Red Team	Green Team	Yellow Team
Number of Bacteriology Tests	440	153	167	120	
Per Admission	3.1	3.1	3.5	2.7	
Number of Biochemistry Tests	3017	918	1091	1008	
Per Admission	21.2	18.7	22.7	22.4	
Number of Hematology Tests	624	148	244	232	
Per Admission	4.4	3.0	5.1	5.2	
Number of Other Tests	102	19	35	48	
Per Admission	.1	---	.1	.1	
Total Number of Lab Tests Ordered	4183	1238	1537	1408	
Per Admission	29.5	25.3	32.0	31.3	
Number of Radiology Exams	270	69	105	96	
Per Admission	1.9	1.4	2.2	2.1	
Number of EKG's & C-V Exams	145	42	54	49	
Per Admission	1.0	.1	1.1	1.1	
Total Radiology EKG & C-V Exams	415	111	159	145	
Per Admission	2.9	2.3	3.3	3.2	
Grand Total for Above Services	4598	1349	1696	1553	
Per Admission	32.4	27.50	35.3	34.5	
Charges for Lab Tests ($)	24187	7261	8728	8198	
Per Admission	170	148	182	182	
Charges for Medication ($) [	5186	1589	1799	1798	
Per Admission	36.50	32.40	37.50	40.00	

Appendix (continued)
University of Missouri–Kansas City Medical School
Table 3

OUTPATIENT SUMMARY

Subject	All Teams	Blue Team	Red Team	Green Team	Yellow Team
Basic Data					
Number of Sessions	60	20	20	20	
Number of Patients	2109	685	743	681	
Average Patients Per Session	35.1	34.2	37.2	34	
Provider Sessions Available	366	105	116	145	
Patients/Session/Physician	176	6.5	6.4	4.7	
Referrals					
Social Worker Cases Opened	12	10	1	1	
Dietician Instructions	207	84	41	82	
Personnel					
Docent	6	2	2	2	
Visiting Staff	7	3	1	3	
Residents	8	3	3	2	
Interns	4	1	1	2	
Pharmacists	3	1	1	1	
Social Workers	3	1	1	1	
Clinical Nurses	3	1	1	1	
Total Appointments Made	2957	980	1025	952	
No of "No Shows"	848	295	282	271	
No Show Rate Per Session	14.1	14.7	14.1	13.5	
% No Show	28.6	30.1	27.5	28.4	

University of Missouri–Kansas City Medical School
Table 4

OUTPATIENT DATA SUMMARY SELECTED ITEMS

Subject	All Teams	Blue Team	Red Team	Green Team	Yellow Team
Number of Bacteriology Tests	123	19	69	35	
Per Visit	.1	----	.1	.1	
Number of Biochemistry Tests	3642	1121	1315	1206	
Per Visit	1.7	1.6	1.8	1.8	
Number of Hematology Tests	492	171	156	165	
Per Visit	.2	.2	.2	.2	
Number of Other Tests	37	6	19	12	
Per Visit	---	---	---	---	
Number of Lab Tests Ordered	4294	1317	1559	1418	
Per visit	2.0	1.9	2.1	2.1	
Number of Radiology Exams	253	85	76	92	
Per Visit	.1	.1	.1	.1	
Number of EKG's & C-V Exams	156	52	52	52	
Per Visit	.1	.1	.1	.1	
Total Radiology EKG & C-V Exams	409	137	128	144	
Per Visit	.2	.2	.2	.2	
Grand Total for Above Services	4703	1454	1687	1562	
Per Visit	2.2	2.1	2.3	2.3	
Charges for Lab Tests ($)	20919	6026	8044	6849	
Per Visit	9.90	8.80	10.85	10.05	
Charges for Medication ($)	15254	5218	5407	4629	
Per Visit	7.25	7.60	7.30	6.80	

Appendix (continued)
University of Missouri–Kansas City Medical School
Table 5

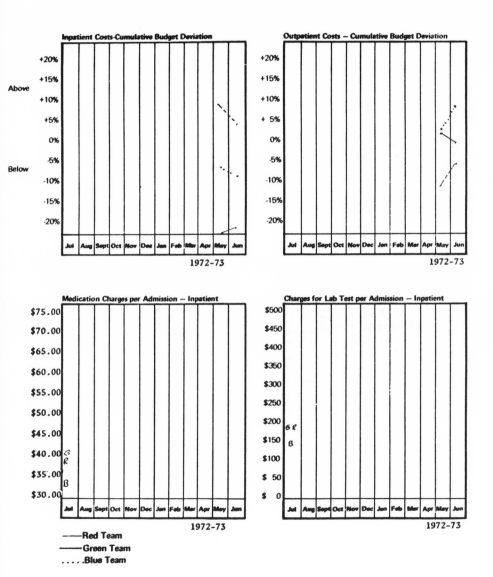

147

University of Missouri–Kansas City Medical School
Table 6

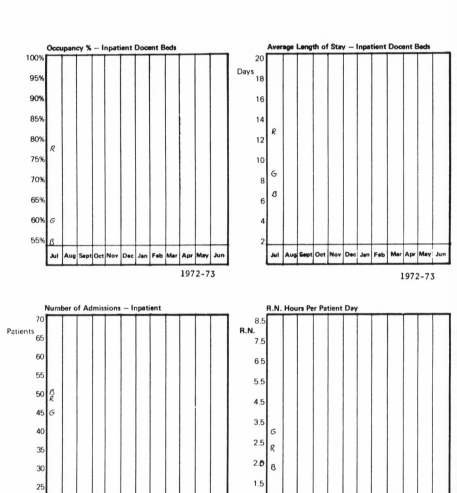

Appendix (continued)
University of Missouri–Kansas City Medical School
Table 7

OUTPATIENT DATA

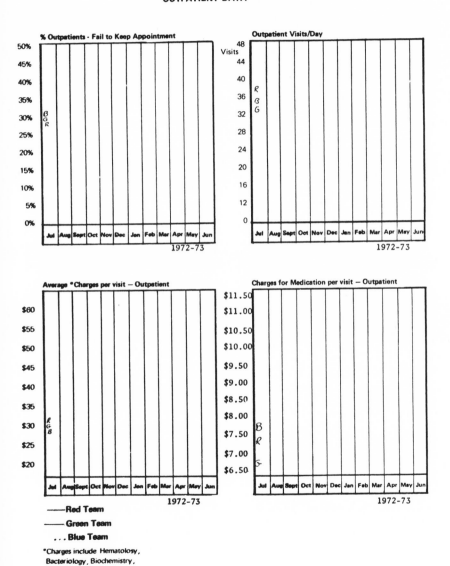

———Red Team

——— Green Team

. . . Blue Team

*Charges include Hematology,
Bacteriology, Biochemistry,
EEG, EKG, Radiology.

149

University of Missouri–Kansas City Medical School
Table 9

INPATIENT DEATHS AND CRITICALLY ILL PATIENTS

Name	Number	Admission Date and Date of Death	Diagnoses	Autopsy	Student Team
			RED UNIT		
	160259	7/25/72 7/26/72	Liver Failure	Yes	
	054494	6/25/72 7/6/72	Congestive Heart Failure. Arterio-sclerotic heart disease.	No	
			GREEN UNIT		
	252171	7/7/72 7/16/72	Intracranial hemorr-hage. Ruptured ant-erior communicating artery aneurysm.	No	
	127594	7/19/72 7/31/72	Metastatic carcinoma to the lungs. Carci-noma, squamous, of the cervix.	No	
	204543	7/24/72 7/27/72	Cerebral infarction, left hemisphere. Hypertensive cardio-vascular disease.	Yes	
	206947	6/18/72 7/2/72	Pulmonary Embolism Metastatic Carcinoma of Breast	No	
	251917	7/3/72 7/6/72	Probable Ventricular Arrythmia. Arterio-sclerotic heart dis-ease. Carcinoma of right lung.	No	
			BLUE UNIT		
	249663	7/23/72 7/28/72	Respiratory arrest Meningitis Emphysema	No	

University of Missouri–Kansas City Medical School
Table 10

INPATIENT DEATHS AND CRITICALLY ILL PATIENTS

Name	Number	Admission Date and Date of Death	Diagnoses	Autopsy	Student Team
			BLUE UNIT CON'T		
	143623	7/23/72 7/29/72	Pulmonary embolism Encephalopathy, Marked Obesity.	No	
	251072	7/11/72 7/12/72	Circulatory Collapse Generalized Carcinoma-tosis.	No	
	251757	6/27/72 7/6/72	Liver Failure Carcinomatosis	Yes	
	190112	7/2/72 7/4/72	Respiratory & Cardiac Arrest; severe pul-monary insufficiency. Bronchial Asthma.	Yes	
	030002	6/26/72 7/5/72	Respiratory Failure Carcinoma of Lung	No	
	248227	7/5/72 7/5/72	Shock-Respiratory arrest. Carcinoma of Lungs with Metastasis.	No	
	009820	6/27/72 7/6/72	Acute pulmonary edema Congestive heart fail-ure. Chronic atrial fibrillation.	Yes	

University of Missouri—Kansas City Medical School

Table 11

OUTPATIENT CARE SUMMARY BY PROVIDER

	Patients Seen Per Month 1	Number of Sessions In Clinic	Average No. of Patients Per Session	*New Patients
Residents:				
	104	20	5.2	
	117	20	5.8	
	99	19	5.2	
Interns:				
	90	16	5.6	
Other: Attending Physicians, Docent, Staff Physicians Listed by Category				
	47	14	3.4	
	1	1	1.0	
	31	12	2.6	
	9	6	1.5	
	1	1	1.0	
	1	1	1.0	
	106	10	10.6	
Medical Students	Patient Encounters Per Month			
Nurse Clinicians	Patient Encounters — Clinic Home			
	34	15	2.3	

*New Patients — A patient being seen in this Docent Clinic for the first time
1. ONLY INCLUDES THOSE PATIENTS FOR WHICH THE PROVIDER SIGNED THE CHART

BLUE

University of Missouri–Kansas City Medical School

Table 11 (continued)

OUTPATIENT CARE SUMMARY BY PROVIDER

	Patients Seen Per Month 1	Number of Sessions In Clinic	Average No. of Patients Per Session	*New Patients
Residents				
	118	16	7.4	
	124	15	8.3	
	70	14	5.0	
	3	3	1.0	
Interns:				
	75	16	4.7	
Other: Attending Physicians, Docent, Staff Physicians Listed by Category				
	54	15	3.6	
	83	14	5.9	
	18	7	2.6	
	2	2	1.0	
	2	1	2.0	
	12	5	2.4	
Medical Students	Patient Encounters Per Month			
Nurse Clinicians	Patient Encounters — Clinic / Home			
	24	8	3.0	
	43	16	2.7	

*New Patients — A patient being seen in this Docent Clinic for the first time
1. ONLY INCLUDES THOSE PATIENTS FOR WHICH THE PROVIDER SIGNED THE CHART

RED

Appendix (continued)
University of Missouri–Kansas City Medical School
Table 11 (continued)

OUTPATIENT CARE SUMMARY BY PROVIDER

	Patients Seen Per Month 1	Number of Sessions In Clinic	Average No. of Patients Per Session	*New Patients
Residents:				
	1	1	1.0	
	193	20	9.6	
	159	20	8.0	
	15	5	3.0	
	1	1	1.0	
Interns:				
	52	15	3.5	
	4	1	4.0	
Other: Attending Physicians, Docent, Staff Physicians Listed by Category				
	77	10	7.7	
	22	11	2.0	
	12	5	2.4	
	27	5	5.4	
	8	3	2.7	
	19	3	6.3	
	25	17	1.5	
	9	5	1.8	
	2	2	1.0	
	5	2	2.5	
Medical Students	5	3	1.7	
	Patient Encounters			
Nurse Clinicians	Clinic Home			
	18	8	2.2	

*New Fatients — A patient being seen in this Docent Clinic for the first time
1. ONLY INCLUDES THOSE PATIENTS FOR WHICH THE PROVIDER SIGNED THE CHART

GREEN

154

University of Missouri–Kansas City Medical School
Table 12

BUDGET PERFORMANCE SUMMARY COMPARISON

Subject	All Teams	Blue Team	Red Team	Green Team	Yellow Team
Inpatient					
Budgeted this Month	53433	18047	17069	18317	
Spent this Month	46664	15324	17201	14129	
Deviation (%)	-13.0	-15.0	-.1	-23.0	
Budgeted to Date Since Last May 1	183679	62013	58661	63005	
Spent to Date Since Last May 1	163945	55135	60398	48412	
Deviation (%)	-11.0	-11.0	+3.0	-23.0	
Outpatient					
Budgeted this Month	4938	1848	1244	1846	
Spent this Month	5084	2163	1135	1786	
Deviation (%)	+3.0	+17.0	-8.6	-3.0	
Budgeted to Date Since Last May 1	16867	6341	4226	6300	
Spent to Date Since Last May 1	16704	6581	3927	6196	
Deviation (%)	-.1	+4.0	-7.0	-2.0	

155

Note for Foundations for Medical Care

Description

This case provides a general description of medical foundations, their objectives, method of operation and extent to which they have proliferated in recent years across the United States.

Teaching Objective

To familiarize the student with a recent attempt at controlling physician fees and medical costs as well as quality of care within the framework of the fee-for-service concept. This note is especially intended to familiarize the student with the foundation concept in a general way.

The case was designed to serve as a background for the case entitled "Foundation for Health Care Evaluation." It can be used alone as a basis of discussion on different ways physicians have responded to the need for controls within the health care delivery system, or it can be used in conjunction with the case Foundation for Health Care Evaluation to provide background for students unfamiliar with medical foundations.

FOUNDATIONS FOR MEDICAL CARE

Definition of a Medical Foundation

Medical foundations are incorporated, non-profit bodies under sponsorship of state and/or medical societies. The specific and primary purpose for which these corporations are formed is to promote, develop and encourage the distribution of medical services by members to people of an area served and adjacent areas at a cost reasonable to both physician and patient; to preserve unto their members, the medical profession at large, and the public, freedom of choice of both physician and patient; to guard and preserve the physician-patient relationship and its numerous benefits; to protect the public health; to work in cooperation with the insurance industry and service plans that provide for periodic freedom of selection of physicians and the guarantee of the physician-patient relationship.[1]

Objectives

The objectives of the foundation movement can be viewed under several headings. Foremost is the desire to place health insurance in the private sector rather than under the control of government agencies. This can only be accomplished, believe foundation supporters, if the foundations can control for and improve the quality of medical care by:
1) extending the scope of insurance coverage to all people,

2) broadening benefits to those already insured,

3) sponsoring prepaid medical care programs that meet foundation criteria,

4) establishing area-wide peer review committees to control for-fee abuse.

5) encouraging the establishment of hospital audit committees for in-patient care.

History of the San Joaquin
Foundation for Medical Care

The idea of a medical foundation was formulated in 1954 in the San Joaquin area of California by a group of physicians under the guidance of Dr. Donald Harrington. The San Joaquin County Medical Society sponsored its formation as a protective reaction to the plan of Kaiser-Permanente to start a close panel prepaid program in the area as well as the possible establishment of a labor union hospital.

The San Joaquin Foundation for Medical Care, as it came to be known, set a precedent for the foundation movement as a whole. One feature of the San Joaquin program was the establishment of *Minimum Standards* for basic group insurance programs. The first group to contract with the San Joaquin physicians, the International Longshoremen's and Warehousemen's Union was dissatisfied with the scope of coverage in their existent plan.

In response, the San Joaquin Foundation undertook full financial risk for physicians' care and guaranteed medical services for a fixed fee ceiling. The Foundation thus guaranteed *Certainty of Coverage*. At this point, a fee consistent with the fixed premium dollar was established as was a close liaison enabling the two groups to renegotiate contractual details. The result was comprehensive coverage for all office visits for union members and a one visit deductible for dependents. In order for a plan to qualify for sponsorship by the San Joaquin Foundation after this initial arrangement, coverage for ambulatory care, outpatient X-ray, laboratory work, consultations in and out of the hospital were necessary.

As the Foundation's operations grew, it sold health contracts on a prepaid basis to over 100 groups; however, the risk assumption was minimal because the Foundation was a front end contractor always writing off risk with a functioning insurance company. Two other California foundations, those of Sonoma and Sacramento, have prepaid groups participating in their programs. The general feeling nationwide is that at such time as foundations assume much of the function of a Health Maintenance Organization*, the practice of insuring groups on a prepaid basis will be more prevelent. The San Joaquin Foundation contracts with groups on a capitation basis but reimburses physicians on a fee-for-service basis with the understanding that excess costs might have to be absorbed through increased membership dues or prorated fees.

There are two categories of foundations currently operating in the United States, the "comprehensive" and the "claims review" types. The San Joaquin Foundation, an example of a "comprehensive" foundation, processes claims for its participating prepaid groups paying hospitals and physicians policies that cover 130,000 people and include 100 groups. The Foundation for Health Care Evaluation, like many other "claims review" foundations, reviews only those claims referred by participating carriers because they exceed fee guidelines; still other foundations review all claims but leave the processing and payment to

---

*A Health Maintenance Organization can be loosely defined as a comprehensive system of medical care that includes all medical specialties and access to hospitals and clinics which is financed by fixed annual prepaid fees.

carriers. In all cases, the patient has free choice of physician and hospital with private office practice guaranteed.[3]

Having ensured Minimum Standards and Certainty of Coverage, the next step was the determination of a maximum fee schedule with the purpose of maintaining *Cost Control*. A decision was made to preserve the actuarial principles of a fixed premium situation, and then establish norms for what were usual, customary, and reasonable fees. Fee schedules were obtained from practicing physicians for various services, low schedules upgraded and regular schedules modified according to changes in the economy.[2]

Other foundations have used different methods for determining fee criteria. The Foundation for Health Care Evaluation of Hennepin County, Minnesota, for example, used the 1963 Minnesota Relative Value Index as a base for determining its acceptable fee reimbursement level. For the most part, foundation physicians in California have been using the Califonia Relative Value Study and the conversion factors agreed on for each local area.[4]

Extent of Foundation
Participation in the U.S.

Although the initial foundations were begun in the middle to late fifties in California as a response to close panel plans like Kaiser-Permanente, by 1971 foundations had spread to 21 states. Foundations in 4 California counties formed a confederation known as the United Foundations for Medical Care (U.F.M.C.) which spawned an umbrella organization, the American Association of Foundations for Medical Care (A.A.F.M.C.). Nineteen foundations serving 32 counties existed in California alone by 1971; 46 county or city foundations were either in existence or in formation across the entire country; statewide foundations existed in New Mexico, Georgia, Kansas, Colorado, Delaware, Illinois, New Hampshire, Ohio, Pennsylvania, and South Carolina.

The scope of the statewide foundations varied considerably. Kansas' foundation covered statewide Medicare and Medicaid peer and utilization review; the Georgia foundation has contracted for care of the entire state's Medicaid population. In 1971, it was estimated that 9000 physicians were involved in some 50 foundations delivering care to approximately 1,500,000 patients. It was predicted that by the end of 1972, over 200 foundations would be in existence.*

Membership

Every physician member of a county and/or state medical society is eligible for membership in a foundation sponsored by it. Membership on the part of a physician carries with it the responsibility to accept all foundation contract obligations with insurers as well as the decisions of peer review committees. This frequently means accepting fee reimbursement as a level established by the foundation. Some foundations require a membership fee; others annual dues. Foundations' Boards of Directors consist mainly of physicians; however, many have been expanded to include other providers and, in some instances, consumers. Even if consumer reps do not sit on the Boards, their collective voice is often heard through the establishment of a community advisory council.

*Emory Bullis, Assistant Director, Office of Program Planning and Evaluation, Health Services and Mental Health Administration, H.E.W., made this estimate in 1971.

Promotion

The initial major cost of creating a local foundation is usually its promotion through insurance brokers, carriers, group insureds, and the general public. Expenditures include the preparation of brochures, bulletins, forms, and other necessary printed material as well as news stories, television and speaking appearances and various group contacts. The history of foundations have shown that brokers must be sold on the idea that a foundation plan is best for their clients, and some of the larger groups have to be convinced that they can afford the added benefits of foundation-sponsored programs.

Administrative Costs

The experience of new foundations generally has been that up to 20% of claims are forwarded from insurance intermediaries for physician peer review. About 2% of these end up being reviewed by a full peer reivew committee. After a foundation has been operating for a period of time, the general experience has been that physicians adjust their charges to conform to fee guidelines and the number of claims referred decreases. If a foundation is of the comprehensive type, it sets standards for medical coverage, receives, processes and reviews all claims, and may issue checks to providers. In order to pay for this administrative function, a foundation might charge the financial intermediary who underwrites the premium in the range of 2.5% to 4% of the total premium; 0.5% of the premium for checking eligibility and around 1% for conducting hospital utilization review. With increasing use of computers to handle these functions, the time lag between submission, of the claim and payment is continually decreasing.[5]

Peer Review

One of the basic tenets of a foundation is that by cooperating to control costs and improve the quality of medical care, physicians will be able to retain control of their profession longer in the face of government intervention. In order to eliminate fee abuses and review for under and over utilization of hospitals, the peer review process has been adopted. In addition to setting ceilings on fee-for-service, some peer review committees investigate malpractice suits and some have the authority to suspend the license of member physicians.[6]

Generally, local physicians undertake individual review of cases as well as serve on Review Committees. After a patient profile and fee guideline is established, deviant claims are referred for peer review. The fact that a claim has been referred to peer review does not mean per se that there is anything wrong with the claim.

A claim that is received in peer review can be subjected to any one of the following actions:

1. The reviewing physician may approve the claim and immediately send it on for payment. Approximately two thirds of all claims sent to peer review are handled in this fashion because it is immediately apparent to the reviewing physician that the services rendered were indeed necessary in the rendering of proper medical care.

2. The reviewing physician may request additional information from the attending physician or other provider. When this is received, the claim is again reviewed and either accepted for payment or referred to the full Peer Review Committee for a decision.

3. The reviewing physician may delete items which he considers represent excessive utilization or unnecessary methods of treatment.

The physician whose claim has been reviewed and, in any way altered, i.e., denied payment for rendered services, has the right of appeal to the Peer Review Committee and the right of hearing.

The review committee may, if in its opinion it is indicated, refer claims which they feel indicate impropriety on the part of the physician directly to the medical society for investigation and such action as a proper society committee deems indicated.

In some cases the physician provider is invited to attend the meeting. In San Joaquin, for example, this direct confrontation has proved to be a highly successful instrument in educating and guiding those doctors whose practice patterns deviate from high quality standards.[6] Peer review has been used to identify under-utilization of diagnostic and consultative services as well as in the establishment of peer justification mechanisms when a new or unusual medical treatment is introduced.

Cost Savings

The United Foundations for Medical Care claims that "the review mechanism usually generates about an 8% reduction as measured in dollars between the submitted bill of the provider and the payment made to the provider." As well, UFMC experience has shown that between 3-5% of the providers account for 90% of the reductions made by the peer review mechanism. According to the executive claims officer of the San Joaquin Foundation for Medical Care, savings from peer review of fees has been only 1.5%; however, hospital over-utilization has been between 12-15%. Somewhat revealing are the average annual patient costs per day of two counties in California. The figure cited for San Joaquin with a comprehensive foundation is $52/day as opposed to $63/day for Ventura County where no foundation is operating.[7]

Foundations as Health
Maintenance Organizations

There is some talk of foundations either qualifying as HMO's should federal legislation be enacted or at least of foundations providing the peer review mechanism for government programs like Medicaid and Medicare nationwide. It is questionable whether Federal guidelines for HMO's encompass the foundation structure; however, there is the possibility that foundations may qualify should physicians be willing to subcontract with hospitals and other facilities to provide the full range of services required. A report published by Blue Cross in 1971 assessed the situation as follows:

> From all indications, foundation activity will increase in coming years . . . While most government involvement in the private health delivery system is mistrusted by medical societies, some recent legislative proposals are being looked upon favorably. For example, through proposed Health Maintenance Organizations, many foundations could become suppliers of medical services which would be purchased by the federal government. If proposals to mandate implementation of peer review organizations for federal programs were enacted, medical societies and foundations could be authorized to set up quality control programs for Medicare, Medicaid and Maternal and Child Health programs under the Social Security Act.[8]

In 1971, HEW provided limited funds via HMO planning and development grants to several foundations, among them the Medical Care Foundation of Sacramento (California) and the Sonoma (California) Foundation for Medical Care, the Metropolitan Denver Foundation for Medical Care, and the Bexar County Medical Society, San Antonio, Texas. Both the Sacramento and Sonoma groups received more than $100,000 each in federal grants to design and develop HMO's.[3] Two other organizational structures contemplated by foundations in the early 1970's in addition to HMO's are the PSRO (Professional Standards Review Organization) and the EMCRO (Experimental Medical Care Review Organization).*

According to proponents, medical foundations have provided one vehicle for controlling physicians' fees. Advocates in the foundation movement claim they have been well received by the physician community at large because of their pledge to maintain freedom of choice of physician and hospital. Their handling of certain state programs such as Medicaid and Medicare have been successful. In California, in particular, they have provided a viable alternative to the large prepaid health programs, through their upgrading of insurance benefits and their effort to provide much needed services in certain areas.

The Fresno Foundation Newsletter, September, 1971 cites the following examples of some specific programs already undertaken by foundations in California:

"The Monterey Care provides services to migrants in their King City Project; the San Joaquin Foundation maintains 2 fixed and 5 mobile clinics for migrants, providing over 8,000 visits per year, and funded by the United States Public Health Service, San Joaquin County Board of Supervisors, and the Regional Migrant Education Program. Regional Medical Programs fund a program in San Joaquin County of multiphasic screening and follow-up care for 3,000 urban poor; this is in cooperation with the Consumer Health Council. Other programs include community-wide utilization programs for extended care facilities; a new concept in certifying hospital admissions developed by the Sacramento Foundation; a coordinated medical utilization program that not only certifies hospital admissions but monitors the length of stay, proper placement of patients after leaving the acute facility, and follow-through at each level of care; a pilot program under Medicare for Kern, Fresno, and San Joaquin Foundations designed to develop patient profile information; and a contract with Pacific Mutual Life Insurance, Pacific National Life Assurance, California-Western States Life, and Occidential Life Insurance whereby the Foundations accept the responsibility of developing criteria of care to be utilized in computerized perspective and retrospective review process. Two Foundations are actually involved in prepaid program for Title XIX. Welfare recipients in the counties of Sonoma, Mendocino and Lake are covered under a prepayment program of Sonoma Foundation for Medical Care, and the welfare recipients of Amador, Calaveras, Tuolumne, and San Joaquin counties are covered under a prepayment contract of San Joaquin Foundations. Both of these contracts give the political subdivisions involved a predictable ceiling on costs for a predictable period of time and have built-in incentives and utilization review procedures.

---

*PSRO's are funded under the federal legislation HR 1 Public Law 92603, Section 249F. The law spells out the procedure whereby organized groups of physicians can assume the peer review function. The EMCRO program provides the foundation with the opportunity to plan a peer review project in the local area and to evaluate both the quality of care and the self-containment of selected categories of care under the terms of an HEW grant. Approximately 11 of these programs have been funded on an experimental basis as a forerunner to the establishment of a PSRO.

Footnotes

1. Quoted from "Concepts Relating to Foundations for Medical Care," Medical Administration Technology Service, Stockton, California.

2. "Address delivered at Regional Conference on Health Maintenance Organizations." July 30, 1971, at the Statler Hilton in Dallas Texas, by John I. Morozumi, M.D. Past President, San Joaquin County Medical Society.

3. Brierly, Carol, "Medical Foundations: Antidote for National Health Insurance?", *Physicians' Management Magazine,* October, 1971, p. 34.

4. Egdahl, Richard H., M.D., "Foundations for Medical Care," *New England Journal of Medicine,* Vol. 288, No. 10, March 8, 1973, pp. 491-98.

5. Egdahl, *op. cit.,* p. 472.

6. Howard Eisenberg, "There's a Medical Foundation in Your Future," *Medical Economics,* September 27, 1971.

7. Egdahl, *op. cit.,* p. 493.

8. From a report on "Foundations for Medical Care," published by Blue Cross Association, Chicago, August, 1971.

Note for Foundation
for Health Care Evaluation

Description

This case is a fairly exhaustive description of the origins and early operation of a medical foundation headquartered in Minneapolis, Minnesota. The case situation involves the Administrator of the foundation who is reviewing with a medical consultant the foundation's accomplishments to date and trying to decide what direction to go in next. The focus of the case is on cost of care provided by individual medical practitioners rather than institutions, and on attempts to monitor those costs. The case raises many questions about the pros and cons of Peer Review in the area of health care delivery and would fit in well with any material dealing with this issue.

Teaching Objective

"Foundation for Health Care Evaluation" provides a vehicle for studying one application of management control systems to the health field. It allows students to consider some of the unique problems of the health field; in particular, the cost and quality control systems which are currently operating in the area of individual care provided by physicians on a fee-for-service basis on their offices, and the difficulty of expanding this control system to institutions delivering health care. Some of the basic and central issues that might be explored in terms of the case material are as follows:

(1) What are the objectives of the control system that is operating in the case?
(2) How do you implement this type of a control system?
(3) How do these systems act as constraints on medical care delivery?

(4) What is really being controlled? Exceptions to customary practice or customary practice itself?

(5) What are the costs and benefits of setting up such a system?

Some of the underlying issues are:

(1) How does one operationally define quality of medical care so that the definition is acceptable and measurable?

(2) Even if you arrive at an acceptable definition, how can you set up a system that is acceptable?

(3) How is such an organization *accountable* to various groups such as

    (a) the consumer

    (b) the insurance industry

    (c) other providers of health care?

(4) Is this a useful approach in attempting to salvage what may be a dying institution—the delivery of fee-for-service health care by the individual practitioner?

The case might also be approached in Public Health courses as a basis for analyzing one organizational approach for monitoring and delivery health care.

The case "Foundation for Health Care Evaluation" can be supplemented by the case entitled "Foundations for Medical Care," which would serve as general background for those unfamiliar with medical foundations.

FOUNDATION FOR HEALTH CARE EVALUATION

Mr. Carl Gustafson, Administrative Director of the Foundation for Health Care Evaluation, had been aware for a long time of the important directions in which the Foundation was heading, some times with great success, other times with less. He was interested in exploring further the reasons for both the success and the problems the Foundation had been encountering, and felt an outsider's view of the Foundation's achievements and operations would be of value. He arranged for Mr. Robert Milton, a medical consultant, to meet with participants, advocates, and opponents of the Foundation's program.

Organizational Design and Board of Directors

The Foundation for Health Care Evaluation is a non-profit, tax-exempt corporation, with a Board of Directors composed of 41 members. (Exhibit 1 is an organization chart.) Medical representation on the Board of Directors is provided by allocating to a term on the Board one physician for each 100 (or fraction thereof) physicians subscribing to Foundation membership within the seven county area.

The Foundation Constitution and By-laws provide for consumer representation on the Board of Directors from the Metropolitan Health Board, Social Welfare, non-profit prepaid health service plans, health insurance industry, and the Minnesota State Planning Agency. In addition, the Board also has consumer members representing management, labor, and hospital administration, and two consumers-at-large. These two groups of physicians and consumer representatives make up the 41 member Board. All Board members serve a staggered three-year term in office.

Objectives

As stated in the April 1972 *Report on Current Activities* of the Health Insurance Council, the main problem areas identified by the Foundation for Health Care Evaluation were:

1) The need to increase productivity of the producer consistent with a criteria of quality care at reasonable cost;
2) The need to achieve optimum utilization of health facilities and services;
3) The need to improve the availability and accessibility of health care to deprived members of our population;
4) The need to expand existing health insurance benefits to provide a full range of ambulatory, therapeutic, preventative and rehabilitative services;
5) The need for an intensified program of health education for all customers.

In the light of this list, a set of objectives for the Foundation were determined. In order of priority, these were:

1) Establishing a system for monitoring and evaluating physicians' judgments and fees in the delivery of ambulatory and institutional care;
2) Broadening the base of coverage in existing health insurance programs;
3) Identifying areas where health care services were not available, or of inferior quality; and
4) Determining the Foundation's role in consumer health education.

In actuality, the Foundation, during its two years in operation, had concentrated primarily on the reviewing and subsequent reduction of physicians' fees. The results, Gustafson felt, had been considerable cost savings. The Foundation's monitoring system has three phases: physicians' fees, hospital utilization, and quality control. Mr. Milton learned that while inroads had been made on the latter two phases in the form of a rudimentary utilization program based on PAS data and a book of norms of health care, opposition from local hospitals had limited these programs.

Origin

The impetus for establishing a medical foundation in Minneapolis-St. Paul stemmed from an OEO study in 1965 which documented the inadequacy of health services in several sections of the Twin City metropolitan area. Spokesmen claimed that the initiative for forming the Foundation for Health Care Evaluation was gaps and shortcomings in the health care delivery system—physician overcharging, inferior care, inadequate health insurance protection, and unjustified costs due to waste and inefficiency—and foremost a desire to do something about them. Above all, increased medical costs as a result of inflation and Medicare led some members of the Hennepin County Medical Society (whose membership includes approximately 70% of the physicians in the Twin City area) to support the idea of a medical foundation.*

---

*A medical foundation is a non-profit organization of physicians sponsored by a state or local medical society. Many foundations contract with industry, unions, or government to provide health care to specified groups of patients on a capitation prepaid basis; others operate solely as a peer review function without assuming any risk. Unlike clinics or group practice arrangements, care is provided in the offices of Foundation members, thus allowing patients free choice of physicians and hospitals. (Howard Eisenberg, "There's a Foundation in Your Future," *Medical Economics,* September 27, 1971, p. 91.)

Mr. Gustafson explained the mechanisms for starting the Foundation:

The year prior to my arrival in 1971, a research and sales campaign was carried out. Once it was decided to go ahead, we had to convince the physicians. This was all done under the direction of the Hennepin County Medical Society. The Society had been concerned with rising costs in medicine. Members went to California twice and visited the San Joaquin Foundation.* It was decided that a foundation like the San Joaquin one wouldn't fit in here. It was also felt that our foundation shouldn't become a claims department. The only thing we had to offer was the expertise of physicians to conduct peer review.

According to Mr. Gustafson, there were several reasons for not modelling the Twin City program on that of the San Joaquin Foundation. Fist, the San Joaquin Valley was a self-contained area populated by 300 physicians, while Hennepin County, Minnesota, had approximately 1200 physicians, Second, insurance carriers in the San Joaquin program had to meet minimum benefit standards established by its foundation; the Twin City group, on the other hand, believed that because most people in the area already had some form of health insurance, they would be excluded from the benefits of the Foundation if their packages did not correspond with the benefit requirements that might be established. In the San Joaquin program, claims against the certified insurance programs were processed by its foundation for a specific fee. This procedure, it was decided, would put the Twin Cities' foundation in the position of competing with with insurance industry in the claims administration function, perhaps at a higher cost to the premium payer.

Promotional Strategy

The next step was to present the concept to the physician members of the Hennepin County Medical Society and medical staffs of the voluntary hospitals in the metropolitan area. The foundation concept was presented twice at the Hennepin County Medical Society's general membership meetings, and to such groups as the Hennepin and Ramsey County Academies of Family Practice, the Minneapolis Surgical Society, the Minneapolis Opthalmology Society, and the Twin City Orthopedic Society.

One promotional strategy heavily relied on was word of mouth. Several prominent physicians in the Medical Society were encouraged to introduce the idea to colleagues and try to enlist their support. According to Gustafson, "the reaction of the physician community had been outstanding. They signed on because they had faith in the doctors who had proposed the Foundation. Communication was not always clear, however. Some didn't understand that we were going to come to grips with fees as tenaciously as possible. While there is difficulty in deciding what problem to attack first, our emphasis has been on monitoring the quality of care."

Gustafson felt that only a small proportion of the public was aware of their attempts at cutting medical costs. He explained that although articles were sent to local papers, not all of them were printed. In addition, Gustafson had appeared on a local consumer-oriented t.v. program for 15 minutes in order to explain the objectives of the Foundation. This brief

---

*The Foundation for Medical Care of San Joaquin, California, one of the original foundations in the country, was a model upon which many others were based. It was begun in 1954 at the initiative of the local medical society in reaction to the threatened penetration of close-panel prepaid health insurance groups such as Kaiser-Permanente into the area.

appearance did not appease the local consumer groups who, through their organization, The Greater Metropolitan Federation, had a direct confrontation with the Foundation's administration in the summer of 1971.

Finance

Further inquiries revealed that the Foundation had been financed from two sources. The first and minor source of income was the physicians' enrollment fee of $10.00 per member, which provided a portion of the seed money for organizational expenses. The budget for the last six months of 1971, in excess of $70,000, was provided by the participating insurance carriers and prepaid health service plans. The individual carrier's assessment of the total budget was based on their market penetration in the Twin City Metropolitan area. For example, if Company X was underwriting 30% of the health insurance coverage in the area, that company was assessed 30% of the Foundation's operating budget. Together, 34 health insurance carriers underwrote 50% of the administrative expenses identified with the operation of the Foundation. The remaining 50% of the administrative overhead was assumed by the nonprofit prepaid health service plans (The Blues).

In 1972, the estimated budget was more than $133,500. The proposed budget for 1973 was $159,000. Once again, funding was procured through the carriers as in 1971. In the following year, however, extensive research and development was to be conducted to effect a Hospital Utilization Program requiring additional personnel and expertise which would exceed the limits anticipated in the operating budget. It was understood that funds might be provided through the EMCRO* grant program under which financing would be available on or after July 1, 1972. This expanded program of the Foundation would make it imperative that financial resources be made available as early as January, 1973.

The professional time contributed by the member physicians, both on the Board and operating committees, was not an expense chargeable against the Foundation program. The additional staff and expenses of office overhead to carry out the work of the Foundation was contained in a separate budget charged to the prepaid health service plans and insurance companies on the basis of volume of business underwritten by each of them in the geographic area served by the Foundation. When asked what the insurance companies hoped to gain from their support of the Foundation, a spokesman for the insurance carriers replied, "Our aim was to put a lid on health delivery costs. We are also interested in quality control through maintaining hospital utilization. As of this time, we can't show on a dollar basis justification for our participation. We are confident that charges have been modified. The rate of escalation of fees has gone up 1.8%. This will be reflected in premiums to consumers although we can't identify how as yet. We don't see broader coverage coming about as a result of the Foundation."

Start up costs of approximately $100,000 were underwritten by the Hennepin County Medical Society. In addition, Gustafson told Mr. Milton that he had applied for grant money with little success. "Other foundations were getting grants, but we haven't received any. Ironically, people are getting grants who haven't done anything about peer review. We had applied for a grant to study the effect of an HMO and fee-for-service plan side by side. The objective of the study was to take a group and establish quality of care while developing doctor profiles."

*EMCRO (Experimental Medical Care Review Organization) is an HEW granted program which permits groups such as foundations to plan and implement peer review projects in a local area.

Physician Participation

In order for the foundation concept to succeed, health experts claim that at least 70% of the physicians in the locale served by a foundation would have to participate in its activities and be bound by its decisions. Sponsorship by a medical society was a reasonable way to insure complete participation. In the case of the Foundation for Health Care Evaluation, 95% of practicing physicians in the four counties west of the Mississippi—Scott, Carver, Anoka, and Hennepin—had subscribed to the Foundation. At the time of Mr. Milton's discussion with Gustafson, this represented approximately 1188 physicians. Any physician duly licensed to practice medicine and/or surgery in the state of Minnesota was eligible for membership in the Foundation. By signing the application card, the physician agreed to abide by those decisions reached by the Foundation Board and its review panels, and was obligated to serve on the Utilization and Peer Review panels when requested to do so. All member physicians were expected to do some peer review for the Foundation. Physicians in the three counties of the Mississippi were in the process of being enrolled as well. The anticipated participation among this group would bring the total of physician participation to approximately 61% of the physicians in the entire state of Minnesota.

During the first year of operation, more than 300 physicians served peer review functions without compensation for their time. In the second year, the figure was estimated at 3600 hours of professional time. This practice of not compensating reviewing physicians differed from that of many other foundations which reimbursed doctors on the average of $25/hour.

Screening and Peer Review

At this point, Mr. Milton wanted a more detailed explanation of the peer review process. Mr. Gustafson referred to a flow chart of the initial screening and review process (Exhibit 2):

> The carriers forward to us those claims which exceed the 84th percentile of the fee guidelines established by the Foundation. When we receive a case, it is date-stamped and duplicated. The first level of review is done in Foundation offices by an individual member physician. In each instance, the one-on-one reviewer practices in the same specialty field as is represented by the case. During the course of the initial review, any additional medical information needed is promptly secured. Insurance carriers are obligated to procure from the physician whose case is being reviewed any additional information which would justify the course of treatment, fee, etc., before being submitted to the Foundation. It should also be noted that a copy of the transmittal form utilized by the carrier to submit a case to the Foundation is sent to the physician.

> The initial reviewer, upon completing his evaluation, will record his conclusions on the standard form. If, in the judgment of the individual reviewer, the case is routine in nature—in other words, without medical complications—and the fee exceeds the 84th percentile guideline, the Foundation Administrative Director will reduce the fee to the guideline. Cases not routinely disposed of by the Administrative Director are placed before the entire Peer Review Panel.

The Peer Review panel is the crux of the entire process. Each panel consists of a specialist in one of 21 specialist fields. When a case for review comes befre the Peer Review Panel, it is usually assigned to the specialist on the panel in that field. However, this is not always possible. After reviewing the case for a brief time, the physician presents his case to the entire group describing its nature, the type of service rendered, the recommendation of the one-to-one reviewer, as well as his own conclusions.

When a final decision is reached, the physician is advised directly by the Foundation. If a physician is not satisfied, he has seven working days to appeal the decision. The carrier is notified after seven days and is responsible for the notice to the patient explaining the level of benefit to be paid. The appeal board is made up of eight physician members. The insurance company also has the right of appeal.

While the majority of cases are presented by third party carriers, cases may be submitted by the provider and/or the patient.

Full panel meetings are scheduled regularly on the same day and at the same hour with each panelist being involved once every fifth week. Such panel meetings are limited to two hours and the case load objective is usually 20 claims. There is a permanent chairman for each of the peer review committees. These eight form a committee of Panel Chairmen which meets every month and is used as a think tank by the Board of Directors. From June 15, 1971, through December, 1971, the fee panels had adjudicated 493 cases with 47.3% of such cases being reduced. It was estimated that in 1972 the contribution of physicians engaged in one-to-one review in terms of time without compensation exceeded 4000 physician hours. The figure did not include time spent in traveling between the physician's office and the Foundation.

While claims referred to the Foundation by the carriers can be reviewed as quickly as two days after they are received, it is possible for an unusual case to require six weeks. Mr. Gustafson indicated that processing time among carriers varied greatly.

> I suspect that some carriers are mailing benefit checks as soon as two weeks from the time they receive the decision. On the other hand, the average time for carriers is much closer to six weeks, and on individual problem cases, it could be as long as four or five months.

Fee Guidelines

Mr. Milton wanted to learn how the Foundation arrived at the acceptable fee parameters. He knew that the Greater Metropolitan Federation, a large consumer group in the Twin Cities, had demanded in the interest of the public that the fee scales be made public. Federation spokesmen were also unhappy about the Foundation decision to use as the cut-off point for reviewing charges the 84th percentile of physicians' charges for the area, and publically advocated using the 50th percentile.

According to Mr. Gustafson, the 84th percentile was arrived at in the following manner:

> In order to determine appropriate charges levels, we collected data from the insurance carriers over a three month period. The guidelines were based on the combined experience of individual insurance companies and the Blue Shield Plan of Minnesota. They reflected the range of prevailing charges for comparable services by practicing physicians in the Twin Cities Metropolitan area. A display of the fee data reflecting the 50th, 75th, 84th, and 90th percentiles was then presented. The doctors who made up the 22 peer review committees decided on the 84th percentile as appropriate and acceptable subject to ratification by the Board. They felt that this parameter would provide for enough claims for review but not too many to be handled administratively. All cases above the 84th percentile would be submitted to the Foundation for review. You have to remember that 90% of area physicians are Foundation members. There was one dissenting vote in deciding on the 84th percentile as the cut-off point. Each year we look at the guidelines and decide which ones need adjustment. At present, we are using the 1963 guidelines from the state medical society, called the Minnesota Relative Value Index. The insurance companies help us collect data. When it comes to adjusting guidelines, there is a difference of opinion.

Initially, fee guidelines were established for 32 very frequent procedures; however, the number was expanded by an additional 47 in addition to procedural guidelines for the specialties of anesthesiology, radiology, and pathology.

Some physician members of the Foundation disagreed with the use of the 1963 Minnesota Relative Value Index as a guide for determining acceptable fees. Their objections were based on the feeling that its fee guidelines were out of date and discouraged the insurance companies from examining individual physician profiles. By the Spring of 1973, it was anticipated that the 1969 California Relative Value Study would become the guide for determining acceptable fees.

Administration of Peer Review

At the time of Mr. Milton's visit, the Foundation staff consisted of five women in addition to the Administrative Director, Mr. Gustafson. The women were engaged in mostly clerical work, although one person with a background in data processing had been singled out to work in this field once the utilization and quality control programs got under way. Mr. Gustafson also indicated that the Foundation was in the process of expanding its staff.

Estimate of Savings

The April, 1972 Report on Current Activities of the Health Insurance Council indicated that the performance of the Foundation up to that time yielded the following results:

1) *Less than 1%* of all claims involving physicians' charges exceeded the guideline limits.
2) Of the 579 cases involving fee evaluation (less than 1% of all claims), 57.4% were reduced and 42.6% were approved as submitted.
3) The general rate of escalation in physicians' fees was 50% below the national average.

Quality Control

The major accomplishment of the Foundation with regard to ensuring quality medical care in the Twin City area was the publication of a *Book of Medical Care Norms*. The guidelines for the ambulatory and institutional services of physicians were developed by panels of practicing physicians usually involved in the treatment of such specific conditions from 21 major specialty areas. The guidelines provided 120 ambulatory diagnoses and 100 for diseases requiring institutional care. Such screens were used to determine when existing practices should be challenged, questioned or submitted to committees for review and evaluation. The compiled material was reviewed by Dr. Beverly C. Payne, author of *Hospital Utilization Review Manual,* who met personally with all 21 committees.

The cost of the initial printing was $18,000. This sum was raised through dues paid by participating physicians and insurance carrier contributions. The book was distributed without charge to all member physicians practicing in the seven-county area around the Twin Cities. The cost for the initial copy of the book outside the seven county area was $50, and $10 for each additional copy. Because of the foreseeable need for addition and amendation, the book was printed in looseleaf format.

Mr. Gustafson explained to Mr. Milton how the current format of the *Book of Norms* and the Foundation's plans for converting it to standards and a retrievable format would lend itself to electronic data processing.

The *Book of Norms* in its present form would best be viewed as the response one would get from a physician if you asked him what he would expect to find in each case record were he to accomplish a chart review on such a patient. In order to convert the *Book of Norms* to standards, the evaluation system must appear to be a group of screens which filter the cases which will require in-depth review, first grossly and then finely; and then after the finest screening will provide the committee with a residue of cases for in-depth chart review which are most likely to be of value to the committee's time. The screening procedures will have to be constructed in such a way that they will not mandate physician time and that the committee will be required to look at only those cases which cannot pass the various screening techniques.

Mr. Gustafson pointed out the three main goals of the Quality Assurance Program and described the strategy for its implementation.

1) Quality Assurance: a guarantee that the health care delivery system in the seven county area delivers uniformly appropriate medical care.

2) Quality Assessment: an activity of the Foundation for Health Care Evaluation, measuring the patterns of care actually delivered against area-wide standards.

3) Quality Control:

(a) The responsibility of each hospital board that the appropriate programs growing out of quality assessment are implemented and that they reach those for whom they were constructed.

(b) A corresponding responsibility of the Foundation for Health Care Evaluation in those areas of ambulatory medical care not subject to supervision by a hospital board.

Standards

During the first years of the Foundation's operation, the standards for the Quality Control Program were to be the *Book of Norms*. Once cooperation would be obtained from hospitals in the seven county area, revised standards based on input from hospital staff committees and converted to a uniform retrievable format would be adopted. Table 1 diagrams the process of revising standards.

Conduct of the Audit

In order to control for deviations, health record analysts would have to be employed by both the hospitals and the Foundation. The role of the Health Record Analyst would be to post the actual practice in the hospital against study criteria, identify and enumerate deviations from the norm. Deviations would be dealt with by the individual hospital staff committees. According to the Foundation program, "the deviations grown out of a comparison of actual practice against the standards (criteria) of the Foundation for Health Care Evaluation should be listed insofar as possible in terms of a per cent. The source of the deviation should be included so we are capable of recognizing whether the deviation occurred with respect to a given patient, a given physician, or is an aggregate deficiency of a department or an institution."

Deviations and Deficiencies

According to the model, the audit committees must seek to justify the deviations identified by the health record analyst. "Those deviations which cannot be clearly justified by good medical practice must by definition be judged deficient practice . . . A deficiency analysis should then include a decision as to whether the deficiency is one of a specific institution, of a specific department or service, or of an individual physician or clinic group. Having identified the deficient person or persons, or possibly even recognizing that the entire profession may be deficient in a given area, the deficiency analyst will require evaluation as to whether it is a failure in knowledge or performance.'' The model also should recognize the possibility that the standards were unjustified in the light of area-wide practice and that instead of a deficiency, the standard might need to be changed.

Corrective Action

Once a deficiency is identified, a decision should be made as to whether it is a result of lack of knowledge or poor performance. If the first, remediation through education is prescribed; if the deficiency is one of performance, it should be determined whether the performance problem is institution-wide or the result of individual activity. If the former, changes in departmental policy of institution rules and regulations are recommended; if the latter, then individual counseling is suggested. The Foundation may become involved in monitoring the correctable action. Deadlines for compliance will also have to be created and monitored through feedback to the Audit Committee.

Control and Certification

As a result of legal precedent, the hospital where deficient care has been delivered is legally responsible for the quality of care delivered within the institution. The Foundation's program is designed to alert the boards of deficient hospitals to the quality of care being delivered therein. At this point, it becomes their responsibility to ensure that corrective action is accomplished. The Foundation for its part will continue to advise the Board as well as provide yearly training programs to hospital boards ''bringing to them attorneys in the health care field to appraise them of the evolving roles of the hospital trustee.'' In terms of long range objectives, the Foundation foresees the following activities once successful implementation of the above quality control is begun: 1) The establishment of standards for ambulatory care; 2) the introduction of a problem-oriented audit for unexplainable diseases; 3) the development of an area-wide mandate for compliance to standards; and 4) the utilization of the material displaying credible medical practice in a public manner. Table 2 outlines the steps to be employed in the Quality Control Program. Exhibit 3 shows some examples of possible standards which could be used to evaluate treatment of such conditions as Myocardial Infarction, Cholecystectomy, Postoperative General Anesthetic Workup, Caesarean Section.

Priorities

Given the overwhelming nature of the task, a method of determining priorities is necessary which takes into consideration the following conditions amenable to audit: Diability, Frequency, Correctibility, Failure Consequences. By so doing, it would be possible to determine which items demand audit first. For example, terminal carcinoma causes overwhelming disability and has a high frequency yet its management has a low correctibility rate. Table 3 is an example of how this might be done by assigning numerical equivalents to each of the four categories.

Pilot Program to Monitor Treatment
of Myocardial Infarction

At the time that Mr. Milton visited the Foundation for Health Care Evaluation, plans were under way for a pilot program to monitor treatment of myocardial infarction in the seven county area. The objectives for the program were the following: "To design a system analysis for myocardial infarction to analyze factors within the physician-patient relationship that shall be related to optimal achievable care. The appropriate monitor parameters shall be defined. A system to audit these parameters throughout the seven county area shall be used to define the diagnostic and therapeutic outcomes and overall quality of care. Such system analysis for myocardial infarction shall be applied by the participating hospitals."

It was anticipated that the program would commence 120 days following funding. According to the prospectus, the purpose of the program would be to define monitor parameters for the following entities:

a) all diseases exceeding 2% of hospital discharges by department.
b) all surgical procedures exceeding 2% of hospital discharges by department.
c) major causes of death.
d) surgical procedures subject to abuse.
e) hospital-acquired infections.
f) 20 most common ambulatory diagnosees.

Furthermore, the prospectus goes on to point out that "success in the study depends on a medical definition of appropriate care. Once appropriate care has been defined, it can be readily decided what a reasonable remuneration for this standard of care should be."

Table 1

Process for Revising Standards

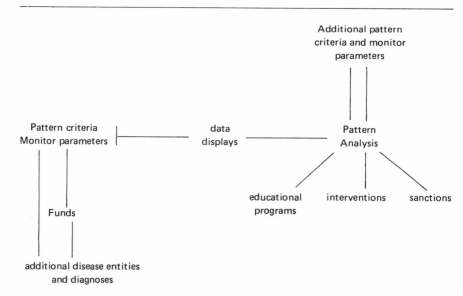

Table 2

Steps in the Quality Control Program

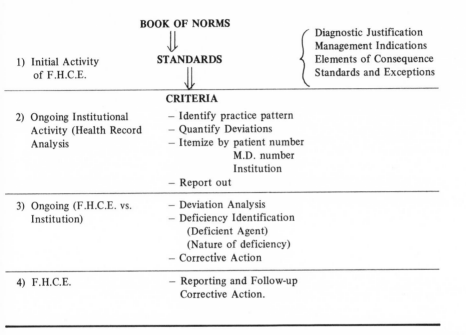

	BOOK OF NORMS	⎧ Diagnostic Justification
	⇓	⎨ Management Indications
1) Initial Activity	**STANDARDS**	⎨ Elements of Consequence
of F.H.C.E.	⇓	⎩ Standards and Exceptions

CRITERIA

2) Ongoing Institutional Activity (Health Record Analysis	– Identify practice pattern
	– Quantify Deviations
	– Itemize by patient number
	          M.D. number
	          Institution
	– Report out

3) Ongoing (F.H.C.E. vs. Institution)	– Deviation Analysis
	– Deficiency Identification
	  (Deficient Agent)
	  (Nature of deficiency)
	– Corrective Action

4) F.H.C.E.	– Reporting and Follow-up Corrective Action.

Table 3

	Cancer of Cervix	Cancer of the Endometrium	Cancer of the Ovary
Disability (1:10)	10	10	10
Frequency (1:3)	3	2	2
Correctibility (1:10)	10	5	3
Failure of Correctibility (1:3)	3	2	2
Priority listing	900	200	120

Hospital Utilization Review

Mr. Milton was impressed by the scope and thoroughness of the systems analysis program outlined in the prospectus on Quality Control of Care and inquired from Gustafson whether the hospitals had been cooperative up to this point and how they felt about a hospital utilization review procedure to be monitored by the Foundation. Gustafson explained that the utilization program was already started and had been quite successful.

> We review each patient and his length of stay. Our cut-off point is the 75th percentile for age, etc. We use the PAS data. This area is overbedded and we have a lot of opposition from hospital administrators who claim we are getting them in hot water. We are trying to set up some sessions with the local hospitals and are going to try to sell them our program. The Foundation has been constructive in terms of hospital utilization. It has reviewed the 100 most typical hospitalizations and come up with figures for proper hospital stay. Our aim is to reduce hospital stay. In our pilot study, length of hospital stay was reduced from 8.6 to 6.1 days. In those hospitals where we make a statement as to why the patient was in longer than normal. Part of the problem is with the insurance companies who differentiate between allowable charges in and out of the hospital. We have two hospital reps on our Board. One is from Minneapolis and one from St. Paul. Conceptually, we wanted them to represent the hospitals, but in reality, they represent themselves and their own hospitals.

The April, 1972 *Report on Current Activities* of the Health Insurance Council indicates that there were two problems associated with compiling guidelines for the 100 most common diagnoses with regard to hospitalization: 1) duration guidelines delineating length of stay where drawn on too liberal a basis with the result that too few cases were submitted for evaluation, 2) carriers were unable to apply a quality screen based on information ordinarily contained on routine claim forms. Furthermore, the Foundation would conduct its review of length of stay on a retrospective basis after the patient was discharged from the hospital with corrective action being applied retrospectively where deemed necessary.

Pilot Program in Utilization Review

For two years, 1970 and 1971, prior to Mr. Milton's visit, a pilot study had been conducted by the Foundation at Bethesda Luthern Hospital in St. Paul. Mr. Gustafson presented Mr. Milton with the following summary of the pilot study:

> Initially, the pilot program was conducted in a single nursing station. Later, the controlled study was expanded to include all adult patients except obstetrics. Upon admission, each patient was coded by age, diagnoses, any secondary diagnoses or complications, and whether surgery was performed. The attending physician was then notified on what date 75% of patients with a like diagnosis, considering as well, secondary diagnoses and complications or operations, would have reasonably been expected to have been discharged from the hospital. Prior to utilization review, documentation was expected from the attending physician to demonstrate why his patient was different from like patients with comparable diagnoses and why his patient should be entitled to continuing stay. The utilization review physician was assigned to a specific hospital ward for six months and all reviews conducted by him were supervised by the chief of the respective service. These reviews were conducted on every patient exceeding the 75th percentile of expected stay to insure the following:
>
> 1. That the patient had a reasonable cause for hospitalization.
> 2. That the diagnostic evaluation and quality of therapeutics were appropriate.

3. That the record reflected the care delivered.
4. That continuing stay was justified.

All cases rejected by the reviewing physician were referred to the chief of service continued to evaluate a sampling of charts which were perviously certified as being acceptable to the reviewing physician.

Patients whose continued stay could be justified by the reviewing physician were given another review date, usually the 90th percentile of expected stay.

This program resulted in a reduction in length of stay from 8.8 days to 6.1 days. Thereafter, hospital stay has stabilized at about 6.8 days. The control group was compared with other patients of the same age and identical diagnostic categories. It is worthy of note that prior to the advent of this program, 27% of hospital admissions as determined by application of the Mid-west Regional Section in the C.P.H.A. Review book, were staying beyond the 75th percentile. The introduction of the review process to the control group resulted in 6% of all hospitalized patients initially remaining beyond the 75th review date—this has now stabilized at approximately 9% of all patients exceeding the 75th percentile of expected stay. This reflects a two-thirds reduction in stay of patients beyond the 75th percentile.

Insurance Company Participation and Scope of Coverage

The objectives of the Foundation with regard to its relationship with third party insurers were stated in the *Report on Current Activities* of the Health Insurance Council, April, 1972, as follows:

1. The practicing physicians will assume responsibility for the screening guidelines, the extent and the scope of the program, and such judgments as might be applied in evaluating the medical care rendered in the community.

2. Participating health care plans and insurance carriers will attempt to stimulate the sale of health insurance benefits meeting the Foundation's guidelines and will apply the Foundation's screening guidelines in their normal claims administration.

Mr. Milton was curious to learn how the physicians and the public perceived the relationship between the Foundation and the carriers.

Dr. Thomas Recht, Chief of Professional Services at the Nicollet Clinic in Minneapolis and Treasurer of the Foundation, told Milton that he felt the relationship between the Foundation and the Health Insurance Council should be that of a partnership. He also felt that insurance companies . . .

. . . have been amply rewarded for their participation in the Foundation.

There is another problem with the insurance industry. To my knowledge, a company like Prudential has a policy of paying any physician's charges under a certain amount without questioning that charge. They feel it is more economical to do rather than to question each small charge.

I feel that one of the Foundation's major drives should be to encourage insurance companies to cover out-patient charges. This would relieve the physician of the chronic statement, "but it's covered when I'm in the hospital." It would also relieve the insurance industry of a tremendous economic burden.

Half of the judgments thus far are in their favor. Among physicians there are chronic under-chargers as well as overchargers.

Mr. Milton met next with Mr. John Jensen, a member of the Insurance Council and Chairman of the open liaison committee that set up procedures for screening claims that were submitted for review. In addition, Jensen was in charge of claims for a large insurance company that writes many of the policies reviewed by the Foundation. When asked about the function of the Liaison Committee, Jensen explained that it was a support mechanism made up of local claims people from the carriers and the Blues and had fifteen to twenty participants. Monthly, as a group, the committee selected participants who sat in on the peer review panels. Two people were chosen—one from the Blues and one from the insurance carriers. The Liaison Committee gathered fee data to determine screening profiles for the coming year. It submited a worksheet of different profiles to Gustafson and the Board who either accepted or rejected it as screening guidelines.

Insurance company support of the Foundation was not viewed positively by at least one consumer group, the Greater Metropolitan Federation. A spokeswoman, Mrs. Grace Lamm, who was head of the Federation's Health Care Committee, publicly criticized the relationship in a newspaper article appearing in the *St. Paul Sunday Pioneer Press* on August 8, 1971:

> There has been a tight circle between insurance companies and doctors since the 1930's and the people can't get into the circle. The GMF "quarrel" is with the whole (FHCE) structure and trying to bring people into it . . .
>
> The GMF maintains there's a further "establishment link" because health insurance companies provide the Foundation with financial support or operating capital—more than $70,000 for the first year.

Although the Foundation was operating on full cooperation with 34 local health insurance carriers and was indeed financed by them, its Board felt it could do little to expand the scope of coverage available to the public. As Gustafson put it, "We have requested that the Health Insurance Council give us evidence of improvement in increasing benefits. For example, the state insurance commission has been given full power to use peer review to handle workman's compensation cases but has not elected to use it. Another problem is that the insurance companies and physicians see themselves as natural opponents. Each is concerned with his private advancement. They really have the same interest—private enterprise—and should get together. In a sense, they have challenged the Foundation to do this. In the event of national health insurance, I see our role as evaluating individuals within the delivery system that is proposed."

Consumer Reaction to the Foundation

Public reaction to the Foundation has been voiced mainly by the Greater Metropolitan Federation. The Federation, started in 1969, is a large, loosely organized consumer group begun by a minister and composed of many local groups with the same goals and little power. Eighty per cent of the member groups are church affiliated. In 1971, it actively engaged in a confrontation with the Foundation over two issues: lack of consumer representation on the Board of Directors and no public disclosure of the maximum fees accepted by the Foundation. The Foundation's *Report on Current Activities* summarized these events:

Shortly after the Foundation's launching in May, 1971, the need for direct representation from the consumer in the work of the Foundation as a reflection of the interest and concern of the recipient of such care was forcefully brought to our attention. The Foundation headquarters were picketed by organized consumers demanding that (1) the prevailing fee guidelines be made public, enabling consumers to shop around for less expensive doctors, and (2) the Board of the Foundation be controlled by consumers. Representatives of the Foundation subsequently held discussions with consumer organizations and learned that their primary concern was the need for direct input of the consumer's point of view in any impact the Foundation might have in bringing about change in the existing system . . . A consumer's advisory committee was formed and one of the first and primary objectives was to identify the areas in the Twin Cities Metropolitan community where the health care needs of its residents were not being adequately met.

One of the Consumer Reps on the Board, Net Wisser, explained to Mr. Milton how he was selected as a consumer representative to the Board of the Foundation.

I didn't participate in the interplay between the Federation and the Foundation. The Federation and other consumer groups submitted names to the Health Board of the Metropolitan Council which is a municipal organization for the Twin Cities and suburbs whose members are appointed by the State. From the names submitted by the Health Board the Foundation selected the original 15 members of the Consumer Advisory Council to the Foundation. These 15 people were from different walks of life. My name was on the list and I was appointed to the Foundation Board of Directors by the Foundation.

The Consumer Advisory Council decided to meet every month. The public doesn't know there even is a Consumer Advisory Council. More information needs to be transmitted to the general public.

A spokesman for the Greater Metropolitan Federation told Mr. Milton how the strategy adopted by the group had resulted in members gaining representation on the Foundation's Board.

After weeks of meetings and skits performed in front of the Foundation offices (to keep public pressure on the Foundation), we arranged negotiating sessions with Dr. Richard YaDeau, president-elect of the Foundation . . . Out of these meetings came a compromise. We dropped our demands for consumer reorientation on the Foundation Board of Directors, that the public have access to fee guidelines, etc. We suggested, and YaDeau agreed, that the Foundation create a "Consumer Liaison Committee" to work with the Foundation. It was agreed that two consumers from this committee would be seated on the Board of Directors. Since neither side would have confidence in allowing the other side to nominate the consumers to the committee, we suggested, and YaDeau agreed, that we ask the Metropolitan Health Board, a regional health planning agency, to nominate consumers to sit on this committee. The Foundation Board of Directors would select the consumers from this third party list. Our other demands would be presented to the consumer committee for their consideration and negotiation with the Foundation. YaDeau then brought Anonson and other key doctors into the negotiations and an agreement was reached as outlined above.

The Federation ultimately succeeded in placing two consumer reps on the Board and in establishing a Consumer Advisory Council; it was unsuccessful in forcing the Foundation to make public the fee schedule. The Federation strongly questioned the Foundation's policy that fee guidelines would be used internally by the Foundation to measure the reasonableness of the rate of escalation of physicians' fees in the community.

Physician Reaction

Some physicians in the Foundation disagreed with the use of the 1963 Minnesota Relative Value Index as a guide for determining acceptable fees. Dr. Harry A. Johnson, Jr., interviewed by Mr. Milton, had the following to say about its use and the review of fees in general:

> First of all, it is important to note that there were no plastic surgeons on the surgical committee which designed the 1963 Minnesota Relative Value Index. There are many discrepancies in the Minnesota Relative Value Index. Most notably, many of the fee schedules are the same regardless of whether a general practitioner, general surgeon, or a plastic surgeon performs the surgery. I have studied the 1969 California Relative Value Study and find this fee schedule is approximately 80 to 90% accurate, in terms of plastic surgical procedures.
>
> In regards to the Minnesota Foundation for Health Care Evaluation, it is my opinion that most of the physicians in the Minneapolis metropolitan area were under the impression that this foundation was set up as a peer review for physicians who overcharged. By "overcharged," we are under the impression that this would pertain to physicians who were charging fees two to three to four times the usual and customary charges for this area. On closer examination, it was found that only minimal numbers of physicians and surgeons fell in this category and that the range of fees charged by the vast majority of physicians in this area fluctuated perhaps 10%.
>
> Insurance companies, most notably Blue Shield, had already set up profiles of all the surgeons in the Minneapolis metropolitan area. Therefore, when the Foundation became an entity, the insurance company seized the opportunity to reduce all physicians' fees above the 84th percentile. In past years, physicians' fees whose profiles ranged above the 84th percentile in specific cases were honored.
>
> What was even more demoralizing is that the doctor-patient relationship was completely disrupted. This disruption came about when insurance companies wrote a letter to the patient stating that the physician had overcharged them and that they were not responsible for the balance. The insurance company informed the patient that the physician's fee was over the 84th percentile of what was usual and customary for such services rendered in the particular area and therefore the patient was not responsible for any balance over that amount.
>
> Another interesting point, specifically related to the field of plastic surgery, is that many of the insurance companies, who had access to our profiles of fees in plastic surgery over a number of years, refused to accept them. Instead, they set up their own fee schedule on a 1963 Minnesota Relative Value Index scale. Consequently, fees which were previously honored were suddenly considered as overcharges.
>
> I would also like to add that the inception of the Foundation for Health Care Evaluation, this created a tremendous amount of paper work and correspondence for the physicians in communicating with the insurance companies as well as the Foundation. At once, the physician was forced into a defensive position in order to substantiate his usual and customary fee schedule. It appeared as though the physician was guilty and had to prove his innocence. Consequently, a great deal of dissension arose between the physician, the patient, the insurance company, and the Foundation.
>
> I believe, in the not too distant future, the Foundation and the insurance companies will realize that the 1963 Relative Value Index represents an impractical guide for fee schedules, particularly where the specialties are involved.

Over the past one and one-half years, physicians representing various specialty groups, have been meeting to determine their fee schedules in correlation with the 1969 California Relative Value Study. From conversations I have had with men representing these various specialties, I find that the 1969 Relative Value Study (California) is in close correlation with the fee schedules in this area. I am not talking about actual dollars per schedule, but rather referring to the unit value per surgical procedure.

On a national basis, plastic surgical fees in the metropolitan Minneapolis area are on average slightly below when compared on a national scale. Since the cost of living index in the state of Minnesota is one of the highest in the country, we feel that our fee schedules should certainly be at a minimum average with the nation and perhaps even slightly higher.

It is of interest to note that the Foundation for Health Care Evaluation is supported by monetary contributions from the insurance carriers. They obviously have a vested interest and it would seem likely on this basis that the Foundation would deal primarily with the best interest of the insurance companies. As a result of this relationship, it has become most apparent that the relationship between the physician and the insurance carriers has deteriorated. The Foundation claims a membership of over 90% of the physicians in the area. This is true, but many of these members are considering withdrawing their support of the Foundation for Health Care Evaluation since their membership has required them in many cases to accept a reduced fee schedule often times as much as 20-30% on routine fees that had been honored by these insurance companies for three to five years prior to the inception of the Foundation.

The Foundation for Health Care Evaluation, peer review system is actually not a true peer review. These peer review sessions are composed of approximately twenty physicians all of whom represent an entirely different specialty. For example, a plastic surgical case might be reviewed by nineteen other physicians of varying specialties, and one plastic surgeon. If that one plastic surgeon cannot attend that specific meeting, you have nineteen other physicians from nineteen other specialties passing judgment on a plastic surgical procedure for which they have very little knowledge.

The most honest form of peer review would be if plastic surgical cases were reviewed by eight plastic surgeons, or an orthopedic case were reviewed by a group of eight or ten orthopedic surgeons practicing in the Minneapolis area.

The vast majority of physicians in the Minneapolis-St. Paul area would really like to see the Foundation for Health Care Evaluation work. Many of us feel this is a last ditch attempt to prevent government control and establish a worthy relationship between the insurance carriers and the physicians. For the Foundation to be successful, however, insurance carriers will have to recognize the existing fee schedules and perhaps be more cognizant of the fact that doctors' fees represent less than 10% of the medical dollar and hospitalization costs represent approximately 90% of the medical dollar.

Nevertheless, it seemed that despite certain reservations, the physician members had heavily supported the Foundation's program. Since activities began, only nine out of the 1965 physicians had resigned; during the first six months of operation, there were 32 cases appealing the action of the Peer Review Panel. Gustafson explained his view of the physicians' reaction to the Foundation.

On the whole, the reaction of the physician community has been outstanding. There is a small nucleus of physicians who want out. They signed on because they had faith in the doctors who proposed the Foundation. Some didn't understand that we were going to come to grips with fees as tenaciously as possible. They thought that the emphasis would be only on quality of care. There are two areas where turbulence has occurred. A number of doctors don't feel it is true peer review because physicians other than specialists in the same field are reviewing charges. This kind of set-up was considered but it was decided that if you left a given specialty to decide on its fees, you know what would happen. When you have 20 other physicians providing input on fees, you get a leavening effect. There is an advantage to having everyone in on the fee decisions. It is a question of whether you are reviewing fees or a pedigree. Earlier, we decided that we were going to review a service. We get some flack from specialists because we try to review the procedure and not the individual. Some doctors see us as representing the insurance industry.

Conclusion

On the whole, Mr. Gustafson felt they had been quite successful in implementing the peer review program. Nevertheless, he had reservations about this potential for success of other problems with which the Foundation wanted to grapple. Specifically, these included expanding the scope of insurance benefits, influencing the availability and quality of health care services, and educating the public. The Quality Assurance Program would attempt to identify areas where health care service was inferior, but without the full cooperation of the hospitals and direct involvement in regional health planning, the Foundation could not hope to accomplish its goals. He was eager to hear what suggestions Mr. Milton as a medical consultant might have to offer.

Exhibit 1

Foundation for Health Care Evaluation

BOARD OF DIRECTORS AND OPERATING COMMITTEES

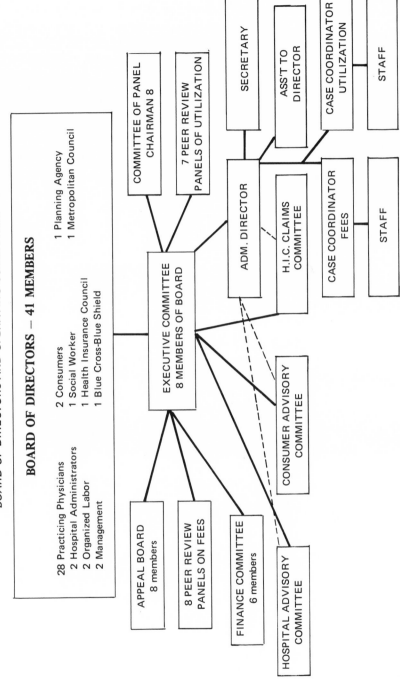

BOARD OF DIRECTORS – 41 MEMBERS

28 Practicing Physicians
2 Hospital Administrators
2 Organized Labor
2 Management

2 Consumers
1 Social Worker
1 Health Insurance Council
1 Blue Cross-Blue Shield

1 Planning Agency
1 Metropolitan Council

COMMITTEE OF PANEL CHAIRMAN 8

7 PEER REVIEW PANELS OF UTILIZATION

EXECUTIVE COMMITTEE 8 MEMBERS OF BOARD

ADM. DIRECTOR

SECRETARY

ASS'T TO DIRECTOR

CASE COORDINATOR UTILIZATION

STAFF

H.I.C. CLAIMS COMMITTEE

CASE COORDINATOR FEES

STAFF

CONSUMER ADVISORY COMMITTEE

APPEAL BOARD 8 members

8 PEER REVIEW PANELS ON FEES

FINANCE COMMITTEE 6 members

HOSPITAL ADVISORY COMMITTEE

181

Exhibit 2

Foundation for Health Care Evaluation

Flow Chart of Fee Screening and Review

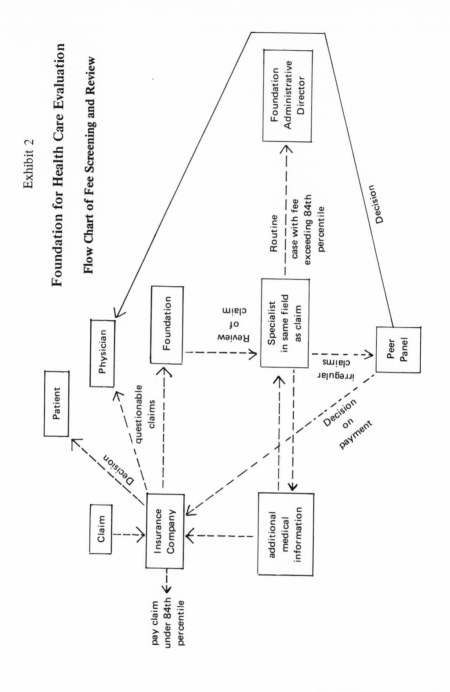

Exhibit 3

Foundation for Health Care Evaluation

Examples of Possible Standards

Enclosed is a worksheet on which standards could be derived. The enclosed standards are just conjectural and are used in part to display the type of standards that might grow out of such an audit program.

Myocardial Infarction:
1. 80% of cases with myocardial infarction shall have the site specified.
2. All patients needing cardioregulatory drugs should have a diagnosis explaining the need for cardioregulatory drugs.
3. 100% of patients shall have serial electrocardiographic studies and serum enzyme studies.
4. 100% of the patients shall be in a special care unit, on a monitor with intravenous therapy and oxygen therapy.
5. All patients with chest pain shall be on a cardiac monitor within fifteen minutes of arrival.
6. The survival rate of patients arriving in the institution alive shall be 85% or better.
7. Appropriate length of stay shall be 14 to 21 days.

Cholecystectomy:
1. 90% of the patients shall have recognized cholelithiasis.
2. Those patients having the removal of a normal gallbladder shall have either:
    a. multiple nonfunctioning gallbladder studies on X ray, or
    b. additional consultation prior to removal of a known normal gallbladder.
3. Cholecystostomies shall represent less than 1% of gallbladder operations.
4. Attempted operative cholangiogram shall be the rule and they shall be successful in at least 80% of the cases.
5. Postoperative fever in excess of a 3° temperature elevation shall include:
    a. secondary diagnosis explaining the fever,
    b. repeat white count, chest X-ray, and urinalysis,
    c. appropriate cultures.

6. Infection rate shall be less than 3% in elective cholecystectomy and less than 10% in acute cholecystitis.

7. Pulmonary emboli shall have an incidence of less than 2%, and each incident will have:
   a. chest X ray,
   b. lung scan,
   c. anticoagulant therapy.

8. Whole blood usage in elective cholecystectomy should be 0%. In acute cholecystitis, it should be less than 5%.

9. The use of antibiotics shall be explained in those elective cases requiring antibiotics. In cases of acute cholecystitis, cultures and sensitivity shall be taken.

10. Overall death rate shall be less than 1.6% and there shall be a secondary diagnosis explaining all deaths.

Pattern Criteria for Preoperative General Anesthetic Workup:

1. A CBC.
2. Urinalysis.
3. Chest X ray.
4. History and physical which includes:
   a. history of allergy,
   b. prior surgery,
   c. current significant medication.
5. All adults prior to surgery who are not immediately postpartum or admitted for Caesarean section shall have a BUN, SGOT, LDH, and serum protein.
6. All patients undergoing an elective general anesthetic shall be evaluated by an anesthesiologist.
7. All patients over 40 shall have an EKG appended to the chart, either done in the institution or in the doctor's office.
8. All patients on digitalis or diuretics shall have a serum potassium and sodium determination prior to surgery.

Caesarean Section:

1. All charts must have a diagnosis explaining Caesarean Section.
2. Caesarean Sections shall be less than 7% of all deliveries.
3. Deaths:
   a. none maternal
   b. none fetal.

4. Classical Caesarean sections — none
   Exceptions: placenta previa, transverse lie (or face presentation), low-lying uterine myoma, technical reasons described in the operative record.

5. No Apgar score of baby below 5.

6. All stays exceeding ten days shall have a secondary diagnosis explaining stay.

7. Transfusion, 20% or less, except where preoperative hemoglobin was less than 10. No transfusions exceeding two units of blood except where preoperative hemoglobin is less than 10.

8. All patients with temperature over 101° shall have:
   a. an explanatory secondary diagnosis,
   b. chest X ray,
   c. urinalysis,
   d. culture of urine and lochia.

9. Antibiotic usage must be explained.

Foundation for Health Care Evaluation

Supplement
TO PATIENT EXPLAINING DELAY

DATE

PATIENT

ADDRESS

Dear _____ ,

Reimbursement for physicians services on the basis of what is the "usual and customary" charge for professional care requires that all information pertinent to your claim be carefully reviewed. We find that additional time will be needed to acquire and evaluate these essential details.

Please pardon the delay while we devote more time to insure that the final decision will be fair to you and your physician.

Sincerely yours,

Insurance Company or
Prepaid Health Service Plan

Foundation for Health Care Evaluation

Supplement
TO PHYSICIAN SEEKING ADDITIONAL INFORMATION

DATE

PHYSICIAN

ADDRESS

Dear Doctor _____ ,

Your patient, _____ , is protected under a health insurance program underwritten by _____ , which provides reimbursement for medical services recently rendered by you. Under the terms of this contract, our obligation to the attending physician is based on what it is "usual and customary" to charge for the professional services you provided.

The information at our disposal does not enable us to evaluate all aspects of this case. So that we can reach a satisfactory conclusion, may we ask that you provide any supplemental information that might indicate whether there were special or unusual factors involved in serving the needs of this patient.

It is not our intention to knowingly do anything to disturb an established patient–physician relationship. Our purpose in seeking this additional medical information is to enable us to readily determine the maximum amount of our obligation to you and your patient under the provisions of this contract.

A stamped self-addressed envelope is enclosed for the convenience of your reply.

Sincerely yours,

Insurance Company or
Prepaid Health Service Plan

Foundation for Health Care Evaluation

Supplement
TO PATIENT EXPLAINING PAYMENT

DATE

PATIENT

ADDRESS

Dear _____ .

Your health insurance program provides for benefits for eligible services based on what it is "usual and customary" to charge for such services in this community.

In determining the proper benefit level it is necessary to evaluate the nature and complexity of the service as well as your physicians usual charge and the customary charge of other physicians in this area.

In many cases, it is necessary to seek outside opinions and bring qualified judgements to bear on complex medical matters. Your claim was referred to the Foundation for Health Care Evaluation in order that all aspects of it might be medically evaluated and every possible consideration given to it. Review by the Foundation means that physicians, who are experts in the field in which you were treated, carefully analyze and evaluate the services rendered and all charges relating thereto.

The Foundation's review of your case resulted in a recommendation that, in their opinion, $ _____ , should represent a fair and reasonable benefit based on what it is "usual and customary" to charge in this area for the services rendered. Our reimbursement for these contract benefits will be based on the Foundation's conclusions.

Sincerely yours,

Insurance Company or
Prepaid Health Service Plan

Foundation for Health Care Evaluation
Supplement
ADJUSTMENT OF FEE

PHYSICIAN   DATE

ADDRESS

Dear Doctor _____ .

As you may know, the Foundation for Health Care Evaluation is a seven county metropolitan organization designed by and under the direction of the medical profession. Its function is to review quality, utilization, and cost of medical care.

Before being reviewed by a Peer Committee, each service is evaluated by an individual physician in the same specialty as is represented by the case. In every instance the identity of the physician whose services are being reviewed is withheld from those making the evaluation.

Eight Peer Review Committees, each consisting of twenty-one physicians representing the major specialties of medicine, are responsible for evaluating and rendering a judgement of each case. One of these committees was recently asked to review the case of _____ .

After taking into consideration all of the pertinent data available and examining the recommendation of the individual reviewer, the Peer Review Committee felt the charge for _____ , on _____ , should be adjusted from _____ to _____ . This judgement was based on _____ .

You may recall that the insurance companies, as well as the member physicians of the Foundation, have agreed to abide by the judgement of the Peer Review Committees, although physicians have the right to appeal to the Board of Directors. Your notice of intent to appeal must be received by the Foundation within the next seven (7) days. If you have questions regarding the activity of the Foundation or its action on this specific case, we will be happy to discuss them at your convenience.

Sincerely yours,

Carl G. Gustafson,
Administrative Director,
At the Direction of the
Board of Directors

Foundation for Health Care Evaluation

ALLOWANCE OF FEE

DATE

PHYSICIAN

ADDRESS

Dear Doctor _____ .

As you may know, the Foundation For Health Care Evaluation is a seven county metropolitan organization designed by and under the direction of the medical profession. Its function is to review the quality, cost, and utilization of medical care.

Before being reviewed by a Peer Committee, each service is evaluated by an individual physician in the same specialty as is represented by the case. In every instance the identity of the physician whose services are being reviewed is withheld from those making the evaluation.

Eight Peer Review Committees, each consisting of twenty-one physicians representing the major specialties of medicine, are responsible for evaluating and rendering a judgement of each case. One of these committees was recently asked to review the case of _____ .

After taking into consideration all of the pertinent data available and examining the recommendation of the individual reviewer, the Peer Review Committee felt the charge for the _____ on _____ , was reasonable for the services rendered. This judgement was based on _____ . This information is being transmitted to the insurance company.

If you have questions or suggestions regarding the activity of the Foundation or its action on this specific case, we will be happy to discuss them at your convenience.

Sincerely yours,

Carl G. Gustafson,
Administrative Director
At the Direction of the
Board of Directors

Enclosure #6

Foundation for Health Care Evaluation
1535 Medical Arts Building
Minneapolis, Minnesota 55402
Phone 339-6871

DATE

TO: PLEASE NOTE: This form is
used as subsequent physician
notification of Peer Review
Panel decisions.

In the following outlined case, the Peer Review Committee of the Foundation for Health Care Evaluation has reached the indicated decision.

Patient's Name _____ Age _____

Description of Procedure _____

_____

Date of Procedure _____ Physicians Charge $ _____

Peer Review Committee Decision of Charges $_____

Explanation:

Intent to appeal this decision must be received by the Foundation within seven (7) days. If you have any questions or suggestions, we will be happy to discuss them at your convenience.

Sincerely yours,

Carl G. Gustafson,
Administrative Director
At the Direction of the
CGG/crk   Board of Directors

191

A 2324 ⊕

Enclosure 7 -- **FOUNDATION FOR HEALTH CARE EVALUATION**

1535 MEDICAL ARTS BUILDING
MINNEAPOLIS, MINNESOTA 55402

SUBMISSION DATE_____

IDENTIFICATION _____

SUBMISSION FORM TO PEER REVIEW COMMITTEE

1. IDENTIFYING INFORMATION

PATIENTS NAME_____ AGE _____ SEX _____

ADDRESS _____

NAME OF PHYSICIAN _____

NAME OF HOSPITAL _____

NAME OF CARRIER _____

ADDRESS OF CLAIM OFFICE _____

2. REASON FOR SUBMITTING CASE: FEE_____ UTILIZATION _____ (If Utilization, Explain)

_____

_____

3. DIAGNOSIS &/OR PROCEDURE _____

_____

4. SERVICE PERFORMED: DATE   CHARGE

_____   _____   _____

_____   _____   _____

5. WHERE PERFORMED:

HOME_____OFFICE_____HOSPITAL _____ECF _____ OTHER_____

6. PHYSICIANS SUPPORTING DOCUMENTS: ATTACHED_____ OR PLEASE EXPLAIN

_____

_____

_____

REVIEW COMMITTEE ACTION: ATTACHED_____ OR PLEASE RECORD HERE

_____

_____

_____

_____

_____

Enclosure 8—FOUNDATION FOR HEALTH CARE EVALUATION

1. Identifying Information:

   Patient's Name_____Age_____Sex_____

   Address_____

   Name of Physician_____

   Name of Carrier_____

2. Case referred because_____

   _____

   _____

   _____

   _____

3. Recommendation to Peer Review Committee_____

   _____

   _____

   _____

   _____

   _____

   _____

   _____

   _____

   _____

   _____

   _____

   _____

   _____

   _____

_____   _____

Reviewing Physician's Signature   Date

Foundation for Health Care Evaluation

DRAFT OF SUGGESTED LETTER FOR MEDICARE PATIENTS

Public Law 89–97 (commonly referred to as "Medicare") requires that this hospital have a utilization review plan to implement the most efficient use of the facility and its services. Under the plan, physician members of our medical staff determine whether the condition of a patient receiving benefits under Medicare is such that further in-patient care in this facility is medically necessary.

In compliance with this statutory requirement, your medical records have been reviewed by representatives of the medical staff and carefully discussed with your attending physician. It has been determined that your condition does not make further stay in this hospital medically necessary. As also required by law, this letter is prompt notification of the decision and the consequent termination of Medicare benefits for your current stay in this facility on ____(3 days allowed)____.

Arrangements for post-hospital care should be made as soon as possible. The hospital personnel will be happy to assist you in arranging for your discharge. If you desire placement in a nursing home or arrangements for home health care, the hospital social worker can assist you.

Questions regarding the policies and procedures established by the Social Security Administration, and implemented by the hospital, should be referred to the Social Security Administration office, telephone number 725-7911.

cc: Hospital Social Worker
　　Attending Physician
　　Patient's Relative

Attachment #6

194

Foundation for Health Care Evaluation
Supplement
PEER REVIEW FORMS AND CORRESPONDENCE

Diagnosis: _____

Second Diagnosis: _____

Initial Review

75% – Notification _____ 75% Review _____

Follow-up Review

90% – Notification _____ 90% Review _____

or

Other Notification _____ Other Review _____

Admit. Date _____
1297.61

Discharge Date _____

Attachment #1

Admission Date   Coding Diagnosis:

_____ 75% Review   _____

_____ 90% Review   _____

_____ Other Review   _____

Attachment #2   Attachment #3

As of tomorrow _____ % of patients with the like diagnosis of _____
_____ have ordinarily been dismissed from the hospital.

If any additional diagnosis or complications have developed to prolong the hospitalization, please include them in today's progress note.

Attachment #4

Note for U.S. Dept. of Health, Education and Welfare (A) & (B)

Description

The A case presents a history of OPS, the Operational Planning System, a form of management by objectives at the Department of Health, Education and Welfare. In this first case three of the agencies of HEW are described, namely the Food and Drug Administration, the Office of Education and Health Services and Mental Health Administration, and their programs outlined in some detail. In the B case their different experiences with OPS are described through the reflections of agency personnel.

Teaching Objective

This case provides a good example of the application of management by objectives to a variety of situations. Whether or not this is a correct and effective application, and why the different institutions experience different results with the technique is a matter of some interest. How one can develop some kind of control system for the complex and differing functions of large institutions like HEW is an intriguing question.

The second theme has to do with the way in which the technique was implemented in the different parts of HEW. This relates to organizational change and methods of implementation and the reader may consider what the different forms of implementation were in the three agencies, and whether these had anything to do with their different experiences.

U.S. DEPARTMENT OF HEALTH, EDUCATION, AND WELFARE (A)

Stu Thomas, the Deputy Assistant Secretary for Management Planning and Technology, studied the reports on each of the agencies in HEW that his Operational Planning staff has prepared. "There just seems to be a different *spirit* from one agency to the next in terms of implementing the Operational Planning System (OPS)," he mused. "It goes beyond whether they have fulfilled all their objectives or not. I wonder what FDA, the Food and Drug Administration, is doing with OPS that other agencies are not? Perhaps I ought to take a look into this right now. I wonder if FDA is doing something special or whether they are just a different kind of agency?" Thomas buzzed his secretary, "Marge, would you please arrange a meeting for me with Read and Jack Markov." (Read Taylor was a member of the Thomas' staff and was responsible for coordination between the OS-OPS staff[Office of the Secretary OPS, i.e., Thomas' level] and the FDA-OPS staff, which Jack Markov headed.) He released

*Frederic V. Malek, "Management Improvement in the Federal Government," *Business Horizons,* August 1971, pp. 11-17.

the intercom button and swiveled his chair towards the window. "I wonder how we can make this whole Operational Planning System a viable part of HEW—useful not only to the Secretary but also to the agencies and regions.

Mr. Thomas had been in HEW since 1966 when he was brought over from the Defense Department to help build a responsive management control system for HEW. He began at HEW as Deputy Assistant Secretary (DAS) for Program Systems and was concerned with long-range planning. He was then appointed to head OPS when it was elevated to the DAS level in mid 1971.

The History of OPS

The OPS came to life under the direction of Mr. Frederick V. Malek during 1969-1970. Within a few years following his graduation from the Harvard Business School, Mr. Malek developed a reputation as a management "wunderkind," and in 1969 was brought into HEW by President Nixon's newly appointed Secretary, Robert Finch. He was appointed Deputy Under Secretary for Management and given what then appeared to be the impossible task of bringing HEW under control. In an article written after leaving HEW,* Malek summarized the kinds of problems which he felt confronted managers in the federal government and which he himself probably faced in 1969:

> Soon after Secretary Finch brought me into the federal government, I learned that when most people spoke of "management" they were really referring to administrative or housekeeping activities. They were not referring to a broader range of functions such as setting goals, motivating and directing subordinates, and assessing performance—activities which I have always considered the essence of management. A great deal of top-level attention was devoted to the more serious problems of management.

> The fundamental problem, and the one which must be attacked first, is the lack of management expertise among officials in top-level positions. In the past, management skills have seldom been given prime consideration in selecting people for sub-Cabinet and other high level appointive posts. Similarly, top career officials are often ill-equipped for the significant management responsibilities they face. Most have had little training or experience in management. Many are narrow, functional specialists rather than management generalists.

> A second problem, closely related to the lack of management expertise, concerns the divided loyalties of many key career officials. As noted above, federal recruiting, promotion, and personnel development practices have encouraged the civil servant to spend his entire career within a single bureau or narrow specialty area. Thus, inevitably, many top career people end up as specialists committed to a single program or discipline.

> As the specialist progresses in his career, he typically become increasingly involved with certain interest or constituent groups and congressional committees. These interest groups often determine the specialist's standing and prestige in his field, are his major sources of employment opportunities outside the government, and are permanent relative to the political leadership.

> The separation of management from policy development is a third problem. Management considerations are often given short shrift when policies are being developed. As a general rule, little thought is given, during the crucial early stages of policy deliberations, to how the policy will be carried out. A key reason for this problem is the scarcity of management expertise among persons at the policy-making levels. It is difficult for those untrained or unskilled in management to

recognize the importance of the less visible and unexciting tasks involved in policy implementation. However, to ensure that a policy can and will be implemented effectively, these tasks must be considered while the policy is being developed.

A fourth problem is the strong tendency among top officials to focus only on high visibility problems and on major new initiatives. This creates pressures which flow through to lower levels, resulting in the concentration of almost all key management resources on a few "hot" items. This tendency has two unfortunate results. First, many management problems or opportunities for improvement in ongoing operations which should be worthy of significant attention go practically unnoticed by most top managers. Second, there is a serious lack of follow-though after a key new initiative has passed its peak visibility. Attention and pressures tend to shift to new initiatives and priorities; forgotten is the equally important task of ensuring that last year's programs are implemented effectively and produce the expected results.

Inability to measure results is a fifth major problem. The difficulties inherent in measuring the effectiveness of most governmental programs have been much discussed in both scholarly and popular publications. The standards commonly used for measurement are recognized as being uneven and arbitrary, and the situation is further confused by the difficulty of isolating cause and effect. Did the poor student do better in reading this year because he had a different teacher, or because he is a year older and more ready to learn? There is little in the public sector that compares with the specificity and concreteness of a profit-and-loss statement in private industry.

In addition, because of the nature of the programs which HEW administered, a large portion (approximately 97% in FY 1972) of its annual budget was funds destined for state and local agencies in the form of grants and loans to carry out specific legislatively authorized programs, such as Project Headstart in 1971 or the National Defense Education Act—which provided loans to certain categories of students. From a strictly line management point of view, these programs were not controllable. That is, HEW was responsible for making the grants or loans to specific agencies, but other than through the initial screening process leading to the grant, HEW had no control over the results produced by the agency to whom the grant was made.

Under Finch and Malek a three part strategy was initiated to deal with these problems. The strategy was to (1) Improve the quality of persons placed in the highest positions in HEW, (2) Rationalize the system for making grants by simplifying its administration and decentralizing the decision making, and (3) Develop a short-range management planning and control system. The last of these became the Operational Planning System which was designed to deal with the problems of providing direction, ensuring follow-through and judging performance. OPS was to fill the gap between long-range planning and the budget by identifying specific goals and making specific plans for what was to be achieved during the next fiscal year. Prior to OPS there was no such "annual plan": The long-range planning process identified three to five year goals, and the budgeting process obtained the money requested by the programs and agencies, but no formal mechanism existed to insure that the programs for which funds were requested would lead to the achievement of the long-range goals established during the planning process.

The Operation of OPS

OPS was basically a "management by objectives" systems. For Fiscal Year 1972 (the first full year of the operation for OPS) the OPS process began with the statement by the Secretary of fifteen priority objectives for HEW to complete during the year. (Beginning with the planning for FY 1973, these priorities were drawn from long-range planning and budgeting decisions and the results of the prior year.) From these priorities, each agency developed five to ten objectives which it felt would help to achieve these priority objectives. Specific programs which would meet the objectives were planned with the help of the field and regional personnel in each of these agencies, and particular attention was given to *how results were to be measured*. These planning activities also provided a set of milestones which could be used to gauge whether HEW or the agency had achieved its objectives. After the year-end status of each objective was assessed, decisions on objective attainment were fed back into the planning stage for the next year, thus reinitiating the cycle.

In describing the OPS system to the case writer, Mr. Thomas stated:

"First of all, the purpose of installing such a management by objectives system was to control and direct resources toward measurable achievements which were stated in terms of impact on a problem or progress toward a long-term goal. MBO is a way of forcing managers to state the results to be expected from the programs they direct. The OPS cycle begins with the attempt by each agency, and by each program within the agency, to specify its activities in terms of measurable, accomplishable, results-oriented objectives which are in line with the general priorities stated by the Secretary (or derived from the long-range planning system as described above).

"As objectives and operating plans are passed up the line from the program managers, they are consolidated into the objectives for that agency. Each individual agency objective is supported by a plan for action which shows all of the critical steps that will be necessary to accomplish that objective. When all of these objectives and plans reach the Secretary's office, they are reviewed, and some number of them (five to ten for each agency) are selected by the Secretary for personal tracking during the year. In this way he can keep an accurate and current view of the status of key programs in the Department. Those objectives *not* selected for tracking by the Secretary are often monitored by the agency heads through their own internal mechanisms. While objectives selected for monitoring by the Secretary may be dropped or revised during the year, none are modified without consultation with the Secretary.

"A central part of OPS's function is the bi-monthly management conference between the Secretary and each agency (and key members from both staffs). These conferences provide a means for discussing and resolving important issues related to agency objectives. First, they enable the Secretary to keep abreast of progress within each agency. Second, they are used to inform the Secretary of any modifications in objectives as a result of problems in either the internal or external environment. Third, they make the Secretary aware of critical issues within the agencies that can's be resolved at the staff level. And fourth, they allow for the concurrence of agency staff and staff from the Secretary's office on matters needing joint attention. These meetings consitute the only regularly scheduled conferences between the Secretary and each agency head on management issues. Prior to OPS, such conferences occurred only irregularly if at all.

"Finally, the OPS operating cycle is closed as the bi-monthly and yearly evaluations are fed back into the long-range planning process. This occurs both formally and by virtue of the fact that, as participants in the management conferences, the planning staff members are aware of the general level of progress and the needs of the different agencies and the Department as a while. By means of this mechanism and the basic operation of OPS, programs are responsive to the facts of HEW's successes and problems. Moreover, the programs themselves are responsive to the needs for progress and completion that HEW demands."

History of HEW

HEW was organized as a cabinet-level department by President Eisenhower in 1953 in order to centralize control of the agencies dealing with human problems. Before this official elevation to department status, the different agencies and offices concerned with health, education and welfare were spread around the federal executive, having been variously placed by the haphazard historical growth of the American social welfare sector. The U.S. Department of Education was founded in 1907, after the Muckrakers and others had revealed the need to monitor the manufacturing and packaging of food and drugs in the U.S.; and the Children's Bureau was organized in 1912 to cope with some of the evils associated with child labor. The Great Depression of the 1930's ahd the greatest effect in accelerating the growth of the American public sector. It provided grounds for the establishment of social security and public assistance programs. These were consolidated in 1939 under the Federal Security Agency.

New agencies and the reorganization of existing agencies and programs constantly changed the size and shape of the department. Perhaps the best illustration of the convoluted development of social agencies lies in the health agencies of HEW. In 1968, the Public Health Service and the Food and Drug Administration (FDA) were merged and reorganized into three new operating agencies; two years later the FDA was detached and re-established as a separate agency. In 1972, the primarily health-related services resided in the agencies of the National Insitutes of Health (NIH), the Health Services and Mental Health Administration (HSMHA), and the FDA. This otherwise neatly delineated structure was complicated, however. by the existence of the Public Health Service and its corps of commissioned officers who were employed by NIH, HSMHA, and FDA but who were also accountable to the Surgeon General in the Office of the Secretary.

Structure of HEW

HEW was headed by a cabinet level secretary, assisted by an under secretary and a deputy under secretary. Connected directly to the office of the Secretary was the Office for Civil Rights, whose job it was to ensure that HEW did not support programs which allowed discrimination by race, origin, or sex. Also in direct line with the Secretary were seven assistant secretaries to advise the Secretary on community and field services, legislation, health and scientific affairs (under whom is the Surgeon General), planning and evaluation, administration and management, financial affairs (the Comptroller), and public affairs. The final member of the Secretary's staff was the General Counsel to advise the Secretary on legal matters. (See Exhibit 1 for an organization chart of HEW.)

The "operating" part of HEW consisted of seven agencies each headed by a Commissioner. In 1972 these agencies were the Office of Education (OE), the Office of Child Development (OCD—a new part of HEW's structure), the Social Security Administration (SSA), the Social and Rehabilitation Service (SRS), the National Institutes of Health (NIH), the Health Services and Mental Health Administration (HSMHA), and the Food and Drug Administration (FDA). (See Exhibit 2 for a brief description of each agency.) In addition to these more or less functionally oriented agencies, there were also programs which were set up to emphasize HEW-wide priority objectives, some of which cut across one or more of the functional agencies. In FY 1972 these priorities were welfare reform, health initiatives, special revenue sharing for education, drug abuse and alcoholism, early childhood development, equal opportunity, the disabled and handicapped, sub and para-professionals, special groups, the aged, consumers and illiteracy.

To carry out HEW's programs at the state and local level, there were ten regional offices located in Boston, New York, Philadelphia, Atlanta, Chicago, Dallas, Kansas City, Denver, San Francisco, and Seattle. Each regional office was headed by a Regional Director, under whom there were regional commissioners for education, social security, and social service, and regional health, child development, and food and drug directors. A problem at this level was the relationship between these regional commissioners and directors for the agencies and the Regional Director on the one hand, and the Commissioner of each agency on the other. In only a few cases did the Regional Director actually have line responsibility over the regional agency representatives.

The FDA

FDA's primary responsibility was to insure that food, food additives, and drugs destined for public consumption were safe. Its primary activities were, therefore, of a regulatory nature, and such operations were relatively easy to monitor—for example, had the proper sample of food manufacturers in Illinois been examined. The other activity of the FDA, recommending legislation for new regulations, was much more complex since it involved decisions based on investigations conducted by FDA. For example, in the cyclamate and hexachlorophene controversies of 1970-1971, which chemicals or products should be banned? What standards should be established for evaluating specific product categories? The importance of this activity can be seen from Exhibit 3: In FY 1972, seven of the eight priority objectives for FDA involved phases of ongoing investigations.

The first three of FDA's FY 1972 priorities indicate the nature of the work involved in different phases of an investigation. The third objective is essentially a preliminary investigation to identify those drugs which lack proper pre-market clearance. The first objective involves a more advanced phase of investigation: to develop criteria for a specific drug class, and from that investigation a method for developing criteria to evaluate other Over-the-Counter drugs. Finally, the second objective relates to the publication of findings of the Drug Efficacy study which was completed in FY 1971.

The actual objective statement and activity plan for Over-the-Counter drug objective provides a good example of how OPS forces the program manager to formulate specific objectives and plans for the year within the context of long-range goals. In this case, the long-range goal is to develop criteria for evaluating each class of Over-the-Counter drugs. The actual objective for FY 1972 was "Develop criteria to measure the safety and efficacy of psychotropic and ten additional OTC drug product classes." In the plan submitted to the Secretary, FDA described its strategy for meeting this objective as follows:

> During FY 1972, FDA will convene a group of high level experts to establish a plan for the review of OTC drug products*. This committee will recommend review priorities and strategy that takes into account the fact that OTCs differ legally, medically, and in method of use from prescription drugs.

---

*Many HEW programs utilize councils and panels of experts from the private sector to advise them or provide guidelines. Appointments to such panels are made by the Secretary.

FDA then expects to classify drugs into one or more of approximately 22 therapeutic classes and will request that industry submit all available data relating to the safety and efficacy of their products. Panels composed of scientific experts will be convened to review this data by class of drugs and recommend the scientific criteria necessary for the Bureau of Drugs to judge the safety, efficacy and labeling for specific formulations. The first panel to be convened will develop criteria for reviewing psychotropic drugs, which will serve as a pilot test for subsequent review panels. We expect this phase to be completed by March 30, 1972, and that by June 30, 1972, FDA will have completed the development of criteria for ten additional classes. The criteria to be developed will be in the form of guidance on: (1) drug components and dosage ranges that are acceptable in each OTC drug class; (2) labeling adequate to permit safe and effective use by the lay person without medical supervision for each class; and (3) identification of those components or combinations where adequate safety and effectiveness data is not available.

The recommended criteria for psychotropic drugs will be reviewed and published by the end of the fiscal year. Industry will then be required to submit clinical evidence of safety and efficacy for those drugs that diverge from the formulation patterns or uses judged to be scientifically justified. If the drug can be reformulated or relabeled to meet the criteria, then supplementary data to effect these changes will be required.

Meeting with Read Taylor and Jack Markov

Stu Thomas got out of his chair and began walking around nervously, thinking about the various issues he wanted to cover in the upcoming meeting. Just then Read Taylor knocked and entered from his adjoining office, although there were still some fifteen minutes yet until the scheduled get-together with Jack Markov. Taylor had come to HEW with a graduate degree in political science from Columbia University in 1968 and had been with Fred Malek's Management Planning group since it was conceived in 1969. Until OPS was elevated to the DAS level and given to Thomas to run, Mr. Taylor had headed the OPS staff. During the initial phases of OPS he had personally handled most of the interfacing with the seven agencies, but now that the OPS staff had been expanded, he had relinquished his personal involvement in all of the agencies except FDA and SSA. His main work was with the overall direction of OPS and with its position in the Department as a whole.

"Stu," he began, "I wanted to get to you a little early, I wanted to get your ideas about how to approach the budgeting people so as to get them to think in terms of the objectives we're generating here." Thomas replied immediately and with great energy—it was an area he, too was concerned with. He spoke on the subject until a second knock signalled the arrival of Markov. Jack Markov, like Read Taylor, had begun his career at HEW in the Management Intern Program. He had gone on to become a personnel officer in the Food and Drug Administration. After he returned in 1970 from a National Institute of Public Affairs Fellowship he had taken at Stanford, he was made head of the newly organized OPS staff in FDA. He too had a subject to broach when he arrived.

"I've really been wanting to speak with you, Read," he began, "because we're having a lot of trouble in bringing together one of the panels of scientists for the Over-the-Counter drug evaluation project. Can you catch the ear of somebody in the Secretary's office on this? It's holding up the whole works." Taylor shifted his attention from the conversation he had just finished with Thomas to the problem Markov had introduced. He indicated that he felt something could be done, and he spoke earnestly with Markov for ten minutes about the actions that were required to keep the project rolling. Thomas occasionally added his point of view although he was not able to contribute too many specifics because he wasn't up to date on many of the facets of the situation. But it was clear he was getting fidgety as the conversation between Markov and Taylor continued.

"Okay, Men," he finally interrupted. "You guys are doing a good job, so I don't want to discourage you, but let me tell you what I want." The other two stopped talking, and listened attentively as Thomas outlined his uncertainty about some of the agencies, and his need for further inputs. He summarized by asking, "Are there any reasons that you two can think of for the smooth running of OPS in the Food and Drug Administration, while it's getting bogged down so much in other areas?"

"Well," Taylor began, "I don't think the relationship that Jack and I have developed is totally irrelevant."

Markov smiled, and added, "But you know, we do have a lot easier job than some of these other agencies. Our objectives, and our general operations, are pretty straightforward when compared, say, to the work going on in HSMHA."

"I don't know if I buy that totally, though," Taylor said. "What are you going to do when you have information that a medication isn't very effective, but when you present that fact, some congressman says, 'What do you mean it's ineffective; it works for me.' "

The three men spoke on, but Thomas started to get impatient again. He wasn't sure he was coming up with what he needed, and he thought to himself, how could he expect to compare the agencies when he was only dealing with one agency at this meeting. After a few more moments, he reminded Taylor and Markov that the time allotted for the meeting had elapsed. He thanked the two men warmly, and instructed them to keep him informed on developments in the attempt to eliminate the impediment to the Over-the-Counter Drug Project. After Markov left, Thomas turned to Taylor and asked:

"I think we need a fresh look at these agencies. Can't we send Mike along to have a look, Read?"

"I guess so," Taylor replied. "Although Mike has been kept pretty busy with those other two reports we gave him to do."

"This shouldn't take him away from those for too long. Could you send him in to see me? Thanks."

Michael B. Allen was summoned to Thomas' office. Allen, who had been working on Stu Thomas' staff for almost six months, had just received his MBA from the Harvard Business School and was one of nine new Harvard MBA's working at HEW in connection with various aspects of OPS. Allen had spent his first six months working on two other special projects in OPS.

"Come on in , Mike. Let's sit down over there." Thomas walked across his office to the informal conference area and sat down. "I just had an interesting conversation with Read Taylor and Jack Markov from FDA about OPS. They were quite enthusiastic about how well OPS was working for FDA, and I couldn't help but wonder how well it is working in the other agencies.

"I know that you are trying to write up a report for me, but I want you to see what you can find out about OPS from the program people in OE and HSMHA. Both OE and HSMHA have some new, ambitious projects that OPS should be a big help on. In particular I'm interested in the new Right to Read Objective that OE has, and two new HSMHA programs—Family Health Centers and Health Maintenance Organizations. You might also take a look at the Disadvantaged objective in OE. I think it is quite an ambitious undertaking. You may also want to talk to some FDA people. I know that FDA is basically different from OE and HSMH—it's smaller and less complex—but I want to know about *why* OPS is working so well out there."

When he returned to his office area, Allen checked with Paul Andrews and John Stans, the two OS-OPS staff members whose job it was to insure that OPS was functioning smoothly and effectively in OE and HSMHA. Since Michael did not have any "working experience" with OPS, he tried to find out what differences there might be between the general OPS mechanism as he understood it and OPS as it actually was set-up to run in OE and HSMHA. Paul, who was responsible for the OE liaison responded:

"Well, Mike, as your question implies, if OPS is to be an effecitve management tool, it has to conform with the operating style of the managers who use it. For that reason OPS looks a little different in each agency. When OPS was first being implemented and the agencies received directives outlining what was expected of them, each responded somewhat differently. Within each agency, the people with whom we work are located in different parts of the organization.

"In OE, OPS is run by the Deputy Commissioner for Management. He believes that OPS should be a staffless system, and he feels that his OPS group is far enough along now that it can run OPS without a great deal of staff support. For that reason OPS within OE is conducted without much paper reporting. Management Conferences are held by the Deputy Commissioner for Management with other Deputy Commissioners, their staffs, and program managers on each objective every month. Also OE, unlike some other agencies, has set for itself what you might call umbrella objectives. These are objectives made up of several sub-objectives which relate in some way to the results expected in the overall objective. For example, the OE objective on the disadvantaged consists of some 18 sub-objectives stated for a wide range of activities in OE directed at problems of disadvantaged children and adults at all levels of education. Given that federal education efforts are targeted only on problems in education that are of national impact, Commissioner Marland finds this kind of objective appropriate to OE.

"While OPS is becoming a more and more effective management tool for the agency top managers—the Commissioner and Deputy Commissions—it has not yet gone deep eoungh in the organization to be of real use to program managers as a management and control tool. At this point, program managers tend to view OPS as a system installed to control their efforts rather than as a system which they can use to manage and control resources for which they are responsible. OE is moving in that direction, however. In fiscal year 1973, objectives for OE will be established at all levels of management in the Office of Education and not all of them will be reported out above the program manager level. The number of objectives developed and tracked in OE should increase from 8 to over 200 in FY 1973."

"What can you tell me about the Right-to-Read and the Disadvantaged objectives? Have there been any major problems?"

"Let's look at the Right-to-Read first. The long-range goal—for 1980—is to achieve 99% literacy among people under 16 and a 90% rate for people over 16. Ideally then, the annual program objectives should be stated in terms of incremental steps toward that goal. The actual objective for FY 1972 was to begin a systematic improvement in state and local reading instructional systems by establishing 120 local reading renewal programs, and by designing and implementing of an interim information dissemination system.

"The strategy calls for a coordinated national effort by all segments of society—public and private, professional and non-professional—to make the necessary resources and skills available to communities in order to end illiteracy. This has been the source of some problems primarily because the director of the Right-to-Read program has indirect responsibility for all reading and illiteracy programs in the nation. So she must work towards redirecting other programs in OE, other agencies in HEW (like Head Start in OCD), and even other departments in the Federal Government (like the Labor Department's Manpower Training Programs).

"Through a variety of reading renewal activities, the Right-to-Read program plans to assist state and local agencies in modifying their reading instructional systems and practices. These renewal activities will assist Secondary Educational Authorities in developing and implementing a delivery system to local agencies. Reading renewal activities are to include: (1) *Redirection programs* in which the Right-to-Read would identify less than successful Federally funded reading programs and attempt to foster redirection and improvement; (2) *Transition programs* in which Right-to-Read would provide assistance to schools without substantial Federal funds and willing to make the transition from their programs to new, more effective programs; (3) *Expansion programs* for schools in which promising practices *are occurring* and which Right-to-Read would extend as exemplary programs in specified areas as well as train and impact staff of satellite schools.

"Basic to the strategy for Right-to-Read is a local commitment to changing existing programs, utilizing Right-to-Read monies as transition resources. This new approach to Federal funding embodies the concept of contingency funding. Part of this springs from necessity since Right-to-Read has no legislative authority for carrying out its program. It has had to take money from other sources and programs to carry out its program. This created some problems last fall, as you can see from this explanation which accomplished an accompanied a revision of the objective (see Exhibit 4).

"We have worked pretty closely with the Right-to-Read Program recently to help them develop objectives which relate not only to where they are spending their money, but also to where they are spending their time coordinating the efforts of other individuals and organizations to achieve the long-range goal. Dr. Holloway is very interested in using OPS to manage her program and good progress has been made.

"On the Disadvantaged Objective, the problem has been primarily logistical. As I already mentioned, there are some 18 sub-objectives being tracked under this umbrella objective. For example, during FY 1972, this program plans to increase the number of students receiving bilingual education (instruction in two languages, one of them English) from 86,000 to 106,000, and increase the number of native-speaking teachers by 15 percent, and reduce by 80 percent the number of projects in which English and non-English speaking students are taught separately, each group in its own language. By heightening the interest of non-English speakers, the program hopes to reduce dropout rates in funded high school projects by 10 percent. OE is to support projects training 9,000 teacher trainers to be more sensitive and responsive to the educational needs of disadvantaged children and is to provide 440 sites for innovative work in teacher training. It also plans to provide assitance to about 60,000 poor children under the Follow Through Program and to sample at least 5 percent of the programs to assess student accomplishment.

"More than a million students in colleges and in professional, vocational, and technical schools above high school level are to receive financial assistance through their schools under OE programs. Of these nearly 733,000 are to be from low-income families—an increase of about 100,000 over the number assisted last year. About 1,247,000 students, including some 400,000 from low-income families, are also to receive guaranteed loans from banks and other lenders.

"More than 160,000 youths are to be helped by the Talent Search, Upward Bound, and Student Special Services Programs an increase of 36,300—and Black and other colleges enrolling large numbers of low-income youth will be special targets for student financial assistance.

"Because of this large number of separate programs or sub-objectives, it is difficult to perform the kind of necessary evaluation on each sub-objective which assures that quality products or outputs are being turned out and that they are being done on time. The fact that there were so many sub-objectives caused problems at the beginning when the objectives were being developed. Because there were not enough people to assist with the development of these objectives, not all of them are stated in terms of results and not all of the operating plans really lead logically to the achievement of the objectives. Consequently, some of these objectives and plans should probably be rewritten to more accurately reflect what's happening in the program. However, only marginal changes in plans and objectives have been made so far. The basic reason why these problems exist is that we and OE did not do a terribly good job of communicating what objectives and plans should look like and what they should be used for."

Michael thanked Paul for his help and then cornered John Stans to try to get the same kind of information about HSMHA and the two programs—Family Health Centers and Health Maintenance Organizations (HMO)—he was supposed to check on. He learned that the HMO program, like the Right-to-Read program, also lacked specific legislative authority—but that this had not created any problems so far. John explained how HSMHA's OPS function had been established, and described the people involved with it. Michael learned that, unlike OE, most of the people staffing OPS at HSMHA were long-term government employees and that HSMHA had established OPS staff positions throughout its Bureaus. In addition, John explained that HSMHA did not yet hold its own agency-level management conferences, although the Administrator planned to start these during FY 1973. John described the two programs:

"HEW's National Health Strategy, in identifying key initiatives for meeting national health needs, called for the support of outpatient clinics to provide primary ambulatory care to meet the special needs of populations in scarcity areas. This initiative served as the basis for development of the Family Health Center Program. In FY 1972, the program is to make available $13 million in project grant funds to support developmental or operational Centers, with the initial funding awards beginning in the Spring of 1972. By the end of the fiscal year, 22 additional Family Health Centers are to make services available to a total of about 250,000 people. Another 13 centers will then be in the process of development and when completed they will serve an additional 200,000 people.

"The Family Health Centers are to emphasize primary ambulatory services to an enrolled population of from five to twenty thousand people drawn from the total population of a defined geographic area that is marked by a scarcity of health services. Services are to be financed on a prepaid capitalization basis, an approach which should enable the Centers to serve as bases for the development of HMO's in the future.

"The planning and development of HMO's is perhaps the most far-reaching of HSMHA's thrusts this year. An HMO is designed to be an integral system of health care to provide comprehensive medical services by a single organization at a fixed, pre-paid annual cost.

"HMO's are to guarantee convenient access to services and fixed costs for patients that are enrolled as members. During 1972, HSMHA is to take the lead in developing Health Maintenance Organizations and plans to fund 80 planning projects and establish 20 working HMO's by the end of the fiscal year. These 100 projects could, at full development, offer the HMO-option to approximately 20 million persons.

"Health Maintenance Organizations are to be a major vehicle for improving the delivery of health services, promoting more effective means of health care, and reducing the financial barriers to essential care. Because they emphasize prevention and early care, they are expected to deliver high quality services and better overall health care at a lower total cost to the individual.

"Here are the actual objective descriptions and operating plans for both programs, you may want to look them over."

Michael thanked John and retired to his desk to look over all the material he had been given. He had his secretary arrange some appointments for him at HSMHA and FDA for the following day, and then settled down to study. He could not help but wonder what he would learn the next day from the people actually being controlled by OPS.

Questions:
1. What are the differences between the A programs and those at OE and HSMHA?
2. How well do you think OPS will work in controlling these other programs?
3. What problems do you foresee in attempting to apply and control system the OE and HSMHA programs?
4. How would you go about implementing OPS in OE and HSMHA to gain maximum utilization of the system?

Exhibit 1

DEPARTMENT OF HEALTH, EDUCATION, AND WELFARE

ASSISTANT SECRETARY (Community and Field Services)	ASSISTANT SECRETARY (Legislation)	ASSISTANT SECRETARY (Health and Scientific Affairs) Surgeon General	ASSISTANT SECRETARY (Planning and Evaluation)

PUBLIC HEALTH SERVICE

FOOD AND DRUG ADMINISTRATION	HEALTH SERVICES & MENTAL HEALTH ADMINISTRATION	NATIONAL INSTITUTES OF HEALTH
Office of the Commissioner Bureau of Drugs Bureau of Product Safety Bureau of Veterinary Medicine Bureau of Foods	Office of the Administrator National Center for Family Planning Services National Center for Health Services Research and Development National Center for Health Statistics Center for Disease Control National Institute of Mental Health Health Care Facilities Service Community Health Service Regional Medical Programs Service Indian Health Service Federal Health Programs Service Maternal and Child Health Service	Office of the Director Bureau of Health Manpower Education National Cancer Institute National Heart and Lung Institute National Institute of Allergy and Infectious Diseases National Institute of Child Health and Human Development National Institute of Dental Research National Institute of General Medical Sciences National Institute of Neurological Diseases and Strokes National Eye Institute National Institute of Environmental Health Sciences National Library of Medicine Fogarty International Center

Regional Food and Drug Directors	Regional Health Directors

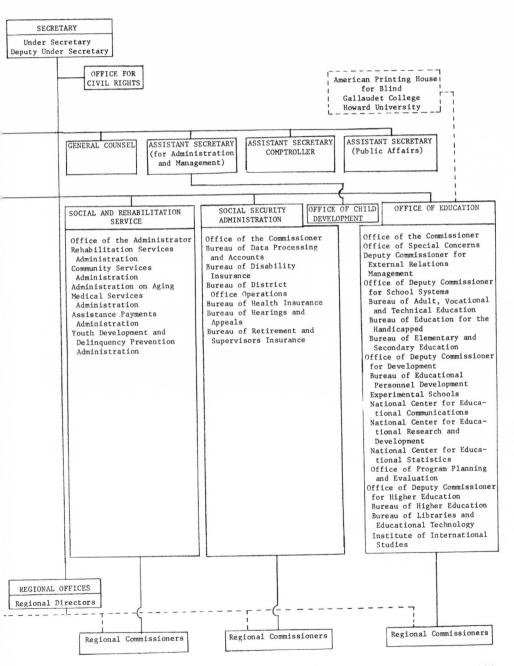

SECRETARY
Under Secretary
Deputy Under Secretary

OFFICE FOR
CIVIL RIGHTS

American Printing House
for Blind
Gallaudet College
Howard University

GENERAL COUNSEL

ASSISTANT SECRETARY
(for Administration
and Management)

ASSISTANT SECRETARY
COMPTROLLER

ASSISTANT SECRETARY
(Public Affairs)

SOCIAL AND REHABILITATION
SERVICE

Office of the Administrator
Rehabilitation Services
Administration
Community Services
Administration
Administration on Aging
Medical Services
Administration
Assistance Payments
Administration
Youth Development and
Delinquency Prevention
Administration

SOCIAL SECURITY
ADMINISTRATION

Office of the Commissioner
Bureau of Data Processing
and Accounts
Bureau of Disability
Insurance
Bureau of District
Office Operations
Bureau of Health Insurance
Bureau of Hearings and
Appeals
Bureau of Retirement and
Supervisors Insurance

OFFICE OF CHILD
DEVELOPMENT

OFFICE OF EDUCATION

Office of the Commissioner
Office of Special Concerns
Deputy Commissioner for
External Relations
Management
Office of Deputy Commissioner
for School Systems
Bureau of Adult, Vocational
and Technical Education
Bureau of Education for the
Handicapped
Bureau of Elementary and
Secondary Education
Office of Deputy Commissioner
for Development
Bureau of Educational
Personnel Development
Experimental Schools
National Center for Educa-
tional Communications
National Center for Educa-
tional Research and
Development
National Center for Educa-
tional Statistics
Office of Program Planning
and Evaluation
Office of Deputy Commissioner
for Higher Education
Bureau of Higher Education
Bureau of Libraries and
Educational Technology
Institute of International
Studies

REGIONAL OFFICES
Regional Directors

Regional Commissioners

Regional Commissioners

Regional Commissioners

209

Exhibit 2

U.S. Department of Health, Education, and Welfare (A)

Agency Descriptions

Social Security Administration

SSA was the largest of HEW's agencies in terms of both budget, where it accounted for 70% (or $47.6 billion in fiscal year 1972) of HEW's overall budget, and manpower, where it utilized half (or 55,000) of HEW's employees. In some ways, SSA was the most straightforward of the agencies. Its main responsibility was to dispense social security and medicare benefits (the benefits themselves form 85% of SSA's costs). One aspect of this operation was to maintain 100 million active work histories with 25 million yearly changes on the largest computer installation under one roof anywhere in the world. But while the nature of most of its job was clear-cut, SSA's operation was not so distinct. In fact, SSA activities were often the least visible of any of the agencies to the outsider, even from other parts of HEW. Claims that its work could be streamlined were usually met with disclaimers as to the critic's ability to grasp the operation of SSA. In 1972, one of the major efforts underway in SSA was the preparation for Welfare Reform, a large portion of which would be administered by SSA.

Office of Child Development

OCD was established in July 1969 to act as an advocate for children, to plan programs for children, to serve as a co-ordinator for federal programs for children and their families and to manage the Head Start Program for disadvantaged pre-school children. It was the smallest of the agencies, with only 400 employees and a $400 million budget. In FY 1972, OCD was concerned primarily with improved management of Head Start, planning to meet welfare reform day care needs, exploration of new programs to meet the needs of children, and following up on the recommendations of the White House Conference on Children and Youth.

Unlike the other agencies, which report to the Secretary, OCD reported to the Assistant Secretary for Administration and Management.

Social and Rehabilitation Service

SRS aimed to help America's vulnerable and handicapped people — the physically and mentally disabled, the aging, delinquents, and the impoverished.

In doing this it administered half the funds for the nation's welfare programs. This was accomplished primarily through grants to states for specific programs. As a fund-allocator, it had the second largest budget of HEW, or $12.1 billion for FY 1972. Following an internal audit of the contracting processes which found severe problems in SRS, a new, more comprehensive management system was put into the works by the agency, and one of its eventual aims was to reach a point where each individual in the department would develop his own, personal objectives. One of SRS's objectives was the separation of the administration of welfare payments from the provision of social services, as this had been shown to ensure more effective delivery.

National Institutes of Health

NIH aimed to improve the health of all Americans, mainly through medical research and the development of health manpower. It conducted its own research at nine institutes located at Bethesda, Maryland and another near Chapel Hill, North Carolina. Cancer and Heart and Lung were the major research efforts in 1972, twenty percent of its research budget of FY 1972 $1.2 billion was devoted to these institutes, with the rest supporting medical research around the country — mainly at medical schools. Aside from its research function, NIH spent an additional $675 million to support institutions of medical education, and the education of health personnel. Its first priority in 1972 was to implement new legislation on health manpower education, with a second objective being the development of longer-range strategies for training medical personnel. In addition, it planned continued attacks on cancer, sickle-cell blood disease, and arteriosclerosis.

Office of Education

OE was the federal wing of America's education program, and accounted for 7% of the total U.S. expenditure for education with its FY 1972 budget of $4.7 billion. Most of this went into programs for the educationally deprived, and mainly at the primary and secondary levels. OE also sponsored research into problems facing the educational system, and the dissemination of results of this, and other, educational investigations. Finally, at the college level, the agency provided student financial aid and support for college libraries and laboratories. In FY 1972, one of OE's objectives was to improve its management. Studies were underway to determine whether more programs and personnel should be transferred to the regions. Other OE objectives were concerned with career education, education for the disadvantaged and handicapped, illiteracy, racial integration, planning for revenue sharing, and educational reform and renewal.

Health Services and Mental Health Administration

HSMHA was responsible for the delivery of health services to individuals and families. With its $1.6 billion budget and its 27,400 employees, it provided medical and mental health care to those designated by law, e.g., Indians and merchant seaman; supported construction of health facilities and mental hospitals; encouraged the dissemination of family-planning information; and attempted to improve the delivery of health services through research and development. Another aspect of its function was to compile health statistics on births and deaths and on disease incidence. Perhaps the boldest and most exciting thrust in HEW during 1972 came from HSMHA's new commununity health systems concept — with its Family Health Centers objective — and its aid to low-income community health projects through the newly-authorized National Health Service Corps.

Exhibit 3

U.S. Department of Health, Education, and Welfare (A)
FDA Objectives Chart

**Overall Status of Objectives
for months of J-A FY 1972**

AGENCY: Food and Drug Administration

OBJECTIVE	CURRENT EVALUATION	Evaluation – Year to Date						
		J-A	S-O	N-D	J-F	M-A	M-J	
1) Develop a plan to evaluate safety and efficacy of **Over the Counter Drug** classes and test the plan in one class	◯	◯						
2) Complete **Drug Efficacy** review	◯	◯						
3) Complete voluntary **Inventory** of all marked drugs	◯	◯						
4) Evaluate the Generally Recognized as Safe (**GRAS**) food additives list	◯	◯						
5) Select a comprehensive approach to **Food Labeling**	◯	◯						
6) Expand examination by 50% of **Import Products** entries	◯	◯						
7) Inventory and classify **Medical Devices**	◯	◯						
8) Product Safety (to be developed)	◯	◯						

Satisfactory ◯   Minor Problem ▢   Major Problem △

213

Exhibit 4

U.S. Department of Health, Education, and Welfare (A)

Explanation for Modification of Right to Read Objective
(Reported at December Management Conference)

December 10, 1971

Revised Objective:

To begin a systematic improvement in State and local reading instructional systems through the establishment of 78 local school reading renewal programs and the design and implementation of an interim information dissemination system.

Explanation:

When original OPS plans were developed, staff members were under the impression that new monies would become available. Since this was not the case, all funding has had to be allocated within the legislative constraints of the designated funding sources.

Because of these legislative constraints, the proportion of **school**-based programs has been reduced; this is the reason for the corresponding reduction in numbers of impact, transition and redirection sites, and the delay in awarding grants.

However, there will be no reduction in the total number of local reading renewal sites; rather **non-school** local reading programs will be instituted, beginning with awarding the necessary grants in February. This involves adding an action step.

U.S. DEPARTMENT OF HEALTH,
EDUCATION, AND WELFARE (B)

Mr. Michael B. Allen, a member of the Operational Planning System (OPS) staff at HEW had been asked by Mr. Thomas, the OPS director, to investigate the effectiveness of OPS in the Office of Education (OE) and the Health Services and Mental Health Administration (HSMHA). [See the HEW (A) case.] Michael had reviewed all the material he could find relating to four priority programs within these two agencies (Right-toRead, Service to the Disadvantaged, Family Health Services, and Health Maintenance Organizations) and was preparing to begin his first day of interviewing at HSMHA. During the drive out to Rockville—HSMHA and FDA were both located in the Parklawn Building in Rockville, Maryland, about 20 miles from Washington—Michael wondered how well OPS would work in the complex environment of HSMHA.

Interviews at HSMHA

Michael's first appointment was with Mr. Holden who headed the HSMHA-OP office and who had helped Michael set up his other appointments for the day.

"Good to meet you, Mr. Allen, I am glad that I could be of help to you in arranging your schedule for today. The people you are seeing should be able to give you a good idea of what's going on. Here is a schedule of the interviews I arranged. The first one is at 10:00. Now I suppose you would like to know what I think about OPS."

"Yes, I was hoping to get some of your reactions."

"Well, as you know this is only the second year for OPS—really the first full year, so we had some problems this year which we probably won't have again. Since OPS was new, we had problems getting people used to the new concept, probably just typical phasing-in problems. One thing that was particularly bothersome, though, was that the Secretary's list of priorities didn't arrive until early May—two months late. And then, rather than readjusting the deadlines for Agency and Bureau objectives, the people downtown required us to meet the original schedules, so the Bureau people had only 2-3 weeks to get their objectives and action plans put together. Hardly much time to do a good job, especially when it is something new! That might not have been too bad in other agencies, but because of our programs' impact on people's health, their impact is non-quantifiable, and the compressed schedule made it even more difficult to complete our plans and to hammer out performance measures.

"Then, the priorities selected for monitoring by the Secretary had more to do with public kinds of programs—extramural in nature—rather than being addressed to the specific problems and programs of internal management. Therefore our managers felt removed from OPS; it was more of an external system. Also, since OPS planning is done after the budget has been submitted, it is hard to budget for the Secretary's of the Administrator's (of HSMHA) priorities—especially if your budget is pretty much committed to on-going grant programs. I guess we need a lot more lead time to pull everything together. That really is a problem with all of these new systems: everybody wants you to meet their deadlines and they don't care much about your problems. I can remember when . . . ." Mr. Holden slipped off of OPS and began to reminisce about other problems he had dealt with during his long career as a public servant. Michael finally had to excuse himself in order to get away in time for his next appointment.

Michael entered the suite of offices where his next interview was scheduled. The secretary look up as Michael approached, "Are you looking for Mr. Myers? In there," she said indicating a room off to the side.

Mr. Myers' office was small and congested. Michael finally managed to find a chair after moving some books. Mr. Myers eyed him suspiciously; he cleared his throat and asked, "I suppose you're here to ask about OPS?"

"Why, yes. You were informed that I was coming?" Michael asked.

"Oh yes, but you might as well save your time. I haven't got anything good to say about that outfit. They just give me a pain in the neck."

Michael tried to defuse the situation. "I'm only here to find out what people think of OPS, so I'd like to hear complaints as well as praise of the system."

"I've only got one complaint. It's a pain in the neck. All they do is get in my hair." Mr. Myers seemed adamant in maintaining his abrupt style.

"You mean OPS doesn't help you accomplish your goals?" Michael elucidated.

"Damn right. All they want to do is fill in their little triangles and squares. They don't give a care about me or our work here."

"What indications do you have of that?"

"Plenty! Whenever I try to tell the HSMHA OPS people that these objectives we have set down here are unworkable, and have to be revised, they come down on me. 'You can't change those,' they say. 'Why not,' I ask. 'Because the Secretary already has this list of objectives.' I tell them, 'But I can't meet them.' They just say, 'Well, you'll have to put down unsatisfactory progress.' What can you do with that sort of business?

"Anyhow, I don't see OPS as anything but a nuisance. They have nothing to do with getting the work done. Like Fred Heinzman (the OPS representative for the bureau to which Mr. Myers' project was assigned), he just gets in my hair. Like I said, him and the whole OPS are a pain in the neck."

Michael was finding the conversation somewhat unpleasant so he excused himself, claiming that he had an appointment with Dr. Robinson, the head of the bureau, even though he had another half hour before his next appointment. "I'll stop back if I need any more information from you," he said brightly as he backed out.

Half an hour later, Michael entered the office of Dr. Lillian Robinson. "How do you do," Michael introduced himself. "I'm on the OPS staff downtown, and I'd like to get your frank reactions to how well the system is operating for you."

"Not too well, actually," she replied "We've had a lot of trouble with Mr. Holden (the director of OPS in HSMHA). We haven't gotten many concrete benefits. Only a lot of extra work justifying why we want to change our predecessor's objectives."

"Oh, you mean you weren't here when the objectives were formulated originally?" Michael asked.

"No. I got here in the fall, when the objectives had already been passed along to the Secretary's office. Now we mainly do battle with the people in HSMHA OPS to change a lot of unreasonable things."

"Don't you find them cooperative at all?"

"Not really," Dr. Robinson continued. "Once an OPS objective has been set, it is not supposed to be changed. These OPS staff people just don't seem to understand how an organization really works. Plans are made ahead of time to help you get organized, but once you get started, the plans have to be flexible enough to let you get the job done. Sticking with the old plan is really pretty foolish when you've found a faster, cheaper way of getting things done. The problem is even worse when you are a new program like we are. Maybe if we were farther along, and it was just a matter of checking off steps within an established way of doing things . . ." here she paused to make exaggerated check marks in the air in front of her "it might be different. But right now we're changing too fast. We don't have a good enough idea about where we are going—and what we need—to be able to benefit from OPS.

"But, even if OPS were flexible enough, I wonder if people understand enough about how it should work for it to succeed. People still have a tendency to put on their best face for their boss, so instead of using the OPS management conferences to get their problems solved, they work up a sweat trying to make certain that everything looks as though it's right on the original plan."

"Yes," Michael agreed, "that kind of attitude would seem to undermine the system."

"Well, the HSMHA OPS staff isn't much better. Their attitude seems to be that everyone is lazy and needs to be prodded if they are going to get anything done. The system might work a lot better if the OPS staff people spent some time working with our program people and really got to know them."

After this meeting with Dr. Robinson, Michael had an hour to get some lunch and collect his thoughts. He was feeling a little depressed about the apparent failure of OPS here at HSMHA. OPS at HSMHA hardly seemed like the OPS he was so familiar with downtown. He hoped that the afternoon would go better, at least he had some FDA interviews to look forward to.

Michael's first appointment of the afternoon was with Ms. Ruth Feinberg, the planning coordinator for one of the HSMHA priorities being monitored by the Secretary.

"Good afternoon, Mrs. Feinberg, as you know I am here to get your comments on the effectiveness of OPS within your project."

"Oh, please call me Ruth," she replied simply. "I don't know if I can help you that much. I *do* go around to the various people to get information on whether we are satisfactorily meeting objectives, but that's a *pro forma* kind of thing."

"How do you mean," Michael probed.

"Well, we really don't follow them that seriously. Like people will just think about the objectives when an evaluation comes around. Otherwise, they just carry on with their work. The in-agency evaluations are much more central to them."

"You mean that OPS isn't a very important part of operations here?"

Ruth Feinberg, a pleasant-looking, personable woman in her early 30's, seemed taken aback. "Well, not entirely. OPS does make you spell out what you are planning to do and then forces you to report against those plans. It's just that the people in our program seem to have forgotten what objectives or action steps they's committed themselves to. I guess maybe that's because OPS seems to be 'external': it's the HSMHA OPS staff that puts our final plan together, so I guess we don't think of it as a 'real' plan. There doesn't seem to be any connection between what we are trying to do and the action steps that OPS is measuring."

Michael left in a disquieted mood. "I wonder if OPS ever works anything like it's supposed to anywhere around here," he thought. "Markov painted a pretty glowing picture of OPS in the Food and Drug Administration, but I can't believe it really works that well even there, after all I've heard so far today."

Interviews at FDA

Michael's first stop in FDA was with the director of a small, new project. Its director, Mr. Barnes, greeted him cheerfully, then sat down to talk.

"This project has been sort of personal fulfillment for me, I was asked by the Secretary's staff to evaluate the possibilities of developing a project of this sort. After my preliminary report, I was told that I was 'it'—to go ahead and begin to implement my recommendations.''

"Where were you in HEW before this opportunity came along,'' Michael asked.

"Actually,'' Mr. Barnes proceeded, "I was in the field on the very same kind of project, actually its predecessor. In fact, I know most of the field people who are now reporting to me from that time and from writing the report for the Secretary. I certainly know the work they do out there.''

"That's really fortunate,'' Michael stated with genuine enthusiasm. "It really gives you a handle on your position.'' Mr. Barnes seemed generally content, so Michael asked him with some optimism, "How do you find OPS affects your work here?''

"Oh, it's very much of a help. I've worked closely with Markov's office both in designing the specific objectives and in figuring the best procedures for accomplishing them. We have a very smooth-working relationship.''

Michael wondered if Mr. Barnes realized that others were not so satisfied. "Do you have any idea of how OPS is working anywhere else?''

"None at all,'' Barnes replied.

Still slightly disbelieving, Michael questioned the typicality of Mr. Barnes' success. "Why do you think things have worked out so well between your project and OPS? For example, do you think there were any special factors like the fact that this is a small project, or that you're new, or that you designed the basic objectives from scratch yourself. Things like that?''

"Well, I honestly never thought of it. I've been trying to make this thing work out—it means a lot to me—and things have just fallen into place. The people in OPS know what they're doing, and they've been able to help me a lot.''

"I see your point,'' Michael said. "Thank you for your time.''

"Glad if I could help you out.''

Michael's last appointment of the day was with Mr. Petritski, the director of one of the five bureau's in FDA. Michael tried to find out more about why OPS seemed to be doing so well at FDA.

"I guess it's a long story. It all goes back to the days of Malek and Finch. Malek devised this brilliant technique—OPS as we now know it—for monitoring important programs. Well, when we got the first directives on this new system, we asked ourselves 'Is this system going to work? Is it going to help us?' We decided to take a wait-and-see attitude. So instead of going whole hog with Malek's system, we fulfilled the letter of his directives and started developing our own system—PMS (Program Management System)—as an in-house evaluation procedure. That allowed us to work more or less at our own pace during the first year. It gave the new PMS staff the time to work with the managers in each bureau in order to put together some really meaningful plans. Then, after the first year of OPS when we saw that they were serious about it and that it could be helpful to us—in the form of PMS—we were off and running.

"We now see OPS, and PMS, as providing us with some real benefits. It helps us get things done. It gives the Secretary a better understanding of our problems and programs, and it has generally inproved communication at all levels. But I think a lot of the success of both systems—they are really parts of the same system—is due to the people and the approach which we took. If we had folowed the Malek line—the impersonal overseer—we probably wouldn't have much more than another paper crunching exercise.''

Michael thanked Mr. Petritski for his time and returned to Mr. Holden's office to collect his coat. He thought about how different some of Mr. Holden's attitudes about OPS and its relations with project managers had seemed. As he left the immense building, he decided that there certainly were differences between FDA and HSMHA—many of them, in fact. Tomorrow he would be working downtown again, at OE. He would just have to wait to see what his interviews there would tell him.

Interviews at OE

Michael's first interview was with Mr. Gil Rowland, a member of the personal staff of the Deputy Commissioner for Management (DCM) at OE. The new Commissioner of OE, Mr. Marland, was quite impressed with the potentialities of OPS, and, through his DCM, he had initiated his own management conferences on a monthly basis. Mr. Rowland was intimately involved in all of the activities revolving around these conferences.

"Good morning, Michael, What would you like to know abous OPS?"

"I would really like to get your frank opinion about OPS. What good things it has done, what problems you see in it—sort of an overall analysis."

"OK. Let's see what we can do. There have been a lot of problems, but there certainly have been benefits as well. I guess that one of the major problems was that we didn't have enough guidance initially, and we still don't have enough technical assistance. No structure or operational level for OPS was suggested when it was first implemented, and we lacked rigid criteria. What criteria we have had, haven't been rigidly applied."

"I'm not sure I follow you."

"Well, since we didn't know enough about how to implement something like OPS, the first plan which we made contained a lot of inconsistencies. Our objectives were not stated in terms of quantifiable outputs, and the milestones in our action plans were defined in terms of administrative processes rather than concrete outputs. As a result, we had little likelihood of meeting our stated objectives even if we completed each of the milestones. We didn't know enough about OPS then, and even though we think we understand it now, we don't have enough manpower to provide the technical assistance to our managers to make sure that our plans and objectives are meaningful.

"There have been some benefits, though. OPS helped us to identify problems, to find out ahead of time where there might be problems, and it does get action from top management. The program managers are aware of the kinds of decisions that OPS has helped bring about, and they are quite enthusiastic about OPS. It does give them increased visibility, especially if they can get their program into a Management Conference.

"The effectiveness of OPS varies from program to program. For example, Jack Spencer, who is responsible for the Disadvantaged Objective has been quite innovative in establishing a system to monitor that objective."

"Oh, really? Can you tell me more about it? I am seeing him right after I finish with you."

"Glad to. Here is a copy of the memorandum he sent out last summer. (See Exhibit 1.) It describes the reports and procedures he has been using. As you may know, the Disadvantaged Objective is quite extensive. It encompasses five bureaus under three deputies and involves 18 different funding sources." (See Exhibit 2 for a description of the Disadvantaged Objective for 1972.)

Michael and Gil spent the rest of their meeting looking over the memo and discussing how that system might work. Soon after, Michael left for his appointment with Mr. Spencer. He was a little bit early, and so he had to wait a few minutes until Mr. Spencer returned from another meeting.

"Come in Mr. Allen. I understand that you are trying to find out how OPS is working."

"Yes, and I've heard about the system which you implemented to help you monitor the Disadvantaged Objective."

"Oh yes. Well, that system was largely the work of Bill Sherman, who is one of your classmates, I believe."

"Yes, he is. I'm glad to hear that he was responsible for it. I'm scheduled to talk to him this afternoon. How has the system worked? Does it complement OPS?"

"Actually, that system *is* our OPS, and it *has* had some concrete benefits. In one of our programs, for example, a shortage of funds forced us to use some of our own staff to accomplish an action step which we had originally planned to have done by outside consultants. In another program, we had to develop an evaluation scheme for grants made to state programs in order to see how effectively we were fulfilling our OPS objective.

"I would say that all of my program directors are quite enthusiastic about OPS because of the visibility that it gives them. On the whole I would say that, given the kinds of programs and institutions which we are trying to control, OPS seems to be doing OK.

"However, we have felt some constraints due to the legislative restrictions placed on funds assigned to specific programs. Consequently, in the review of the Disadvantaged Objective which is now underway, we are looking at the charter of each program to see how much discretion we may have to modify it. Then, if we can change a charter, we examine what the significance of different changes might be in terms of facilitating the accomplishment of our objectives. Hopefully, the result of this review will be a more meaningful, better coordinated set of objectives to fulfill the Secretary's priority for serving the disadvantaged."

Michael thanked Mr. Spencer for his time, and hurried over to his next meeting with Mr. John Conners. Mr. Conners had been assigned the responsibility of monitoring the activities of one of the priority programs for the DCM (and thus for OPS). Michael had arranged this and his next meeting in order to get the perspective of some program people, those being controlled by OPS.

Mr. Conners got into this view of OPS quickly, almost as soon as Michael arrived. "Well, Mike, I would say that OPS hasn't done much for us this year because it was only its first year of operations and we didn't know where we were going. Right now we are only trying to survive for the rest of the year and hope that our efforts and understanding will produce better palns and objectives for next year. Our objectives just weren't right this year. 'Make so many grants' is not a very meaningful objective; it doesn't say anything about the quality or outcomes of the programs we are funding. OPS is potentially a beautiful system. It is a followup to PPBS—it checks on policy implementation.

"However, I am afraid that I see some more basic problems that may need to be solved before OPS can really succeed. I think that we will really need some kind of a reward system for program managers if we want to get their cooperation. Right now the program manager is more concerned with the autonomy of his program—and he probably has an interest group and a lobby to support him. In addition something has to be done to tie a manager's performance under OPS and the budget into some sort of overall managerial evaluation. Right now I don't think that program people pay much attention to anything but the budget."

"I hadn't reckoned with that category of problems," Michael thought as he left Mr. Conners' office. "They would certainly interfere with OPS, and with the running of HEW as a whole, for that matter. In fact, if these problems were significant, they could really sandbag

OPS.'' Michael's last meeting of the morning was with Ms. Marion Wakefield, a special assistant to one of the bureau directors involved in the Disadvantaged Objective. What Michael heard from Ms. Wakefield seemed to underscore what Mr. Conners had said. Ms. Wakefield was fairly pessimistic: ''OPS seems to create a basic conflict between bureaus like ours and the Secretary's office. One of the program directors in this bureau was forced to spend some of his discretionary funds to meet an OPS objective when the funds budgeted for that activity were not approved. As a result of cases like this, I think that program directors may become much less cooperative in committing themselves in the future. OPS seems to threaten the independence—the power base—of the bureaus.

''Sort of akin to that problem, a major premise of OPS is that you have authority or resources—in the proper ratio—to commit, and that is just not always the case. First of all we have a lot of categorical funding with specific legislative restrictions—not much flexibility there. Then, the budget, which precedes OPS anyway, is never certain until Congress gets around to passing it. That can mean a whole year of inactivity if the budget is not approved until the last minute—and you still don't know how much of the proposed total will be authorized. Then, when the manager sees OPS on top of all that, it is very difficult to expect him to be either interested in it or to cooperate with it.

''There are some specific disenchantments with OPS, too. People cannot understand why many of what they considered to be high priority objectives were not selected for monitoring by the Secretary, while some seemingly low priority objectives *were* selected. And, you can't forget that most of the program managers—where things are supposed to get done—are educators, not managers. That may be a partial explanation for the difficulty that we had putting together our initial set of OPS objectives and plans. The program people need to be educated on how to use OPS. They need to understand the need for it, and how to develop meaningful objectives and milestones. I don't know, maybe we need to have an outside consultant come in—that would get away from some of the internal politics.''

Michael had a lot to think about during lunch. While his previous interviews had only seemed to indicate problems with the implementation of OPS, these last two raised much broader questions. Could OPS be made to work in this kind of environment? What kinds of basic changes might have to be made at HEW in order to implement such a management system? The afternoon promised to be interesting. Michael's classmate, Bill Sherman, had arranged a meeting with the OPS coordinators from each of the five bureaus encompassed by the Disadvantaged Objective. The meeting moved quite quickly and touched on many of the problem areas that Michael was becoming familiar with. Some of the more important comments were as follows:

''One of our major problems is measuring our results. How do you get feedback or evaluate the effectiveness of a program, especially one that is as broad in concept as Disadvantaged? It may take two or three years, or more, before you can see any results.''

''Perhaps the Disadvantaged Objective is really only a general goal. Maybe we need more specific objectives to use as a basis for planning and evaluating our results.''

''How can you coordinate an objective as wide-ranging as this one? There appears to be little convergence of interest or effort among the bureaus. I guess that the source of the problem is caused by the specific intent of the legislation which established and supports each bureau. OPS tries to superimpose a set of executive priorities and objectives on top of the priorities and objectives which already exist for each bureau in the form of legislatively created and funded programs. It creates conflict at a very basic level.''

''The planning process seems to be out of phase. It would make more sense to start with broad statements of goals and priorities *before* the budget is prepared and submitted. As it is we have already made our plans before we know what priorities OPS may want to monitor.''

"We have already recognized this problem of phasing to some extent. In the Office of Program Planning and Evaluation (OPPE) we are beginning to do some long-range planning for OE. However, there is quite a lag in getting something going. We are now considering FY 1974—which still leaves 1973 without any formal tie-in.''

"But OPS still has no relationship to the actual allocation of resources. Our program needed to come up with a revenue sharing plan, but there were no extra funds appropriated for it. To really make OPS work it might even be necessary to tie in the Salary and Expense budgets.

After the meeting, Michael and Bill adjourned to Bill's office and continued their discussion of OPS. Michael found that Bill, as someone he had known in the past, was willing to be completely frank.

"One of my main concerns, Mike, is about who is actually running OPS. I am afraid that right now OPS is primarily being run by staff people. We couldn't really find out much about that in our meeting just now because they were all staff! But I don't think that OPS can really work unless we get the line manager—the program directors, bureau chiefs, and deputy commissioners—involved in setting their own objectives and making their own plans.''

"We actually are trying to do some of the things that we talked about in the meeting. For instance—you've seen our control plan?''

"Yes, Gil Rowland gave me a copy of it this morning.''

"Well, we may have been overambitious, but if you look at attachment 3 and 4 (See Exhibit 1.) you can see that we are trying to get people to plan their spending in terms of their program responsibilities. Right now only some people are providing us with all of this information, and unfortunately, we haven't been able to look very closely at the results. We just haven't had time, and even if we did, the current accounting system doesn't have the capacity to provide the information that we need.

"Here is something else that you might be interested in seeing. Those of us who have been working with OPS have found several difficulties with the present version of OPS, so, rather than let those difficulties slide into the background and be forgotten, we put together this short paper which summarizes and discusses the problems we saw.'' (See Exhibit 3.)

"Great!'' Michael exclaimed, "This ought to be a big help in my report to Stu Thomas.''

"We have also been working on some recommendations for improving the overall control system. I guess that the thrust of our proposal is the integration of Long-Range Planning, Operational Planning and Budgeting. We just don't see how any control system can work unless long-range plans are first developed and used as the basis for planning the current year. And it certainly makes little sense to try to plan your budget until both long-range and short-term—this year's—plans are known. Well, I hope that I have been able to help you, and I hope that your report will result in some improvements in OPS.''

Michael thanked Bill and hurried back over to his office. He wanted to catch Paul Andrews before he left for the day. He got there just as Paul was preparing to leave.

"How did your interviews at OE go today?''

"Pretty well, Paul, but they did leave me with a few questions. Do you have a few minutes?''

"Sure, go ahead.''

"Well, most of the people at OE and at HSMHA felt that the OPS effort was hindered by a lack of coordination between it and both long-range planning and budgeting. Is there anything in the mill to deal with that problem?''

"They're right. Coordination between OPS and the budget and long-range planning processes has been a problem in the past, but we're now spending a lot of our time trying to integrate these systems. For example, in fiscal year 1973, guidance for long-range planning and for operational planning will come in the same document and the goals and priorities for both will be the same. Long-range planners will review all the objectives of the agency for conformity with the long-range plans of those agencies. This kind of review will also take place in OE prior to the submission of objectives. Long-range planners are now involved in all management conferences and the evaluations of progress toward the achievement of objectives. Finally, all evaluative material on successes and failures of OE and other agencies in meeting objectives are being fed into the long-range planning process so that policy can reflect reality at the operating and at the delivery level. As for the budget process, we are pushing towards including a statement of objectives in the Department's budget to Congress for each line item or request for funds. By achieving this objective we will not only have integrated the budget process with the OPS but we will also be in a position where the Department is committing to a set of results prior to the allocation of resources. The budget objectives submitted by each agency would be come sort of a shopping list for the top managers in the Department for which they can select the results they are willing to purchase for the coming year.

"I don't mean to imply that we've made it in terms of integrating these systems, but we are spending an awful lot of our time in achieving that objective and we know that the successful institutionalization of OPS depends on our ability to tie these systems together."

"Thanks a lot, Paul. Now I feel better about chances for success."

Michael spent another two hours at his desk trying to piece together what he would report to Mr. Thomas.

Questions:
1. What do you see as the major problems of OPS?
2. What changes do you think should be made in the system?
3. What should Michael recommend to Mr. Thomas?

Exhibit 1

U.S. Department of Health, Education, and Welfare (B)

MEMORANDUM

TO: OPS Coordinators

FROM: Acting Associate Deputy Commissioner for Higher Education

SUBJECT: Monitoring and Controlling the Disadvantaged Objective

In order to assure full responsiveness for achieving the sub-objectives for the Disadvantaged Objective, we would like to explain our efforts for monitoring the Disadvantaged Objective in some detail.

First, attachment #1 is a chart indicating the key staff members designated by each Deputy Commissioner as responsible for specific sub-objectives. We intend to hold meetings in advance of the monthly conferences that the Deputy Commissioner of Management (DCM) will hold on the Commissioner's Objectives. We anticipate that you will encourage and support this monitoring effort by your staff since this will make our monthly meetings with Dr. Ottina more productive, give better representation of your bureau's activities, and will help to insure successful completion of the objective.

Second, Attachment #2 is a progress report which should be submitted to our office one week before the DCM's monthly Management Review session for the Disadvantaged Objective. It requires that each Deputy Commissioner report progress on each action step and action taken to remedy problems. We are assuming that the people noted on the organizational chart (Attachment #1) will be responsible for insuring that these monthly reports are accurate and timely.

Finally, Attachments #3 and 4 are monthly reports on program and controllable administrative funds. These reports will require an initial effort to plan expenditures for the Fiscal Year as well as monthly up-dating. The intentions of the two forms are to have more detailed information on how each Deputy Commissioner plans to meet sub-objectives under his responsibility and to have reasonably current information.

Again, we will appreciate your full support in our efforts to monitor this Commissioner's Objective and, of course, are welcome to any suggestions for improvement.

John F. Spencer

Exhibit 1 (cont'd)

Organization for Monitoring the Disadvantage Objective

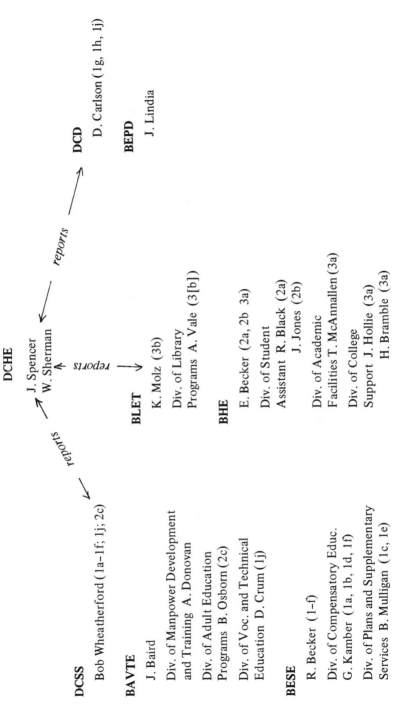

DCHE

J. Spencer
W. Sherman

reports

DCD

D. Carlson (1g, 1h, 1i)

BEPD

J. Lindia

DCSS

Bob Wheatherford (1a–1f; 1j; 2c)

reports

reports

BAVTE

J. Baird

Div. of Manpower Development and Training A. Donovan

Div. of Adult Education Programs B. Osborn (2c)

Div. of Voc. and Technical Education D. Crum (1j)

BESE

R. Becker (1–f)

Div. of Compensatory Educ. G. Kamber (1a, 1b, 1d, 1f)

Div. of Plans and Supplementary Services B. Mulligan (1c, 1e)

BLET

K. Molz (3b)

Div. of Library Programs A. Vale (3[b])

BHE

E. Becker (2a, 2b 3a)

Div. of Student Assistant R. Black (2a)
J. Jones (2b)

Div. of Academic Facilities T. McAnnallen (3a)

Div. of College Support J. Hollie (3a)
H. Bramble (3a)

Exhibit 1 (cont'd)

Interim Report

Problem and Variance Analysis

for month of _____ FY 1972

Overall Evaluation: ☐

Organization: _____

Objective: _____

Subobjective: _____

Person Responsible: _____

Action Step (s)	Problem Description (including effect on objectives)	ACTION	
		Underway/Completed	Recommended

Exhibit 1

Attachment 3

Monthly Financial Report for Program Funds
(in 000's)

Subobjective	Person Responsible	Sources	Total Source	Current QTR				Year to Date			
				Plan	Actu.	Var.	Cum % of Total Source	Plan	Actu.	Var.	Cum % of Total Source
DcDev 1g	D. Carlson	EPDA, Part D	22,000								
1h	"	EPDA, Part D	5,000								
1i	"	EPDA, Part B-1	74,100								

Exhibit 1

Attachment 4

Monthly Financial Report for Controlable Administrative Funds
(in 000's)

Subobjective	Person Responsible	Sources	Total Source	Current QTR				Year to Date			
				Plan	Actu.	Var.	Cum % of Total Source	Plan	Actu.	Var.	Cum % of Total Source
DcDev lg	D. Carlson										
1h	"										
li	"										

Exhibit 2

U.S. Department of Health, Education, and Welfare (B)

Office of Education
Serving the Disadvantaged Objective

Goal 1972-77

Eliminate education barriers to low-income and disadvantaged youth by supporting changes in the educational system and by providing financial assistance and supportive services to meet the special needs of economically disadvantaged youth. Specifically: (1) at the elementary and secondary levels, the primary thrust will be to improve academic performance of disadvantaged to the extent that achievement profiles of low-income students are the same as the achievement profiles of high income students; and (2) at the post secondary level the primary thrust will be to eliminate inequalities of educational opportunity to the extent that by 1977 students coming from low-income backgrounds will enter post secondary education in the same proportions as students in the two highest income quartiles.

Objective – Fiscal Year 1972

To initiate activities for the achievement of the long-range goal to eliminate educational barriers at all levels of education, increased efforts will be made to target financial and technical assistance to meet the special needs of low-income students. The following subobjectives are proposed for FY 1972.

1. **At the early childhood, elementary and secondary levels,** to improve the delivery of educational services and other assistance to low-income students. Specifically:
    a. Improve effectiveness of supportive services of ESEA, I by strengthened technical assistance to SEA's and LEA's and assure that 75% of the LEA's meet ESEA, I comparability criteria by the end of FY 1972 and that the remaining 25% have adequate plans.
    b. Establish criteria on the basis of which 20 exemplary projects supported under ESEA I, III, VII, and VIII are identified. Develop an implementation strategy for the exemplary projects for Fiscal Year 1973.
    c. Increase the number of students receiving bilingual education from 86,154 to 106,000 and increase the effectiveness of ESEA, VII by reducing projects with segregated instruction by 80%, reducing dropout

rates in the high school projects by 10%, and increasing the number of native speaking teachers by 15%.

d. Reduce by 20% the number of students dropping out of the ESEA, VII target schools.

e. Target $3 million of ESEA, III to continue 25 projects to deal with special educational needs of disadvantaged students. Utilize $2.7 million to continue projects involving reading for disadvantaged students.

f. Provide assistance to about 60,000 poor children under the Follow-Through program and by using sampling techniques and appropriate site visitations in at least 5% of the Follow-Through communities examine the accomplishment of students. On the basis of findings, create model procedures for change from exemplary practices identified.

g. To retrain the trainers of educational personnel, involving 5,000 participants who will be sensitive and responsive to the educational needs of disadvantaged children.

h. To support projects that train and retrain 4,000 trainers and aides in the area of Early Childhood Education.

i. To provide 440 sites for the innovations reform of teacher training component to effect the disadvantaged child through the SEA, LEA, and IHE's with community involvement on a systematic, cooperative and coordinated basis utilizing the Career Opportunity, Teacher Corps, and Urban/Rural School Development Programs.

j. To provide effective career training for 970,000 secondary, post-secondary, and adult students who are disadvantaged under the States grant program for vocational education.

2. **At the post secondary level**, it is proposed to increase the targeting of student financial aid on low-income students and to provide additional educational opportunities for disadvantaged youth. Specifically:

a. Provide financial assistance under the college-based programs to 1,043,700 students of whom about 732,900 will come from families earning $7,500 or less — this represents an increase of about 99,500 low-income students assisted during FY 1971. (Also, 1,247,000 students will receive guaranteed loans including 399,000 low-income students.) In addition, further modify during the current fiscal year the FY 1973 application and application process to reinforce the targeting of EOG and CWSP funds to low-income students.

b. Provide assistance to 161,600 students under the Upward Bound, Student Special Services, and Talent Search Programs representing an increase of 36,300 students assisted in FY 1971. Of the 64,000

Upward Bound and Special Service Students, assure that at least 90% will come from families with incomes at or below the poverty level as defined in program guidelines. Among Talent Search students, assure that at least 85% will come from families with incomes of $7,500 or less.

c. Provide educational opportunities for 724,000 students under the Adult Education Program and increase effectiveness of SEA through increased technical assistance to States.

3. **At Black colleges and other institutions**, target increased financial assistance to those institutions enrolling large numbers of low-income students with particular emphasis on the traditionally colleges. Specifically:

a. Increase the percentage of funds awarded to these institutions over the FY 1971 level as follows: Developing Institutions Program from 70% to 74%; EPDA Part E Institute Program from 29% to 40%; fund all acceptable applications under the HEFA III Interest Subsidy Program.

b. Target 100% of College Library Resource Program to at least 600 institutions that are disadvantaged or have a high enrollment of disadvantaged students.

Strategy

The strategy will be implemented by coordinated and intensive utilization of all USOE authorities which have a special mission for serving disadvantaged children and which provide discretionary funding authority to the Commissioner of Education. In carrying out the objective and subobjectives stated above, the Office will pursue the following set of strategies:

a. Identify and disseminate effective programs and components which have been funded by Follow-Through, ESEA Title I, ESEA Title III, and other programs serving disadvantaged children;

b. Provide training and technical assistance to improve the effectiveness of SEA's and LEA's who are engaged in Federally funded projects and activities;

c. Increase in-service teacher training facilities and programs and target training efforts to specific school areas serving large numbers of disadvantaged children;

d. Improve client participation in educational programs serving disadvantaged children through parent advisory committees and other forms of parent involvement;

e. Provide higher levels of Federal financial assistance to support needy students in post-secondary education through loans, opportunity grants, and other work study programs;

f. Expand and strengthen post-secondary programs which have as their specific mission the identification of able and needy students for upward mobility programs participation;

g. Provide direct financial and technical support to higher education and other institutions serving the needs of disadvantaged students;

h. Develop techniques of measurement to assure attainment of goals and objectives for serving the disadvantaged.

Resources Needed

The proposed strategy is dependent on existing program authorities as indicated below.

Bureau	Authority	Amounts (000)
1. Elementary and Secondary Education	ESEA III, VII, VIII	49,500
	GEPA, FOLLOW THROUGH	59,425
2. Adult, Vocational, and Technical Education	VEA, AEA	108,100
3. Libraries and Educational Technology	LSCA, GEPA, HEA	47,400
4. Higher Education	HEA II, III, IV, VI	711,000
	NDEA, EPDA	397,000

Exhibit 3

U.S. Department of Health, Education, and Welfare (B)

General Findings and Observations

1. **Secretary's Guidelines Submitted Late**

   The Secretary's guidelines and priorities were submitted late. This delay caused confusion and indecision in OE. For example, most Deputy Commissioners never disseminated their versions of what their respective bureaus ought to accomplish for the forthcoming year. Ideally, we perceive that the Commissioner ought to interpret the Secretary's guidelines and formulate OE guidelines. (that is, Commissioner's Objectives); the Deputy Commissioners, in turn, ought to interpret the Commissioners Objectives and formally give guidance to the bureaus. The bureaus would then have a general framework in which to work. The net result was a strong 'bottom's up' approach that allowed the bureaus great leeway and freedom in determining what would be in the objectives. In addition, it appears that the Deputy Commissioners did not act as managers but rather as 'sign-offers' in the formulating of the Commissioners Objectives.

2. **Little Relationship to the Five Year Plan and Budgetary-Decision**

   There was no apparent or logical tie-in between the Operational Planning System and the Five Year Plan. Similarly, the time dimension of the budget cycle did not appear to support the OPS, or vice-versa. Ideally, it would seem that budgetary decisions (especially concerning S&E money) should be made after initial objective statements have been clarified but before detailed objective statements and work plans have been made. Of course, there should be a certain degree of inter-meshing between the OPS and budget decisions. Note that presently all objective statements and work plans are in final form and S&E budget decisions have yet to be made. (S&E is salary and expenses.)

3. **Commissioner's Objectives Contains Many Routine Items**

   The essence and thrust of the Commissioner's Objectives may be lost in that most objectives are stated in a comprehensive, global fashion. This is to say that nearly anything dealing with the disadvantaged, for example, has been included under the Disadvantaged Objective. The danger is that the Objectives may well become meaningless and a paper work exercise. If, on the other hand, limited, non-routine objectives are stated, it seems that there would be a greater likelihood that OE could accomplish some significant, tangible results.

233

4. **OPS Has Made Several Mistakes**

   Apparently, OPS at one point revised the Commissioner's Objectives and submitted them to the Secretary's Office without the approval of the respective Deputy Commissioners. In addition, it made revisions without informing the relevant bureaus and Deputy Commissioners.

5. **The OPS–OPPE Role is Quite Unclear**

   No one, including the people in OPPE seem to know OPPE's role in formulating the objectives or in monitoring results. Notions of guidance and advice seem to be nebulous, especially in OPPE as noted above.

6. **A Conceptual System or Plan for Tracking the Objectives Does Not Appear to Exist**

   The question is, who will track and monitor the objectives? OPPE? the Deputy Commissioners? Dr. Ottina's special staff? Will a uniform system be used throughout OE?

7. **There Is No Detailed Statement Specifying What Division (or Branch within a Bureau) Will Be Accountable for Achieving an Objective and Will be Accountable for Seeing That Funds are Allocated as Planned**

   Furthermore, there is a real question as to how effective the Budget Office can be in checking to see if funds were spent on achieving objectives. This brings up the real question as to what management system is being used by whom to track the objectives.

Recommendations & Next Steps:

1. Conduct a more detailed analysis of what went wrong with OPS and document the findings. Getting submissions from those in the bureau and planning staffs who endured the experience would surely be illuminating. Make recommendations.

2. Prepare a detailed plan for the next-go-around that will insure smoother results.

3. Within a short time, reach decisions on how the monitoring and tracking system should work. Concurrently, begin to introduce responsibility and accountability to people for the actual monitoring. The Deputy Commissioners seem to have relinquished this function. Given the present comprehensiveness of the objectives, it may be hard to track them in a meaningful way.

CHAPTER 4

THE USE OF GROUPS AS A MANAGEMENT TOOL

This chapter deals with four facets of groups in organizations. First, the development and function of the informal work group, second, the use of groups (as opposed to individuals) as a means of furthering action, third, decision making groups, and last, some practical approaches to the problems of running effective groups. Since the average manager spends one third of his working life in groups which are often ineffective and time wasting, their proper use and management would seem to be desirable.

THE WORK GROUP

What produces the behavior observed in a particular work group? Why are some work groups more productive than others? Why do some groups resist innovations in technology or organization while others welcome them? The answers to these and related questions are important for any manager. They not only enhance his understanding of his own behavior, but also that of peers, superiors and subordinates.

The answer to these questions lies in the factors which determine the behavior of the members of a work group (Seiler, 1967). Individual inputs are one important input to the subsystem from the individual members of the unit, and reflect the personalities of the members of the group. Two other clusters of factors which affect behavior in a subsystem are imposed from the larger organizational system and were described in chapter three. The first is the nature of the work assigned to the unit. The second is the formal organizational practices (supervisory arrangements, control systems, procedures, rules, etc.) which are usually defined by the management of the larger system.

These three factors are interdependent. They interact with each other. For example, an organizational input (personal selection procedures) may affect the kinds of individual inputs in the system. Similarly, the character of organizational inputs may be affected by the task inputs. When a highly routine task is to be performed, management may find it feasible and efficient to rely heavily on formal rules and procedures to regulate the work, but when a more uncertain or problem-solving task is to be performed, it may be impossible to rely on such predetermined procedures. Recognizing the interdependence of the inputs is crucial because it means that when a manager thinks about altering one of them, he should be aware of the effects on the other inputs if he is to keep the system operating effectively.

Inputs not only interact, but this interaction creates a fourth determinant of behavior in the work group—the emergent social controls and structure—which in turn interacts with the inputs to produce the behavior which emerges in the subsystem. By social controls are meant the traditional ground rules or norms about how members should behave which develop in a work group and which guide behavior, and the methods which develop within the group to enforce these norms through feedback. Social structure includes such ideas as the status hierarchy which develops informally in any group, the established power relationship in the group, and the stable pattern of friendships which supports this pecking order.

Although social controls and structure are treated more fully below, it is helpful to illustrate the interdependence of this set of variables with the technical, organizational, and individual inputs. One obvious example of this interdependence is the degree of physical proximity of group members required by the task. If they must work in a confined space together, this is likely to result in more stringent norms about behavior such as one should not talk loudly if it will disturb others. Organizational inputs, such as compensation schemes and measurement methods, can also affect the extent to which a group develops into a tightly knit subsystem with strong social controls and a well-defined social structure. In those situations where measurements and financial compensation emphasize group accomplishment versus individual output, stronger social controls are apt to develop. The interaction of individual inputs with social controls and structuve is even more obvious. As an illustration, the needs, interests, and skills a member brings into the group and the way he is perceived by others will have a great deal to do with the position he ends up with in the group social structure.

As pointed out earlier, social controls and structure are different from the other factors discussed above in that they develop within the subsystem out of the interaction of task, organizational, and individual inputs. Social controls refers to the norms about appropriate behavior for subsystems members which develop in a group and the mechanisms employed to gain compliance to these norms. Social structure is the hierarchy of membership positions which actually emerges in the subsystem.

The relationship between these social forces and behavior is highly inter-dependent and the distinction between them is very subtle. In fact the only way that the social controls and structure which exist in a subsystem can be tracked is by observing the behavior over a period of time. This is so because social controls and structure represent relatively enduring subsystem-wide expectations about how members should behave collectively and individually. Actual behavior can and does deviate from these expectations but, in general, the social controls constrain be-havior so that it supports and reinforces structure. The connection between behavior and social controls and structure becomes clearer as their development in a sub-system is examined.

Why do people become actively involved in work groups? After all, just because one is formally assigned or working in a subsystem is not sufficient reason to become involved in a process of social control. The answer to this question is simple enough, whether the subsystem in question is defined on the organization chart or whether it just grows up in the organization without formal sanction. People become involved in work group activity because it meets certain of their needs. First, by joining a group, persons are often able to accomplish task objectives they cannot achieve alone. For formally established groups, this may be the solution of a complex problem one person could not solve alone or the manufacture of a com-plicated product. In such cases, the member is satisfying important ego needs for mastery or competence as well as meeting the task requirements of the larger system. Put another way, the needs of individuals and the primary task of the subsystem are consistent with the requirements of the larger system.

But in other situations the group's primary task is not the same as the task inputs defined by management. For example, a group of workers that has developed a healthy distrust for management may implicitly define as its primary task protecting itself from management pressure for higher productivity. By banding together, the workers can resist attempts to get them to work harder. Alone they could not accomplish this, but by coordinated activity, they can protect themselves from what they perceive to be a hostile environment.

Both these examples suggest the same essential fact: By joining into subsystem activity, members get things done which could not be accomplished alone. At the same time, they are also meeting important internal needs. By joining together to accomplish work, they can manage their drives for affection and aggression, get reinforcement, and gain a sense of self-esteem from the acceptance by others.

As members work together on a task and satisfy their needs, the group as a whole develops certain expectations about what is appropriate behavior. In the second example above, for instance, the group would expect that members should not produce more than a certain number of units of output per day. Such shared expect-ations about behavior are what is meant by group norms. Variations in individual behavior from such work group norms can have major negative consequences for the group and the individual. First, it can prevent accomplishment of the task. Eventually, if a group ceased to fill such a major purpose, this could lead to its breakdown. Second, since people have needs which are being satisfied by group membership, itself, as well as task accomplishment, they are reluctant to see this happen and they become involved in maintenance behavior aimed at controlling norm-breakers. This often painful sanction is what is meant by the process of social control.

Attempts at social control are a form of feedback and often consist of verbal sanctions, such as sarcasm, invectives, jokes, etc. If these types of punishment do not work, the ultimate weapon is disregard or ostracism. Whether or not these controls will work on individual members depends on the extent to which they value subsystem membership. If the group is an important source of need satisfaction for them, they will comply. If the group is not important to a member, he can safely disregard these sanctions. This point is closely connected to the formation of social structure, but before this is discussed one last point about norms and social control.

In the discussion above of norms aimed at restricting productivity, it was suggested that the social controls of the subsystem would be operating in opposition to the organization and task inputs defined by the larger system. While this often is the case, equally often social controls support the accomplishment of organization objectives. An example of this is reported by Blau (1955) in his study of a government agency. In this agency, the group of investigating agents had developed a norm stipulating that the more competent agents should help the less competent ones when the latter were having difficulty. While this norm was contrary to a formal rule that agents should only confer with supervisors, Blau concluded that this inter-agent consultation improved the quality of agent decisions and contributed to the overall effectiveness of the agency. Obviously, the negative consequence of this norm was that it tended to weaken the authority of supervisors. However, the problem in this situation was not so much the norm but the rigid rules which seemed inconsistent with task requirements and social controls.

Turning now to the issue of social structure, different members may value subsystem membership to differing degrees. Similarly, certain individuals are more or less important to the group. This importance can take the form of contribution to task accomplishment or to their role in the maintenance of the group. For example, in Blau's group of agents the competent agent was an important member because of his ability to help others in task accomplishment. Simultaneously, the group was important to him because it fed his sense of self-esteem. These competent agents were high in the social structure of their group. In another situation a person might become a central member of a group because of his capacities to help maintain group cohesion at times of stress. For example, in a task force of managers working on a complex problem, one of their number who was skillful at reducing tension through the use of humor might become a valued group member with high status. Also, one's status in group social structure can be determined by external characteristics like age, skill, etc. Which characteristics will be important depends on how task, organizational, and individual inputs interact with these social factors to shape the activities and skills that group members value. What is essential to remember is that such hierarchies do develop and people's positions in them are related to their contribution to the group. At a minimum, such a contribution means adherence to group norms.

One way to illustrate these points is to describe four categories of group membership identified by Zaleznik, Christensen, and Roethlisberger (1958). The lowest of these on the totem pole is the isolate. This is a person who has been isolated from the group. This can happen because he has so little to offer the group that they isolate him and because the group is unimportant to him that he chooses to stay out. In essence, he has signalled that group membership either is not important to him or he is not capable of meeting group expectations and the group, through its rejection, has indicated that he is not important to them. Next in lowest standing is the so-called deviant. He deviates from the expected patterns of behavior but is still tolerated by others. This tolerance may be because he is making some important contribution to the group in spite of his deviance or because other group members feel that there is still hope that he will conform to group behavior standards. In either case, a deviant can be identified because, instead of being ignored like the isolate, he will be the focus of much interaction directed at bringing his behavior back into line.

Next in line up the social structure is what these authors called the "regular." As the name implies, such members are squarely in the group. They adhere to most, if not all, group expectations about behavior, so they are making the contributions expected of a good member. In exchange for this contribution they are rewarded by being included in the group. Finally, at the top of the pecking order are the "leaders." In this case, the leader is not necessarily defined by the social structure. What is meant are those subsystem members who are seen by others as making the greatest contribution to the group. As a minimum contribution these members adhere to group norms. But beyond this, they make some special contribution which others value. It may be the contribution of helping others as in the case of the agents of Blau's study, or it may be a tension-reducing role like the task force example above. Whatever their contributions, the leaders can be identified because they will be at the center of the group in the receipt of interactions and in terms of influence. In fact, this relationship between interaction and positions in the group can be seen throughout this discussion of membership roles. The more central a person is to the group in terms of his contribution, the more he is apt to be involved in positive interactions with others. This is another example of what is meant by the interdependence of behavior and social controls and structure.

Two other points need to be made about leadership in subsystems. First, throughout this discussion the plural term leaders has been used. The reason for this is that most subsystems often have a number of leaders playing slightly different roles. One very visible example of this point is in the top management subsystem of larger organizations (like Children's Hospital), where two or three executives play different leadership roles based on their unique competences. Such an arrangement has been formalized in the Office of the President in many companies. One executive may deal with external problems such as finance or marketing, while another devotes his efforts to internal issues of management development, organization, etc. Such division of leadership is frequently agreed on among the top group and is not necessarily officially recognized in titles or job descriptions. This is an example of the fact that in human organizations of any size leadership must handle both task and maintenance functions, but it should be noted in passing that for one individual to do both is often difficult.

The final point about leadership has to do with the concept of authority. Too often, authority is seen as coming from a formal position. This certainly is one basis of authority. But, as this discussion suggests, authority in organizations is also derived from the special contribution a leader makes to the subsystem of which he is a member. Often in management it is the particular competence a man demonstrates which makes him a valued group member whom others respect and are willing to follow. While this view of leadership and authority is more complicated than conventional ones, it is also more accurate. For leadership, behavior like the behavior of any other subsystem member can only be understood in terms of the inputs and the issues of social control and structure that have been described.

THE USE OF GROUPS
AS A MANAGEMENT TOOL

Naturally the politicians preferred to decide such questions in close conclave. In time of war, the need for secrecy became more critical, and as carelessness was more likely to arise from a large cabinet, so smaller ones were favoured. And lastly, there was the undeniable fact that many holders of great household offices were not clever men, and their opinions were more likely to befog than clarify business. These factors resulted in the early development of a small inner cabinet which met frequently and consisted almost entirely of the political officers of the Household—the Lord President, the Privy Seal, the First Lord of the Treasury, the two Secretaries, and the Lord Chancellor—the men who bore the burden of government. They met informally wherever it suited them best, sometimes at the Cockpit, which housed the Treasury and the Secretaries, but frequently in their own homes; sometimes one of the Secretaries jotted down their decisions or made a few notes, but many meetings have gone unrecorded. Once this inner ring, or 'efficient cabinet' as it is called, had determined its policy, it had little difficulty in imposing its views on the large cabinet which from time to time was required to meet to give a more formal sanction to certain acts of State.

When a treaty or a negotiation was on foot, Walpole would dine with each of the chief ministers or spend a night with them in their country houses. In the benevolent and easy atmosphere induced by good food and better wines, Walpole would air his views, counter criticism and plant his suggestions. The ground prepared, the efficient cabinet meeting would be called. Unanimity, in the heyday of his power, did not take long to achieve. Once the inner ring was certain of its line, the Lords Justices or the formal cabinet would be summoned and, with alacrity and little discussion, formalized the decisions previously taken. Sir Robert Walpole: The Making of a Statesman.

(Plumb, 1972)

Neither fashion nor a manager's natural affinity for, nor abhorrence of, groups would allow him to ignore the dictates of clearly defined objectives in the determination of whether to use a group, what kind of group to use, and how to run it. Thus, if the purpose is to seek ratification of a decision rather than to have a group to consider what decision it wishes to make, this will dictate the way the agenda is set up and the meeting is run. For example, an administrator was concerned to get ratification of a decision to merge from his board of trustees. He was, to be blunt, not interested in having them explore the issue but come to a rapid and affirmative conclusion on it. He therefore carefully planned the agenda so that they would exercise their emotions and concerns on a series of relatively trivial issues early in the meeting. He dropped in this issue close to the end, at which time they were all exhausted and ratified it unanimously with little discussion. By contrast, Mr. Staton in the B.H.W. case is interested in using the group format to build a team, and to provide an emotional safety valve, as well as for decision making. These purposes will be undercut if he tries to be too task oriented or manipulative. Some purposes of assembling a group are to share information (which may be done even while an unrelated task is being completed), to educate the members of the group (which may or may not center on the task), to solve a specific problem (probably synonymous with the task), to make a decision or ratify a decision, to inhibit an action (this would often be a hidden purpose, perhaps only visible to the person assembling the group), and to get to know people (which could occur while an unrelated task was being performed).

Groups are not appropriate devices to serve all purposes. In general, groups are better for identifying problems than for solving them; better for ratifying decisions than for making them; better for identifying information needs than for information sharing.

What kind of grouping of people would serve an identified purpose? The alternatives are the following or some kind of combination:

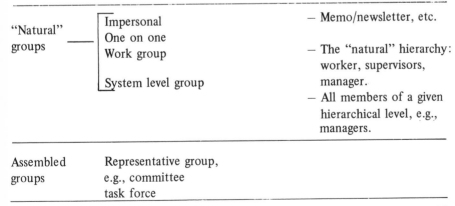

"Natural" groups	Impersonal One on one Work group System level group	— Memo/newsletter, etc. — The "natural" hierarchy: worker, supervisors, manager. — All members of a given hierarchical level, e.g., managers.
Assembled groups	Representative group, e.g., committee task force	

Generally speaking, the manager should be guided by the above rules of thumb. If there is variability of opinion, seek some reduction by sounding out individually. Representative groups need time to return to their constituencies. Task forces can effectively and efficiently get a lot of work done as long as they contain the necessary skills for information assembly, and the implementation phase is recognized as critical. (The membership may need to change.) Task forces (and representative groups) may have problems of conflicting loyalties between the temporary group and the back home group which may be hard to reconcile. Thus managers from different hospitals met in task forces to explore what the problems of different functional groups would be in the event of a merger. In order to promote free and open discussion of the widest range of alternatives, a ground rule had been set (and agreed) at the beginning of the task force meetings that all discussion should be confidential until a final report was written which would then be shown to the directors of the hospitals concerned. However, in one of the task forces a manager prematurely showed his hospital director the intended final report for approval much to the consternation and anger of his fellow task force members who had not yet seen it. In fairness to him, that particular hospital had been marked by a fairly rapid turnover of managers, and he was not unreasonably concerned with protecting his own interests in the light of this. But this does exemplify the need not only to set rules in a task force which are clearly understood by the members, but for these rules to be enforced by whatever means are appropriate. This in itself is quite difficult, because a task force leader rarely has many sanctions that he can invoke. Paradoxically, the better the temporary group functions through good rules and leadership, the more painful may be the conflict.

Which grouping is chosen will to some degree depend on who should be in the group, for some groupings are natural and members cannot be omitted without setting precedents. While skill and knowledge are key determinants for problem solving, representativeness is crucial where constituencies are involved, as is power for the implementation of action. Task forces' recommendations often fail because they possess the skills for problem solving, but not the power to enact. Outsiders (e.g., consultants) can be helpful if the purpose of the group is to reconcile internal differences.

The timing of the group's meetings, i.e., length, frequency, and time of day, can also be important. Often an organization will not give a group the time it needs for the work it has to do, or the conditions of meeting may be inimical (phone ringing, people called out). There is a tendency to think in stereotypes—"all groups meet for two hours weekly"—when an intensive all day session off site may get much more done. Sometimes interim tasks must be accomplished, or time taken to assimilate and reflect or check out with colleagues. Group meetings (conferences) could often be improved by clarification of the agenda ahead of time, with some use of simple questionnaires. These issues are discussed at greater length in the last two sections of this chapter.

DECISION-MAKING GROUPS

Groups are generally effective vehicles for decision-making where more information and information sharing is valuable, where more approaches to a problem gets out of ruts, where participation increases acceptance, and where better comprehension of the decision is important.

Groups are poor where social pressure leads to conformity (the minority opinion may be correct), there is pressure for a decision rather than the best decision, there is a dominant individual (an authority or expert) and it gets to be a win-lose issue.

The following factors can lead to good or bad results. Disagreement can lead to bad feeling or innovation. If there is a mix of different and mutual interests, there is need to separate goals, obstacles, and solutions to get to the mutual interests. Groups can do a "risky shift" and be more risk-taking than individuals. More time is required by groups. If agreement means changing positions, and the constructive person changes, then poor decision may result.

The leader of a group should facilitate cooperative problem solving not selling. He should receive and relay information and communication, integrate and not take a personal position or sell a personal solution.

However, there may be circumstances where groups are extremely ineffective decision-making vehicles not only because they may be unwieldy but because of the operation of the kinds of strong social norms described in the first part of this chapter. The way in which these norms operate and the sometimes appalling consequences have been very vividly described in a recent book on groupthink (Janis, 1972).

According to Janis, poor decision-making by highly intelligent individuals is often due to the fact that people in groups become more concerned with retaining the approval of their fellow members than with coming up with valuable and fresh solutions to the problems at hand.

Members tend to evoke informal objectives to preserve friendly intergroup relations and this becomes part of the hidden agenda. A general pattern may even be assigned to this in-group behavior. Members endeavor to be as amiable as possible, they show warm feelings and pride of solidarity, and seek concurrence on every important topic. This tendency is maintained only at the expense of ignoring realistic challenges, for at the first possible sign of dissent, considered a threat to the group's ring of confidence, disdain and derision are displayed and the "nonconformist" is cast aside as an unfaithful turncoat.

Hence, the multiple results of group pressure in decision-making can be listed as the deterioration of mental efficiency, reality testing, and moral judgment. These defects mean, among many other things, that group discussions: (1) do not include all possible options; (2) fail to reexamine initial decisions; (3) neglect courses originally considered to be unsatisfactory; (4) neglect to obtain information from outside experts; (5) choose through selective bias, thus eliminating all ideas which do not appeal to their prejudgments; and (6) fail to consider contingency plans, favoring to continue already decided on action even when the policy is working badly. Seemingly, a change in mid-road policy represents insecurity and failure for the image conscious group.

Eight main symptoms run through the case studies of historic fiascoes. These include an illusion of invulnerability, shared by most or all the members, which creates excessive optimism and encourages taking extreme risks. Collective efforts to rationalize in order to discount warnings which might lead the members to reconsider their assumptions before they recommit themselves to their past policy decisions. An unquestioned belief in the group's inherent morality, inclining the members to ignore the ethical or moral consequences of their decisions. Stereotyped views of rivals and enemies as too evil to warrant genuine attempts to negotiate, or as too weak and stupid to counter whatever risky attempts are made to defeat their purposes. Direct pressure on any member who expresses strong arguments against any of the group's stereotypes, illusions, or commitments, making clear that this type of dissent is contrary to what is expected of all loyal members. Self-censorship of deviations from the apparent group consensus reflecting each member's inclination to minimize to himself the importance of his doubts and counterarguments. A shared illusion of unanimity concerning judgments conforming to the majority view (partly resulting from self-censorship of deviations), augmented by the false assumption that silence means consent. The emergency of self-appointed mind-guards—members who protect the group from adverse information that might shatter their shared complacency about the effectiveness and morality of their decisions.

Not all cohesive groups suffer from groupthink, though all may display its symptoms from time to time. A group whose members have properly defined roles, with traditions and standard operating procedures that facilitate critical inquiry, is probably capable of making better decisions than any individual in the group who works on the problem alone. And yet the advantages of having decisions made by groups are often lost because of psychological pressures that arise when the members work closely together, share the same values, and above all face a crisis situation in which everyone is subjected to stresses that generate a strong need for affiliation. In these circumstances, as conformity pressures begin to dominate, groupthink and the attendant deterioration of decision-making set in.

In light of these glaring problems, Janis proposes several possible conclusions to be drawn from the groupthink theory which may help all decision-making bodies to come to more realistic grips with their responsibilities and needs. The leader of a policy-forming group should, for example, assign the role of critical evaluator to each member, encouraging the group to air all objectives and doubts. He should be impartial at the outset, instead of stating his preferences and expectations, so as not to cast a prejudicial tint over the proceedings. His briefings should be unbiased statements about the scope of the problem and available resources.

Furthermore, the organization should routinely create independent planning and evaluation groups to work on the same question, each group headed by a different leader. One or more qualified colleagues within the organization, who are not members of the policy-making group, should be invited to each meeting and encouraged to challenge the members' views. At every meeting, at least one member should play the role of devil's advocate to challenge the opinion of those who support the majority position.

Finally, after reaching a preliminary consensus, the group should hold a "second chance" afterthought and get together preferably in a relaxed atmosphere where the members could express their residual doubts or retackle the entire issue from a revitalized standpoint.

Only by meeting issues head-on with ever new appraisals and fresh solutions can the problem of fault-ridden decisions be curtailed if not eliminated from all organizational levels. Each problem is new and different and should not be handled with the usual barrage of old responses, for the security of concurrence is too often merely the shield of superficiality, giving constant invitation to recurring nonsolved tasks.

PRACTICAL APPROACHES TO EFFECTIVE GROUP MANAGEMENT BY ERIC NEILSEN

(a) What Are Some Basic Guidelines for Changing or Simply Coping With Groups in an Organization?

Informal group behavior is almost inevitable. It is possible to change who talks to whom, or a particular structure, or a particular group's resources, etc., but the phenomenon itself is not likely to go away. It is thus important to keep in mind all the things an informal group does for its members before attempting to change it. For instance, it may be blocking a formal work flow to a certain degree but simultaneously be training new personnel, free of charge, for the organization. Here the following questions are worth asking: if something is done to the group's ability to block the work flow, will it still perform the socializing function? If not, can the latter be done on a formal basis? Would the cost of doing so be greater than the rewards to be gained from removing the blockage in the work flow? In short, there is always likely to be a trade-off involved.

Get to know as much as possible about the group to be changed. Use a system perspective to assess the inputs, so as to develop hunches as to why its various features have developed as they have and what might cause each of them to change. Evaluate the plan of action on a move-by-move basis. What response will there be to each move taken alone?

Order moves so that the most revocable changes are made first and the least revocable last. Listing moves in this way, besides minimizing risks, may help to identify intermediate steps not thought of. Group members who are most willing initially to tell outsiders about their society often have low status within it. They may be deviants or scapegoats and, as a result, color their descriptions with feelings and interpretations which do not represent those of the leadership or regular members. Their data may be valuable but needs to be interpreted in this light.

Because so much of group life is not explicitly defined, the character of its leader, his personality, style, etc., is likely to be the best barometer for gauging the group's orientation and its attitude toward the larger organization. If the members of a group deny they have a leader, look at the person who supports this position most strongly. He is either the leader or the chief contender.

Coopting an informal leader is an excellent way of gaining more control over an informal group, but the process is more complex than one might think. If the cooptee is not given real influence, his group will soon abandon him. If, on the other hand, he is given influence, he is likely to use it at least in some degree to advance group interests.

If the work flow is such that informal groups are bound to control various aspects of it, adapt by periodically shifting personnel. An informal group, like any organization, needs time and practice to become expert at using its resources.

(b) What Does It Take To Run
an Effective Task Force?

Agreement in as clear detail as possible by all group members and by every individual who can interfere directly with the activity of any member on as many as possible of the following items: the group's objective(s); procedures to be used to attain the objective(s); a method for gauging progress toward the objective(s); the resources members may use and in particular any ways in which they may not use them; a division of labor, responsibility, and control within the group; an equation for rewarding individual and group performance; the sanctions to be used in enforcing the above; a method for deciding when and how, if at all, to socialize new members; and a method for deciding when and how to renegotiate, whenever the members themselves or all those who can control their behavior feel this is necessary.

Many groups operate without complete agreement on all of these issues, either among the members themselves and/or among people who can interfere with the group's operation. Sometimes they do so and are still considered useful and effective. It should be noted, however, that they do so at a risk. Sometimes the risk may be worth taking. For instance, discussion of negative sanctions is often avoided because it creates anxiety. Sometimes a procedure may be followed which has not been agreed to by a powerful outsider in hopes that either he will never discover it or that he will change his opinion in light of the effects following the procedure provides. Sometimes powerful parties are not contacted and negotiated with under the assumption that they would agree to all these items if approached and would be annoyed unduly by being asked to discuss these issues. Frequently, managers are ordered to use their own judgment in defining these issues, under the assumption that they will act in the best interests of the more powerful people who have given them these orders.

Clearly, there are limits to the time and resources a manager may use in laying the groundwork for a task force activity. He should make sure he considers the ramifications of all potential disagreements and focus his energies on those areas which are most critical to the success of the team as he sees it. The more he understands about the people he has to deal with, and the nature and traditions of his organization, the better he will be able to do this. The less he knows about his would-be colleagues and the more unusual the activity to be undertaken, the more effort he might have to put into this preliminary work.

(c) What Does an Effective Meeting Look Like?

An agenda is chosen which is consistent with what those present can do given the resources they are willing and able to commit. By resources are meant the following: the influence members have on the rest of the world (as a group or individually); their motivation to work together as a unit; the skills they have developed for working with each other; the time they have to meet; their ability to communicate with each other; and their energy levels and ability to concentrate.

The agenda is stated clearly and everyone understands it. Procedures for treating items on the agenda are well understood and accepted by all present. People actively attempt to proceed according to the above. A procedure is well understood and accepted for adjusting the agenda and the procedures for following it. Deviations from the agenda and/or procedures for following it are recognized as they occur by all present, with the following results: Either adjustments are made in the resources particular people have decided to commit in order to make up for missing resources which have caused the deviation, so that the agreed upon agenda and procedures can be reasserted, e.g., Joe is supposed to present the solution to problem X but can't, so Sam helps out. Or the absence of needed resources is recognized and the agenda and/or procedures are adjusted, e.g., it turns out that no one has the solution to problem X, so people agree to devote time and energy to solve it in the group. Such adjustments may involve an agreement to adjourn until more work has been done outside the group. They may even evolve the dissolution of the group if people agree it can't do what they want it to.

(d) What Are Some Characteristics
of a Good Agenda?

Content, of course depends on a multiplicity of factors, but there are some general guidelines for selecting and sequencing items.

Selecting items. Avoid items that could be done more effectively by subgroups or individuals. Use the group for group activities. Don't overload the agenda. Try to agree to just a little more than you think you can get done. One controversial issue is usually enough for one meeting. If treatment of several is critical, provide for rest periods between discussions of them.

Sequencing items. The first item on the agenda of any meeting, naturally, should be a discussion, however brief, of the agenda itself. Any clarification in or adjustment of the procedures for following the agenda should come next. If possible, make sure the items build on one another. Do what you are likely to agree on first, then broach the issues most likely to make heat. If a routine has been well established over a series of meetings, try breaking it occasionally to avoid boredom. A poorly sequenced item can occasionally be handled well by an effective group, and, if it cannot, at least justification for more careful sequencing will be reestablished.

(e) Problem Solving in Groups.

Problem solving is a response to the feeling that something is not as it should be. This feeling is a response to one or more signs in the actors' environment, and one must be careful to consider whether the signs describe the problem itself (what one wants to treat most) or are simply symptoms of that problem. Thus, formulating the problem is a task in itself. This involves the accumulation of indicators which arouse the feeling that one must act, their analysis, and the formulation of a problem which takes as many of these indicators as possible into account.

The members of a meeting need to decide how long they will spend defining a problem before they attempt to move on to the next step of proposing solutions. Groups generally work better when they consider a number of proposals for the solution to a problem before they evaluate any one of them. Evaluating one proposal at a time discourages comparison among the proposals themselves and encourages personal commitment to a proposal before the fruits of group discussion are reaped.

The next step of forecasting the consequences of various proposals and evaluating them, benefits most from hard data, and yet this kind of data is also the hardest to get. Consequently, a tradeoff must be made between putting time and effort into getting hard data and doing everything else. Frequently, the greater the variety of evaluation methods used, the better the evaluation.

The recycling of problem solving activity from initial formulation through idea production and idea testing to reformulation of the problem is a sound practice which should be seen as a major advantage of group discussion.

Action taking is both a problem in itself and an activity which can cause recylcing of the entire problem solving process. Thus, the solution proposed may be good but implementation poor and vice versa.

Those who take action should be made as aware as possible of the process through which the group went to formulate the problem. Otherwise, they might misunderstand their instructions, or not be committed sufficiently to them. Ideally, the implementer should also have taken part in formulating the problem and the plan for resolving it. The problem of creating a task force is a good example.

Note for "The Use of Groups as a Management Tool Boston Hospital for Women" (A), (B), and Video Tape

The (A) case in this series gives background information on the hospital and the members of the Administrative Cabinet (the group studied) and describes very briefly several meetings of the group which the casewriter observed. The (B) case consists of an interview with the Executive Director in which he discusses the group, one of its meetings, and his goals and leadership style both in the group and in general. The (A) case is designed to serve as preclass background reading. Case issues are not raised here but instead can be found in the video tape.

This tape, which is approximately 50 minutes long, opens with a ten-minute section in which BHW and the Cabinet members are introduced. The remaining 40 minutes are a film of the third of the three meetings the casewriter attended and described in the (A) case. The meeting lasted about one hour; sections were edited to allow the class to focus on the most interesting issues discussed and relationships revealed. This tape could stand alone as the basis for class discussion, but benefits from the use of the (A) case.

The (B) case is designed to be distributed at the end of the class discussion of the meeting; if the case were read beforehand, it would give away some points which should come out in class discussion. This case does reveal certain new information about the Executive Director. Perhaps more interesting, however, are two issues he mentions which may not have been completely clear from the tape alone: (1) he encourages the group to act out some of their emotions in the weekly meeting; (2) there is a great deal of uncertainty in the hospital.

That the group sometimes serves as a kind of encounter session is stated by Mr. Staton on page 1 of the (B) case when he says ". . . This meeting is a forum where we let off pressure. As far as I'm concerned that is one of the major functions of the meeting." In the casewriter's original interview with him, Mr. Staton made this point more strongly. The casewriter attempted to pave the way for Mr. Staton's comments by describing two other meetings she had attended. In the first and last paragraphs on page 6, (A) case, incidents are described in a rather round-about way. Actually these incidents were extremely emotional with the strong personal involvement particularly of Ms. Brooks and Mr. Cobb.

Perhaps it would not be going too far to interpret the extreme amount of laughing and joking around the planning of the party in the taped meeting to be an emotional catharsis comparable to that which usually took place in a more serious vein in the other meetings.

The amount of uncertainty in the hospital might be somewhat difficult to infer from the cases. However, this uncertainty can indeed be traced back to the experimentation Mr. Staton describes on page 4 of the (B) case. This in turn is clear from the cases:

There has been substantial turnover in top management as evidenced by the fact that no one in the Cabinet has been in his or her present position for more than two years

The people who constitute top management now have been shuffled around considerably and their responsibilities changed [(A) case, pp. 0-0]

No organization chart exists for the hospital [(A) case, p. 0]

No policy for salary increases existed in the hospital (video tape) and so on.

In general, the cases were designed to illustrate small group behavior and the relationship of the group leader's behavior to that of the group members. The instructor can consequently analyze the meeting from a number of points of view and ask questions such as: What are the goals of and for the group; how do personalities affect the working of the group; how do decisions get made in the group; what role does Mr. Staton play in the group; etc.

In addition to the organizational behavior issues, a set of issues centering on management control can also be discussed. Questions of performance appraisal, incentives, and rewards, etc., are discussed by the group in the video tape. The class discussion could cover both the group's handling of the problems and the problems themselves as they arise in other situations.

THE USE OF GROUPS
AS A MANAGEMENT TOOL
BOSTON HOSPITAL FOR WOMEN (A)

In November 1973, Mr. James Staton, Executive Director of the Boston Hospital for Women (BHW), was discussing his use of small group meetings to facilitate consensus decision making at BHW with a casewriter from the Harvard Business School. In particular, he was describing the Administrative Cabinet, a group consisting of five nonmedical BHW managers, himself and his administrative assistant. "My goal with this group is basically to deal with some of the operational concerns of the hospital," he explained, "but the meetings also serve as a forum where we let off pressure. I am interested in exploring the effectiveness of these meetings: how well are we meeting the goals I set for the group? Are these meetings serving a useful purpose, both from my point of view and that of the cabinet members? Are we succeeding in making the necessary decisions in these meetings, especially in the area of operational policy?"

Mr. Staton and the casewriter agreed that the latter would attend several of the meetings, video-taping one of them. Mr. Staton and the group would then be able to use the casewriter's report and the tape to find their own answers to Mr. Staton's questions and decide what changes, if any, should take place in the group's process or composition.

History of BHW

BHW, a not-for-profit hospital located in Boston, consisted of two divisions located one mile apart; the Parkway, a 90-bed facility specializing in gynecology, including surgery, and inpatient and outpatient fertility clinics; and the Lying-In, with beds for 121 obstetrical patients, 51 gynecological patients and 141 bassinets, including special care facilities for newborns.

Prior to the merger of the two facilities in 1966, the Parkway Division had been known as the Free Hospital for Women since its founding in 1875. The Lying-In Division was formerly the Boston Lying-In Hospital, and had been established in 1832. Both hospitals were well known for pioneering efforts in medical care for women, with each serving as the Harvard teaching hospital in their representative fields of gynecology and obstetrics.

In 1973, BHW was involved in plans for further merger or at least a joint venture with two other area hospitals, Robert Brigham, a small hospital specializing in care of arthritis and rheumatis- patients, and Peter Bent Brigham, an adult medical-surgical hospital. The three hospitals had begun planning for their future venture in 1960 with the creation of Affiliated Hospitals Center (AHC) which had originally also included Children's Hospital. A number of plans had been made and discarded over the past 13 years. In 1973 the AHC members believed that they would remain in their present physical facilities for the next five years, at least. The practical pressures of maintaining outdated and limited space forced the BHW administration to make decisions regarding capital expenditures, space allocation, etc., as if there were no plans to move at all. Potential administrative changes were also largely ignored in determining day-to-day organization of the hospital and administrative structure and responsibility, although the entire hospital had some awareness that some day things might change.

The Organizational Structure of BHW

Since becoming Executive Director of the hospital in 1972, Jim Staton had seen several major changes in medical staff and brought about a series of organizational changes, major redistributions of responsibilities, and a number of changes in administrative personnel and their titles.

In January 1973, Dr. Kenneth Ryan became Chief of Staff, filling a position vacated by retirement and which had been temporarily filled by an acting Chief of Staff since 1971. Dr. Ryan was characterized by the hospital administration as a dynamic, strong leader who had raised morale and standards in the hospital and created firm medical leadership when it was needed. Besides his position at BHW, Dr. Ryan was also Chairman of the Department of Obstetrics and Gynecology at the Harvard Medical School and maintained a small private group OB-GYN group practice with several associates.

The other major change in medical personnel had been in Ambulatory and Community Health Services. Traditionally an area which was considered a minor part of the hospital and thus operated on a shoestring budget, Ambulatory Services was reorganized in 1973 with a physician, Dr. George Ryan, as Director. He was responsible for the administration, medical and nursing staff in the area, and had succeeded in integrating the staff, and expanding the services offered.

The major organizational changes in the administration of BHW had included:
—the creation of the position of Associate Director, with responsibility for operations
—the appointment of a Director of Fiscal Affairs, with the Controller and Director of Data Processing reporting to him
—the Assistant Director for Professional Services reporting to the Executive Director began reporting to the Associate Director, then became Director of Professional Services reporting again to the Executive Director
—the addition of an Administrative Assistant to the Director's staff.

Although Mr. Staton had issued no formal organization chart during his administration, the diagram in Exhibit 1 generally indicates the lines of responsibility as they existed in December 1973.

The Administrative Cabinet Members

This group first began meeting in June 1973. When the casewriter began observing the group in late November 1973, it consisted of the following members:

Jim Staton—Executive Director

Carol Brooks—Director of Nursing

Richard Cobb—Associate Director

Bob Emerman—Director of Professional Services

John O'Shea—Director of Fiscal Affairs

Jeanne Tannenbaum—Administrative Assistant to the Director

In December, Stan Burchfield, Administrative Director of Ambulatory and Community Health Services, joined the group for the first time. All of the members of the group except Mr. Tannenbaum were nonmedical managers of BHW. Besides meeting as the Administrative Cabinet, everyone except Mr. Burchfield also met once a week with the joint medical-administrative staff members: the Chief of Staff and the directors of areas such as Ambulatory and Community Health Services and the Anesthesia Service, which were headed by physicians. This larger group, the Management Council, served as the in-house policy-setting group and dealt with a number of issues that were beyond the scope of the Administrative Cabinet.

Mr. Staton had become Director of the Hospital in 1972, after working closely with BHW through Affiliated Hospitals Center for two years as Assistant Vice President. Prior to joining the AHC staff, he had served in the Army for three years, received a Master's degree in Hospital Administration from Duke University, and worked at an assistant administrator level in the University of Kentucky Medical Center for three years.

Ms. Books, whose academic background included a Master's degree in Nursing Administration, was Director of Nursing in two other hospitals before coming to BHW. She had extensive experience in nursing administration in pediatric hospitals and OB-GYN services.

In the Administrative Cabinet meetings she considered herself as primarily a representative of the nursing staff. This identification with the nurses reflected her strong interests in nursing as a profession and as an opportunity for women to play an active part in hospital decision making. In her administration of the nursing area, she tended to emphasize professional growth through education, increased responsibility of nurses, and integration of nursing with physicians and administration. She felt that it was important to prove to her staff that they could be heard and their roles could change. She was not militant in her bids for change, but she was firm in supporting the nurses and presenting their concerns and needs to the medical and administrative staffs.

Mr. Burchfield, who first began attending the Administrative Cabinet meetings in December 1973, came to BHW late in 1972 as Administrative Director of Ambulatory and Community Health Services (ACHS). In his role at BHW, he was directly responsible to Dr. George Ryan, Director of ACHS, but made many administrative decisions himself. Mr. Burchfield had an MBA from the University of Nebraska and had worked in higher education management before coming to BHW.

For some time he had felt that he was not receiving the proper administrative information through the existing channels of the hospital. Once a week, he went to the Administrative Cabinet meetings where, he felt, he could both represent the ACHS (which he felt had been the stepchildren of BHW for too long) and find out firsthand what was happening in the administration of the hospital. The decision to have Mr. Burchfield attend the Thursday meetings had been made by Mr. Staton and Dr. George Ryan. The group itself was first informed of his participation when he came to the December 7 meeting.

Mr. Cobb came to BHW from the New York University Medical Center, where he held the post of Assistant Administrator for four and a half years. There he was one of four assistant administrators responsible for the operations of the 636-bed hospital. Like Mr. Staton, he had received a Master's degree in Hospital Administration from Duke University.

Mr. Cobb joined BHW as Associate Director in January 1973. At that time he was theoretically given extensive responsibility for day-to-day operations of the hospital, with these responsibilities to be exercised gradually as he came to know the hospital well and to establish a good working relationship with Mr. Staton. By December his position and responsibilities still were not completely clarified, a situation which was difficult for him and for the other members of the administration who were responsible to him.

Of all the members of the Administrative Cabinet, Mr. Emerman and Mr. O'Shea had been at BHW the longest. Mr. Emerman joined the staff in 1970 after graduating from the University of Chicago with an MBA specializing in hospital administration. In his original position, he had staff responsibilities as an Administrative Assistant and line responsibilities as Director of Medical Records. In 1971 he became Assistant Director for Professional Services. He continued to handle the same administrative areas and became more involved in providing administrative support to the medical staff. He became Director of Professional Services in October 1973, at which time he began attending the present Administrative Cabinet meetings.

Mr. Emerman was primarily a liaison between the medical and administrative staffs and specifically held administrative responsibility for anesthesiology, fetal monitoring, radiology, ultrasound, pediatrics, blood bank, pathology, social services and the clinical, cytology and hormone laboratories. He also worked closely with the medical staff committees in a support role.

Mr. O'Shea came to BHW from a Chicago hospital in 1969. His background included a Master's in Hospital Administration from Trinity University in San Antonio, Texas, and work toward an MBA, specializing in finance and computer management, which he was continuing in 1973. His original position at BHW was multifaceted: he was Director of Outpatient Programs, Administrative Assistant to the Chief of Staff, and in addition he worked on long-range planning. He was appointed Director of Fiscal Affairs in May 1973. In this role, he had responsibility for general accounting and cost accounting (areas which the Controller, Mr. Granger, supervised), data systems (in May 1973 under Mr. Menning), and a new area, patient services. The latter was an attempt to integrate the personnel and duties of pre-admissions, admissions and accounts receivable into one system so that an incoming patient would be assigned a single hospital liaison to handle all these procedures during the patient's association with the hospital. This area was still in the planning stages in December 1973.

The final person who attended the Thursday meeting, Ms. Tannenbaum, also had an office in the far wing of the hospital, but she often worked at a desk in the corner of a room near the Director's office. She joined the staff in May 1973 as Administrative Assistant to the Executive Director after receiving an MHA from Duke. Before graduate school she had worked in hospital personnel in Boston for five years. Her role as Administrative Assistant was not clearly defined, but rather had developed throughout the six months she had been there, and was intended to provide entry level administrative experience. She worked with the Board of Trustees, particularly researching special-interest topics for them; she acted as liaison with the Ladies Board Service League and as Chairman for the Housing Committee and the United Fund drive. In the Administrative Cabinet meetings, she played a limited role, primarily keeping a record of topics covered and occasionally providing specific information to Mr. Staton. In December, she had announced her intention of leaving BHW in the summer of 1974.

Administrative Cabinet Meetings

In addition to the meeting of the management cabinet on December 13, 1973, video-taped excerpts of which are available, the casewriter attended two other meetings of this group, on November 29 and December 6.

The meeting on November 29 began about ten minutes late, when everyone was called into Mr. Staton's office. Mr. Cobb arrived shortly thereafter. The seating was as below:

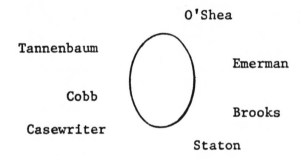

Although everyone except Mr. Cobb arrived with notes in hand, the meeting did not have a hard and fast agenda. Mr. Staton introduced the first topic and other participants introduced other topics later in the meeting. Issues covered included peer review policy, space utilization and allocation, employee raises, and policy for the special-care nursey. Discussion of several of these issues became rather heated. Ms. Brooks, in particular, raised some issues of responsibility and lines of command very strongly with Mr. Cobb. He then became involved in defending his actions. Finally, Mr. Staton intervened and told Ms. Brooks to put her requests in writing. Throughout the meeting, the other participants were less intensely involved, with Mr. O'Shea generally providing comic relief in tense moments, at times with the help of Mr. Emerman, and with Mr. Staton smoothing things over. Ms. Tannenbaum was largely uninvolved. Toward the end of the meeting there was a period of somewhat frivolous brainstorming in which everyone participated before being brought back to business at hand by Mr. Staton.

The next meeting, on December 6, was the first attended by Mr. Burchfield. Mr. Emerman was absent for most of the meeting. Everyone was a little late arriving and went into Mr. Staton's office at 11:05. Mr. Staton was on the phone; he finished his conversation, joined the group, and apologized for being detained. Mr. O'Shea arrived shortly thereafter. Seating was as below:

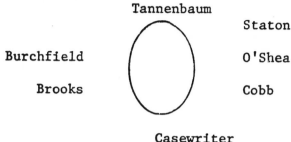

Tannenbaum

Staton

Burchfield

O'Shea

Brooks

Cobb

Casewriter

Issues discussed in this meeting included pay raises for employees, fees for second trimester abortions and policy on providing this service, medical staff committee structure, peer review policy, and energy and emergency planning.

This meeting was similar in several ways to the previous meeting. Mr. Burchfield, who was quiet at first, became more involved in the meeting as it progressed. Ms. Brooks again became involved in a heated discussion, this time with a certain amount of support from Mr. O'Shea and in opposition to Mr. Staton. Mr. Staton continued to attempt to bring the group to consensus. Ms. Tannenbaum was only slightly more involved than previously. Toward the end of the meeting, Mr. Cobb, who earlier had made several jokes, reintroduced a topic on which discussion had been completed, expressed his concern about its resolution, and then quickly brought up several other issues which he felt should be covered by the group. By this time the meeting was running overtime. Mr. Emerman had come in, Ms. Tannenbaum and Ms. Brooks had left, and generally issues were not resolved. Rather, the remaining people left while still discussing the issues. Messrs. Emerman, Cobb and Burchfield all went into the hospital snack bar for lunch, still talking.

The December 13 Meeting

The casewriter and Mr. Staton had agreed that this meeting should be video-taped because meetings for the next month would be affected by Christmas parties, vacations, and other external factors and participants were aware ahead of time of this. The casewriter arrived early and set up the equipment in a corner of the room.

The participants anticipated that they would be constrained by the presence of the camera, although the presence of the casewriter had seemingly had little effect on their behavior. This proved to be true to a certain extent. Principally, the meeting was less emotional than usual.

The main issue discussed in the meeting was employee raises. This topic had been discussed off and on for several months, often with input from the Director of Personnel. Several major factors had led to the decision to give employees a raise: other area hospitals had done so, the federal guidelines allowed raises within established limits, the hospital unions were canvassing BHW and drawing attention to the salary scale. The members of the group had now to decide to confirm or take action on several points, some of which involved questions of policy:

(1) Should increases be merit raises or cost-of-living increases and
(2) Should all employees, including administrative and medical personnel, receive raises?
(3) Should pay scales be changed, that is, should ceilings in each employee category be raised?
(4) Should the increases be four, five, or six per cent of current salary or another figure in that range?
(5) Should each department be allotted a lump sum for pay increases or should each department request a certain amount based on an assessment of specific employees?
(6) When should an increase become effective?
(7) When should an increase be announced, and how?

Everyone except Mr. Cobb and Ms. Brooks came into the office about 11:00. Mr. Cobb cane in a few minutes later and the meeting began. Ms. Brooks arrived around 11:15. The seating arrangement was as follows.

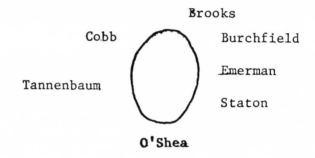

Exhibit 1

Boston Hospital for Women (A)

The Use of Groups as a Management Technique

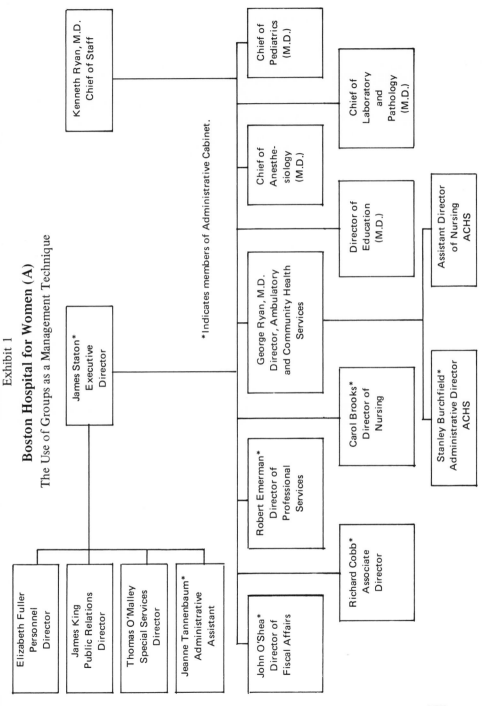

*Indicates members of Administrative Cabinet.

THE USE OF GROUPS
AS A MANAGEMENT TOOL:
BOSTON HOSPITAL FOR WOMEN (B)

Several weeks after the December 13 meeting of the Administrative Cabinet, the casewriter (CW) met with Mr. James Staton (JS), Executive Director of Boston Hospital for Women. The casewriter opened the interview by asking Mr. Staton for a brief description of the group, its functions, and its goals from his point of view.

JS: This group is a hybrid of a group by the same name that I inherited when I got here. Basically it is the administrative side of the organization without any of the joint medical appointees.

My goal with the group is basically to deal with some of the operational concerns and consequently I try to bring at least one structured topic to the meeting each time. Sometimes we have discussed the issues before or we have a draft to go over or we are revising a policy. This gives the beginning of the meeting a structure and then the participants can bring up anything they want. They know this—that there will be 30 or 40 minutes available so they can get into as much detail as each wants or as others are willing to react and respond to. It is an effective vehicle for letting off some pressure, for getting some initial reactions to people's thoughts about our direction.

I use things that come out of these meetings to go in one of two directions: back to my inner palace guard, the Personnel Director, Public Relations Director, and Special Services Director; or to the Management Council, which is the in-house policy setting group and which includes a number of medical appointees.

I don't need to go beyond this group for certain decisions, those that relate only to the functional areas represented by the group: interaction of in-patient nursing activities and support services are mostly covered there.

CW: What about the last meeting? What did you think of it?

JS: I could have predicted what was going to happen—the Hawthorne Effect: a microphone on the table and a camera in the background. People won't act exactly the way they do in the absence of that. To that extent I'm a little disappointed that we didn't have something that demonstrated that this meeting is a forum where we let off pressure. As far as I'm concerned that is one of the major functions of the meetings.

CW: Could you tell me a little about the problems you inherited, how you've handled them, what you see happening in the future?

JS: I think that the biggest operational problem that I inherited was replacing the Director of Nursing who resigned at the same time the hospital Director resigned. I was interested in finding a replacement who both expressed and had demonstrated a philosophy of collaboration with other disciplines in planning and directing patient care. After extensive interviewing, we hired Carol Brooks. Several members of the nursing administrative staff, who had participated in the interviewing, had mixed feelings about the selection. I was convinced that Carol Brooks' attitudes and abilities in relating to the hospital staff would overcome these problems. The recruiting of a new Director of Nursing related to another operational problem: There were breakdowns in communication and team spirit between medical staff and nursing staff and between some hospital departments and nursing staff. So, I made it clear when we recruited Ms. Brooks that she had a dual responsibility to both Dr. Ryan, the Chief of Staff, and myself, and I have done everything I can to foster the commitment of Dr. Ryan to giving her direction in areas that relate to patient care.

Because BHW is an institution with over 16,000 admissions per year and over 1000 employees, the traditional lines of authority and organization had to be seriously reconsidered. I think we are moving in the right direction with the creation of smaller operating units within the hospital. One of these units with which I'm very pleased is Ambulatory Service. We have a Director of Ambulatory and Community Health Services, who has responsibility for directing all aspects of the Ambulatory Care Program. The Director of Nursing provides guidance and consultative support, but the line responsibility of the Assistant Director of Nursing in Ambulatory Services is to the Director of Ambulatory Services.

This was an example of the problem of clear identification of organizational responsibility in this institution. I am trying to move the organization toward identifying functional components and then getting people who can effectively run particular functions, control the necessary resources to make decisions, and make their functional component responsive to the mission and objectives of the hospital. We're moving in that direction with Ambulatory Services. I want the whole educational component developed along those lines. We will move in that direction with pediatrics and ultimately with labor, delivery and operating room suites, key areas for patient care and support activities.

On the support side of the organization, I really inherited a pheonomenal fiscal mess. When I became the Director in June 1972, a conversion from a second generation to a third generation computer which was supposed to take a month had been going on for six months. Part of the problem was a very ineffective relationship between the Director of Data Processing and the Controller, both of whom reported to the Director of the hospital. After first attempting to coordinate that relationship myself and then putting them both on a committee which was chaired by someone else, I finally decided to put a third person in charge of fiscal affairs and have them both report to him. Eventually, I had to move the individual who had been responsible for data processing out of that role and bring someone else in.

Originally there were five assistant directors, four of whom had responsibilities for supporting areas: Mr. Emerman, Mr. O'Malley, Mrs. Nye, and Mr. McGoon. I felt that I needed a number two person responsible for all of those operational areas. None of those people were appropriate to assume that position. When I let my feelings on that become known Mr. McGoon decided to take another position. I brought in Mr. Cobb and basically I've consolidated the functional day-to-day operations involving plant services, housekeeping, dietary, laundry and personnel under him.

In addition to these problems there was activity associated with Affiliated Hospitals during this time. My objective was to spend as much time as I needed in both camps getting the planning for the Affiliated up to a certain point where it did not need much executive action while learning a fair amount about the internal operations so that I would feel comfortable delegating major parts of both activities, staying in touch with both, and coordinating both. But the Affiliated plans had not come to fruition by the spring of '73 as I had anticipated nor even by the fall of '73 so I had to spend a lot more time on details of Affiliated than I would have like to spend. Consequently I have had less time to get internal concerns to a level where I felt I could delegate more responsibility.

So basically the timing has been thrown off, particularly in the relationship between Mr. Cobb and myself. We have just not been able to spend the necessary amount of time getting to know each other's style, developing smooth working relationships so that I would feel comfortable leaving him alone with most of the internal operations and leaving me to handle more external affairs. That's the situation now. Furthermore, I have realized that the original concept of assigning to him a major responsibility for day-to-day operations was somewhat unrealistic. There's more to that job than either of us anticipated. Finally there is some resistance on the part of a large number of both the medical and administrative staff to accept his decisions as the final word on a subject.

CW: Would you talk a little bit about yourself, your style, its costs and benefits, and your personal goals as manifested in this style?

JS: There are many catch phrases to describe styles. I would say that I practice more of a consensus style. I believe in attempting to surround myself with capable people and in creating an environment where they solve as many problems as absolutely possible without me having to formulate the solution. The liability of that is that it produces an awful lot of wheel spinning. People have to feel comfortable working with each other, accept that they have the responsibility to put their heads together, and marry up the resources they individually control in order to get a satisfactory solution whenever possible. Lots of people feel more comfortable in presenting their cases to an authoritarian individual who then makes a decision.

I still question the extent to which the consensus style can be successful, particularly as the group grows and as people periodically misinterpret the strength of their positions and the importance of the resources they control. Sometimes you have to shut off debate and tell the people that it's just going to be this way.

Because I am relatively new in this position and a lot of my staff is also new, we have had to go through a period of arm wrestling, getting to know one another's strengths and weaknesses, before I felt comfortable in deciding to exercise or in exercising more authoritarian leadership. We are now in a period when the individual members of the administration team find out what is important to me in making decisions, what I want them to consider when they make decisions, and what general factors I want brought to me when they want me to make a decision. That's a slow learning process, because what is important to one person doesn't always seem important to another. So we just have to spend some time going back and forth and reviewing these team formations that reflect the pressure points.

CW: So basically you need to feel that the people who work with you share your administrative goals. Then you can give them more responsibility because you know that decisions will be made within a consistent framework.

JS: Yes.

CW: It hasn't all been easy so far.

JS: There have been disappointments and frustrations and I have learned a lot from the process. I think the people who are here have learned a lot too. If I ever get an opportunity to do this again, there are some things I would do differently. But there are some other things that I think have been done quite well. There are areas where we are still making progress. The building of strong working relationships among the medical, nursing and administrative people is something of which I am quite proud.

Dr. Kenneth Ryan, Chief of Staff, is committed to the same kind of integration. He understands fully that there must be major medical input into the administrative processes of considering issues, formulating solutions and implementing and evaluating performance. The Trustees recognized that there was a need for a major commitment to give the medical staff administrative and supervisory responsibility. There are people now who are learning what it means to have administrative responsibility for the abortion service group, ambulatory care, and Associate Chief of Staff positions. These people are engaging in an administrative process rather than saying, ''Oh, that's a financial concern, an administration problem.'' They are becoming very acutely aware of the financial condition of the institution as a whole and of the revenue potential of various services.

CW: There seems to be some uncertainty among the members of the Administrative Cabinet about exactly what constitutes your ''Master Plan.''

JS: To a certain extent I am still experimenting. I don't think I have assembled all of the right people yet. I don't think that relationships are as clear as they ought to be. I am still testing, watching, and feeding the line out gradually, pulling it back in pretty often. We have some problems. I admit it and acknowledge it and I think people have been very patient in watching the process.

To a large extent people are uncertain, and I am sure that to some extent my uncertainty shows. My timing has been thrown off by developments at the Affiliated. There is a great deal of uncertainty about what the heck is happening with that project. Starkweather has done some interesting work on hospital mergers. He points out that without the help of very far-sighted community people, basically trustees, these things never come off. I see that definitely. But Dr. Ryan and I and some of the other people who have to deal with it on a day-to-day basis get so damned frustrated that we say: ''Look, we have 6,000 babies born here every year and 9,000 surgical procedures. It is ridiculous to keep wasting our time planning the AHC. If it hasn't happened by now we ought to just put it on ice, and try it another time.'' Any time we start to talk like that the Trustees say: ''Well, you know, you fellows are new at it. We've been at it for ten years. Just be patient. It's a good idea, and the longterm viability of the institution really depends on it.'' So we keep trying.

CHAPTER 5

STABILITY, CHANGE, AND ADAPTATION IN ORGANIZATIONS

ADAPTATION AND CHANGE

At the outset it is necessary to distinguish between the important processes of adaptation and change. The distinction between these is somewhat fuzzy; essentially change is an alteration in the state or level of some subsystem variable. For example, at one time it may be very easy to get skilled labor as a human input to the organization, and because of economic changes, at another time very difficult. This represents a change in the level of the human input to the system. Adaptation is the adjustment which the organization subsequently makes in order to accommodate the change in the level of such a variable. Thus, when the availability of skilled labor drops, the organization has to do something about it. If it does this "something" effectively, this is called adaptation. If it fails to do this effectively, this is failure to adapt. Adaptiveness is the ability of a system to modify itself or its environment when either has changed to the system's disadvantage, so as to regain at least some of its lost efficiency (Ackoff and Emery, 1972).

There is a tendency to think of change in organization as being only such dramatic alterations as the introduction of automation or formal reorganization. But there are several kinds of change which should at least be touched on that appear all the time in less evident ways. Most organizations are growing in size, just like the human organism, and this continual growth necessitates continual readjustments. For example, as an organization expands in size, it is apt to develop more subsystems which somehow must be linked. A further "natural" and continuing change is the movement of people through an organization. People leave and are replaced by others. As new people join, they and the organization have to undergo adaptive processes so that the newcomers can become effective replacements for their predecessors. This process of socialization is part of the social control mechanisms described earlier. As the new member is socialized he learns the norms and expectations of the subsystem and the subsystem learns what it can expect from the individual. For a while during this period deviant behavior on the part of the newcomer is tolerated as part of the learning process. This period may be as long as six months, but shortly thereafter organization members feel the newcomer has had time enough to learn and meet their norms and expectation (Weiss, 1956).

It is also useful to make a distinction between change which originates outside the subsystem to which the subsystem must then adapt, and change which originates within the subsystem. As suggested above, most subsystems have a capacity to initiate change in themselves as well as in others.

Change may occur in any aspect of the system. For the organization as a whole, there may be changes in inputs so that the availability of raw materials, of financial support, or of appropriate personnel may vary; there may be changes in outputs so that the organization's position in the market environment changes; there may be changes in processes so that a new technology is developed (as, for example, the introduction of automation); last, there may be a change in the political environment, so, for example, the Federal Government may decide to regulate more closely. The changes of most concern to subsystem members are those which have to do with the nature of the task, the means by which the task is performed, or the way in which people are formally organized. A task may be changed, technology may change, or there may be the reorganization of a department and and two groups which have hitherto worked separately may now be required to work together. In practice, because of the interdependence of subsystem variables, such changes rarely occur singly.

Before the dynamics of change and resistance to it are described, it is necessary first to relate change processes to the concept of feedback. By feedback is meant information received within the system or subsystem comparing actual events with expectations. Essentially feedback describes the comparison of actual output with expected output, and the linking of information back to modify the input-output process. In the strict cybernetic sense, negative feedback reduces discrepancies between actual and expected outputs, or variations from a norm, while positive feedback increases such discrepancies or variations. In popular usage, positive feedback describes information which supports a given direction or output, while negative feedback is critical of it. If the comparison is unfavorable in relation to the desired state of affairs, it is called negative feedback; if it is favorable it is defined as positive.

The channels through which this information moves are feedback loops. One obvious example of feedback is the attempt by subsystem members to influence deviants to conform to group expectations. The feedback loop is between the subsystem and the deviant, with information moving in both directions. The deviant is receiving information about the consequences of his behavior; the rest of the system is learning whether or not their sanction is having an effect. Most changes in organization or in subsystems occur because of information going through such feedback loops. Thus, if the environment changes, producing a market which is more competitive and therefore requiring a change in outputs, feedback loops conduct this intelligence through the marketing department to the production department. Here a series of decisions might be made depending on the situation: technology might require altering, people might require reorganizing, or costs may have to be reduced. As these internal adaptive changes are made the effects on output will be measured by the organization's capacity to compete in the market. Some feedback loops prompt alterations in the internal organization to improve its task performance and ability to compete in the external environment while other feedback loops may stimulate organizational changes which are not related to such outputs. For example, an organization may be performing effectively, but its members may still feel that feedback from the internal environment demands change. Employees may be dissatisfied or alienated and so managers decide that an internal reorganization would increase their feelings of satisfaction with employment. This whole area of large-scale internally determined change processes to improve the nature of the organizational climate is frequently termed organizational development.

STABILITY AND RESISTANCE TO CHANGE

The negative feedback loops which permeate an organization, and are described above, are important sources of damping down unwanted fluctuation and thus of stability. But they may be so stabilizing that the system becomes difficult to change. Ironically, what is now a source of resistance to change and a problem may once have been the very set of activities which constituted the organization's success. A typical succession of events might be as follows. A new leader enters an organization and through dint of hard work, persuasion, and an understanding of motivation and the systems that support it begins to point an organization in a new direction. He selects people whom he regards as fitting the kind of organization that he wishes to create and measures people on the kinds of activities that he values. He rewards those that are successful. If he is not only successful in creating a system but it is also successful in its environment, the measurement and reward systems become not only an instrument of his will, but also a means of reinforcing the organization's behavior as it is successful. Feedback to the individual not only tells him that he is doing well in terms of the performance of his unit but that he pleases those who matter.

An example is one of the more successful, prepaid health plans, which for some years provided very high quality patient care through superb physicians who were encouraged by the reward system of the organization to practice excellent medicine and to attract new subscribers to the plan. As long as prepaid group practices were relatively novel, such a strategy was slowly but surely highly successful in attracting new subscribers away from private practitioners and in providing them with excellent sick care while generating the kinds of funds flow that would enable the organization to grow. However after a number of successful years, the pressure on cost control from the third party reimbursers and rising costs to the plan began to cut into the dollar margin and to make the care of sick patients a barely break-even proposition. This meant that the plan had to begin to cut back on the kind of care it provided, and to appeal to a larger and larger segment of the population that would be well and not sick, for these people provided it with premiums and therefore were a source of funds, but did not incur significant costs. However, this required that the plan would not only attract but retain new subscribers who would be well, and it had to do this in the face of competition from other plans. Previously the plan had been geared to attracting new subscribers, for the incentives reinforced this, but somewhere on the order of 50% left the plan after a year (and there was no penalty for this loss). Moreover, a high proportion of those who remained were those who had some kind of ailment that required treating. To keep more of the "well" half meant offering "well" services such as eye glasses, periodic medical examinations, etc., at times that the well population could manage, such as evenings and weekends. But physicians value caring for the sick and do not like working unusual hours. Thus the system, once carefully designed and attuned to a successful strategy, was now reinforcing a set of behaviors that could lead to financial disaster.

Control and information systems are there both to check and monitor but also to damp out behavior. Current mechanisms in an organization are probably capable of coping with small environmental shifts, but if the environmental shift is qualitatively different or rapid, some new mechanisms of adaptation may be required. How does one detect the difference between a significant and trivial environmental shift? This obviously involves periodic scanning and checking back against the organization. Feed forward, i.e., the scanning of the immediate and distant future, has therefore to be damped by feedback so that the capacity of the organization to cope with future situations is constantly evaluated. It becomes extremely important therefore to link planning to the organization and not have it existing simply to scan forward without some feedback link (see below). Part of the feedback link would be a continuing assessment of the state of the organization. The strategies for changing a system would thus have to start with an understanding of the dynamics by which the old was successful and which now were creating problems.

A not dissimilar situation was encountered by the author when he attempted to develop a family-oriented cancer care unit on a highly successful oncology ward. In addition to the high quality medical care that had always characterized this unit, several new services were offered that enabled the patient and his family to identify and cope more successfully with the problems encountered in terminal cancer. This involved the author working with the nurses on the ward to train them in working closely with the patient and family. While the unit itself began to be effective, and the nurses showed extraordinary ability to change their behavior in relation to the cancer patient, the repercussions on the rest of the system were ignored and the importance of the enduring stability of the nursing hierarchy was underestimated. The hospital suffered a chronic shortage of nurses, exacerbated by the frequent occurrence of nurses reporting off sick especially in low morale wards. As morale rose on the oncology ward, a higher and higher proportion of its nurses regularly attended and thus were available for floating to other wards, so success was penalized. Further, as the nurses more and more engaged in "talking-behavior" with patients, the supervisors began to feel more and more out of touch and resorted to controlling those activities that they understood, namely, the administrative rituals of completing forms. This became both a problem for the supervisors who felt inadequate and for the nurses who needed additional supervisory support as their emotional loads increased.

The inordinate stability of some systems does not only stem from the past successes of behavior rewarded by incentive systems, but may come from the intrinsic attachment to certain values embedded in the way that the organization operates. In Chapter 2 the high value for autonomy and for the privacy of the doctor-patient relationship of physicians was noted. The kind of measurement (and public scrutiny) of doctor-patient relationship as proposed in the Foundation for Health Care Evaluation is not without controversy. Many physicians feel that this is an intrusion into an area where they ought to have complete authority. This value set is a reason for the continuing power of many physicians in health institutions, and the frustrating situation whereby this continuing power goes along with a lack of interest in the management of anything but clinical affairs. This is slowly changing as more and more physicians are beginning to appreciate the desirability and necessity of managing health care organizations better and to realize that if they do not learn how to do so and how to participate in the process, they will lose control completely. But meanwhile change in any aspect of the stable system incorporating their values may well be resisted by physicians who recognize quite accurately that it threatens the loss of important controls for them. At one medical clinic, the appointment system was computerized. This might be regarded as an opportunity for the physicians to improve their use of time, to minimize mistakes, and to be a boon to all. However, it was resisted and indeed bitterly resented by the physicians, who valued their personal interactions with their secretaries. They also recognized that instead of their appointments being made through people who could be influenced by them, an impersonal machine would now manage their time and would reduce their amount of control over it.

This raises an important issue in the consideration of the implementation of any new kind of health technology. However efficient and effective it might be, if it disturbs valued relationships in the system, it will be resisted for that reason alone. Moreover, physicians dislike documentation, and any system involving significant addition to documentation may well fail on that alone.

Logic and rationality may under certain circumstances be powerful tools, but rarely in organizational change situations. Logan *et. al.* (1972) produced a superb analysis of the Liverpool Hospital Region in England, in which they found that lengths of stay were, for most hospitals and many conditions, significantly longer than in any other group of hospitals in England. His team demonstrated conclusively that there were reasons associated with this phenomenon which had much more to do with habits of medical practice than with the kind of patient population being in any significant respect different. The cost of this difference to the national health service was considerable. In spite of their reporting their findings to all appropriate bodies, the most that they could point out some two or three years later was that one committee or another had finally reviewed their work and made some comment on it, while there had been negligible change.

So organizations may over a period of time, through the efforts of their leaders, identify the key behaviors necessary for a successful operation and incorporate these. They reinforce their success and provide a means whereby new members of the organization can rapidly learn similarly successful behavior through organizational socialization. At some point this adaptive behavior becomes maladaptive and problems result from the disjunction between the organization and its environment. Thus it is not many years since many health care organizations in the United States were shaken by the realization that their communities no longer felt that they were providing them with humane and effective health care. This maladaptiveness comes about because any system tends to have boundaries around it and may well, if successful for long enough, become relatively closed and impermeable to new influence. Moreover, since such new influences as they emerge in a changing environment may be seen and experienced as threatening, the separation between the organization and its environment is reinforced. At some point eventually the effectiveness of the organization is threatened sufficiently that it has to make some kind of change, but this may be too late.

To summarize, when a change is made in any aspect of an organization, whether in technology, task, or the arrangement of people, such changes frequently are met by the people they affect with concern, if not active resistance. People have become very accustomed to doing certain things in certain ways and even if new ways are suggested which are in fact improvements, they will still be resisted. There are many reasons for this. A few examples are

(1) Any change involves the introduction of some uncertainty. What is affected and how is never entirely clear until it happens. Therefore, some individuals tend to prefer what is familiar.

(2) Change usually involves the introduction of new things, and dropping of old things. As a result a psychological sense of loss may be experienced, and this is uncomfortable.

(3) Very often people's sense of competence at work is closely related to their having mastered a particular way of doing a task. When asked to change this, they may feel a lessened sense of competence.

(4) Changes often also entail an alteration in valued interpersonal relationships.

People may no longer have the same intensity of contacts with former associates or may be required to interact more intensively with strangers.

(5) Finally, people may react to the way the change is introduced. If the change is imposed on them unilaterally, they may resist the change to counteract their feelings of powerlessness.

It should be stressed that these factors are not mutually exclusive, nor is this list exhaustive. Furthermore, in any given situation one particular reason for resisting change may be more important than others. This means that an important task for a manager engaged in making changes is to determine why his subordinates and associates are resisting a change. It is inevitable that people involved in a change will experience feelings such as those described above, but an effective manager can minimize the effects of these feelings.

The forms this resistance takes are many. Sometimes there is an explicit rejection of the new proposal. Sometimes indirect manifestations of behavior will indicate resistance such as an increase in people reporting sick or mistakes being made. After a period of initial resistance, there is usually a period of waiting and seeing. At this time people are convinced that the change is going to be made but are not prepared to support it in case the effort fails. They will do nothing to undermine it but also they will do nothing to help it. Finally, if the change persists, people will incorporate it as part of their everyday life and accept it.

MANAGING CHANGE ORGANIZATIONALLY

There are several important implications about change which stem from this systems view. First the manager must recognize the stage of the relationship of his organization to the environment, and what is needed at each stage. Greiner (1972) has suggested that not only do organizations adapt to shifts in the environment, but they generally seem to go through a succession of identifiable stages as they pass through their own life cycle. The stages that he has identified start with that of creativity, in which the entrepreneur initiates, with excitement and imagination, a new organization which tends to function highly informally. As the organization grows and the number of people as well as tasks becomes ever larger and more complex, there tends to be a leadership crisis in which the organization has to case the need to develop organizational systems. There is some loss of the kind of informal interpersonal relationships which were previoulsy possible. Further growth and the passage of time result in a third stage in which there is now greater delegation of authority from the previously centralized management structure to decentralized units. With yet further growth and expansion, these begin to take on some life of their own and there is a crisis of coordination in which the decentralized units must be linked more effectively and finally must work together in a collaborative stage.

The importance of these last two stages cannot be underestimated. They not only form the last two stages of the life cycle of organizations identified thus far, but become extraordinarily important processes given the kinds of turbulent environments in which most organizations, including health organizations, now function. Thus with limitations on the availability of health resources, including both people and money, the provision of the best kind of health care to most people will necessitate some kind of allocation of resources between health organizations as well as within them. Whether this, as in America, occurs through the third party reimbursement system and informal means, or as in several countries in Europe, through a centralized national health service, the issue is basically the same: the need to coordinate and collaborate so that limited resources are used effectively.

Second, the manager must recognize the complex interrelationships of many variables in producing behavior. Managers who rely on an overly simplistic view of human behavior instead of the systems view presented here run great risks of selecting an inappropriate course of action. Understanding the functioning of a system cannot only guide the manager in working out his own behavior, given the constraints of the social forces and inputs facing him, but can be curcial in determining which of the various inputs to alter. Such understanding may be the difference between the successful introduction of action in general and of change in particular. The stability referred to earlier may mean that the only chance for real change that will not be damped out by the existing system is to replace key managers or to start a totally new side by side organization.

A third major point for the manager to recognize is that an important element of the behavior which occurs in subsystems is the feelings of the members, produced by the interaction of subsystems inputs and social mechanisms. It is these feelings which lead to the manifest behavior called resistance to change. In thinking about action taking and change, managers must recognize and deal in some way with these feelings because they are as real as the electronic hardware in an operating theater.

The manager must also recognize that in groups, members work together to control their environment and to satisfy their own needs. A unilateral introduction of change can upset the members of the subsystem and can create negative feelings about a management action. It is therefore important to educate group members to the rátionale and details of change, and wherever feasible to foster their active participation in the planning and implementation of change. While a manager has the responsibility to make certain decisions, it is clear that the quality of these decisions and their implementation will be greatly enhanced if the manager is open to feedback from others in his subsystem. In fact, as a manager makes a diagnosis of the problems facing him, he is engaged in the process of collecting feedback about the current state of his subsystem. The more open he is to this feedback, the more adequate will be his diagnosis.

Greiner (1967) has summarized approaches to the introduction of change as unilateral, delegated, or through a shared strategy. The unilateral approach includes by decree, by replacement, or by structure. The delegated approach involves case discussion or the T-group, and the shared strategy utilizes group decision making and problem solving. The forces for change, both external and internal, must be identified and there should be a recognition of need, if the change is to be successful. Further there needs to be a diagnosis of the symptoms, the problem, what should be done, and what the outcome will be as well as an exploration of alternative methods and strategies and limiting conditions. After this a selection of the method and its implementation and then evaluation. Since change may be associated with an individual manager, and die out when he moves, attention must be paid to the problem of institutionalizing it. Acceptance (and commitment) can be enhanced through involvement, and as an example, the participative approach was used by a group of hospitals which, intending to merge, set up a series of management workshops for their functional managers. Groups of managers with similar functions met regularly with an outside consultant to recommend to the hospital directors approaches to the merger task as affecting their areas, and the optimal future organization of their function. The process diminished considerably their potential resistance to merge, enhanced the accomplishment of the merger task, and provided the directors with invaluable information.

Lastly, it is extremely important to be alert to the unanticipated and unintended consequences of an organizational change. It may be that the new process will throw out a new elite or power-holding group and that the change be resisted by those who will lose their previously held power.

There is an important distinction worth making between organizational change and organizational development. Frequently the first resort of an organization in trouble is to send its managers to some kind of management training program. Failing that, they will consider making organizational changes, usually in response to specific problems, and often trivial in nature. (Of course, organizational changes as described above may also be made regardless of any pressing need thus the institution of more effective technology.) Organizational development describes the systematic review of the way that the organization functions and the making of changes that would enhance the organization's capability to operate or attractiveness to its members. It is not therefore necessarily dictated by the presence by any kind of problems although the review may well reveal some. It is usually an activity of a personnel department.

MANAGING CHANGE AT
THE INDIVIDUAL LEVEL

While organizational change techniques and strategies are explicit about how to deal with resistance from a variety of sources, few studies are concerned with the factors governing the individual's favorable or adverse response. Recognition of the individual's feelings and values in relation to those of the group allows the manager to develop change tactics which take into account the likely reactions of individuals.

During periods of organizational transition, two factors seem to be closely linked to the individual's reaction to major organizational changes.

The first factor affecting reaction to change is the set of beliefs and values of the individual as stated in Chapter 2. Individuals react differently when organizational changes are in agreement or disagreement with their beliefs or professional ideology. It can be expected that organizational changes consistent with an individual's beliefs and values will be better received by the individual, other factors being equal.

The second factor identified as relevant for predicting an individual's reaction to change is his predisposition either to function independently and autonomously from groups of other workers of the organization, or to seek membership and support in such groups. Autonomy, as used here, may be defined as the degree to which individuals prefer to operate separately within an organizational structure and to maintain control over their own job activities. The polar opposite of a high need for autonomy is considered to be a need for inclusion and support within the organizational framework. Persons with a strong need for autonomy will react negatively to situations of organizational change which result in increased integration of their roles into groups and subsystems to the organization.

Individuals require different degrees of autonomy in their work situation. Some persons function most satisfactorily and effectively as organizational members when they are tightly enmeshed in the influential organizational group, with close affiliates to whom they can turn for support and guidance. Others, in order to satisfy individual needs for freedom from constraint, gravitate toward positions of isolation from the care groups of the organizational framework. The predisposition to function independently or autonomously from intraorganizational peer groups will make the individual less subject to the influence of such groups.

Formal and informal groups within an organization may be said to develop or adopt certain orientations, or sets of beliefs concerning the primary tasks of that organization. As a set of beliefs becomes widely accepted in attitudes and behavior of members.

An idea or belief system can have power as an important organizing force affecting definitions of correct role performance among organizational members. The dominant group is the major collectivity in an organization which shares a common idea system and acts to influence other organizational members in the direction of this model orientation. Such dominant groups can represent important and influential groupings of organizational members during a time of change (e.g., physicians). When faced with the ambiguities of major organizational changes, the dominant group will tend to influence individual reactions to change in directions consistent with its own orientation.

Different intraorganizational groups may serve as sources of support and influence for individuals in the same organizational setting. An individual's work group may be a greater source of support and guidance than the group of individuals within the organization who share the same profession. As noted earlier, individuals predisposed to function independently or autonomously from intraorganizational peer groups will be less subject to influence of those groups. Such autonomous individuals, other factors being equal, can be expected to attempt to avoid influences from a dominant group.

An individual has several alternatives with regard to his position vis-à-vis the members of an influential core organizational group. He may be (1) a member of a dominant group, fully accepted by others and fully accepting of the orientation and influence of the other group members; (2) a peripheral member of the group, deviating in ideology and/or somewhat immune to the social pressures of the group; (3) an isolate, completely out of touch with the pressures of the group; or even (4) an isolate with an orientation incongruent with or antagonistic to the orientation of the dominant group. Isolation may be the result of either deviant orientation or an individual preference to function separately. When the orientation of the dominant group changes to be consistent with the individual's orientation, certain constraints and pressures on the individual are removed. If his isolation results from differences in orientation rather than from a personal need for autonomy, then there will be increased satisfaction for the individual after the change. He will stay within the organization and will once again become a member of the dominant group. Until such time as that group makes major moves in its orientation toward his point of view, he will remain an isolate.

As long as a deviant ideology prohibits such a person from obtaining full membership, support, and sanction by the dominant group of peers, the individual will feel discomfort in a peripheral or isolated position. The alternatives open to this individual depend on: (a) the intensity and magnitude of the differences between his orientation and the central group's orientation, and (b) his personal need for membership and support by the dominant group. These options include: (1) changing his orientation to that of the dominant group; (2) attempting to change the ideology of the group; and (3) remaining a peripheral member complacent in his divergent orientation. He also has options to either "leave the field," by quitting the organization and going to one where his orientation is consonant with the model orientation of the dominant group, or to adopt an isolate position. The more deviant his orientation, the more likely it is that he will stay within the system and change his attitudes.

The directions in which individuals will move in the face of change consistent with the orientation of the dominant group may be thus clarified by use of a general typology. This typology considers the individual dimensions of ideological orientation and need for autonomy and the influence of the dominant group in terms of that group's normative standards toward changes. The specific alternatives open to an individual vary depending on his organizational position and his formal or informal power in the situation.

Situations in which change becomes a threat can cause the organization to lose individuals who are important to its successful operation. Although changes in personnel may often be for the best, the administrator or other individual interested in facilitating the change process would want to avoid unnecessary losses of valuable personnel.

The key to a successful transition is to avoid forcing into isolation those individuals to whom the change is disturbing and for whom isolation is uncomfortable. For nonautonomous individuals whose basic orientations are distrubed, it is important to keep them in contact with the central group. Rejection by the dominant group will lead to further dissatisfaction and feeling of isolation, thus leaving open only the alternatives of leaving the organization or ceasing to function as a viable member of it. By developing a role for the individual in which he can communicate with the dominant group, he need not isolate himself and his service and he can thus keep the service a productive part of the organization.

By placing the individual who deviates conservatively from the dominant group's orientation into a position where communication channels from the deviate to the dominant group may be kept open, the deviate will be to some extent, subject to the influence but not coercion of the central group. This adaptation will obviate the necessity for the individual to withdraw from the organization.

On the other hand, the individual who has an isolated position due to a personal need for autonomy and whose orientation is very progressive with regard to the movement of the core group may serve as a groundbreaker for the progress of the central group. Once this groundbreaking function had been served and the central group begins to move into the groundbreaker's territory, this individual cannot be expected to meekly come into the fold. He must be given the opportunity to continue to move ahead of, and separate from, the central group. If such alternatives are not opened for these individuals, the group's progress will be threatened and the individual will be faced with only the alternative of leaving the organization.

To prevent complete isolation and loss of productive individuals who need autonomy but possess conservative orientations, it is necessary to legitimize roles in which these individuals may autonomously serve the traditional functions which their orientation dictates while remaining in contact, even if peripherally, with the central group. If these roles are sufficiently well designed, the conservatives may still provide useful services to the organization while satisfying their personal needs.

The specific tactics needed to implement these strategies will, of course, vary from situation to situation. One must be able to see clearly which alternatives are open and which ones will result in a smoother transition and a smaller loss to the organization of valuable personnel.

ADAPTATION AND PLANNING

Adaptation involves sensitivity to environmental shifts, and if an organization is to remain adaptive, it needs continuously to scan its internal and external environments and make timely adjustments. This is a function of planning.

Planning involves the guidance of change (Friedmann, 1967) and the systematic management of assets (Chamberlain, 1965). Planning includes (1) ideological aspects, the framing of objectives and the use of value systems to limit or prescribe instruments for achieving goals; (2) technical and economic aspects, the most efficient hypothesized means; and (3) organizational and political aspects, the manipulation or contrived coherence of participants. Planning, apart from its function of coordinating people and the technical aspects of operations and its function as a process of bargains or varying degrees of sacrifice of system objectives to subsystem goals, has additional potential uses: (1) the symbolic representation of progress, (2) the mobilization of external resources, (3) the redistribution of power, (4) the building of consensus, and (5) the stimulation and acceptance of development. Some of these additional uses may be inimical to the purposes of planning. In systems terms this process of self-guidance may be concerned (1) with the differential growth of subsystem components, (2) the transformation of system structures and processes, (3) the maintenance of system boundaries during change, and (4) the alteration of systems boundaries. It should involve a cycle of comparison of expected and actual performances and the exertion of controls if variances are observed and discrepancies exist.

Planning in the health field is usually a reaction to inadequancy and consequently, episodic rather than continuous. To what extent should the planner (a change agent) model the very processes he wishes to implement? To what extent should planning be a profession, or a separate organizational function, rather than an integral function of operating executives? The planner, if professionally separate, may have real difficulty in challenging basic assumptions in the area crucial to his plan because of his lack of relevant knowledge. The planner, if functionally separate, may not have the power to influence events.

Planning should therefore either be a function of the top manager, because he is responsible for implementing its results, or should be concerned with involving the manager in the assimilation of information for making decisions rather than the passive provision of information, which often results in it being ignored. Planning involves helping the manager think through the future of the organization strategically. This strategy formulation requires an organizational system to develop intelligence about the future on which to base a policy.

Every planner or administrator has to work in the future, but his roots may lie only too solidly in the past. The need for a more radical future orientation is self-evident in the time lag seemingly inevitable in curriculum change or change in social services where five years is a pitifully small period. Yet the real interest in long-range planning and forecasting, in spite of this long lead time, is remarkably small, perhaps in part because those most engaged in problems tend to have a different time cycle from those responsible for change. Thus short-lived governments have to plan long-range, and tenured faculty deans must respond (or not) to the imperious importuning of a momentary student. But there is also more scorn, skepticism, and caution concerning long-range planning than is warranted by defects in technique. The tearing of the veil offends. Other constraints include (a) the absence of willing organizations, (b) the pressure to use other factors for decision-making, especially the immediacy of day-to-day problems, (c) the difficulties in interpretation of problems, (d) the issue of credibility and the self-fulfilling character of predictions, (e) poorly defined objectives, and (f) the poverty of data.

A forecast is an opinion about the future and the process of forecasting is the intellectual activity of forming such opinions. Current prediction techniques attempt to determine possible or probable alternative futures thus to facilitiate the selection of the most desirable. This process is already being institutionalized in the form of such "surmising forums" as the Futuribles, the Hudson Institute, and the Institute for the Future.

While industry has seized on the admittedly imperfect techniques of technological forecasting with apparent success, most health planners still rely primarily on trend extrapolation, a technique fraught with assumptions and there is something of a feeling that a new technology, such as that of the anti-tuberculosis drugs that effectively eradicated T.B. and emptied much valuable real estate, is regarded as an unpredictable irritant in the smooth flow of events disrupting nice, straight line graphs in the most impolite fashion. The prediction of health manpower needs, especially of physicians, has been notoriously poor. There have now been several studies dealing with the future of the health care system (McLaughlin and Sheldon, 1974).

The dilemma facing the planner is how to get his management to take notice of his warning signals about current or future function as evidenced in his analytic and predictive studies. Strategic thinking is unusual in health as a form of behavior, and it is far more common to build a health organization piecemeal without consideration of consequences. Thus, the director of a community hospital was prepared to expend several million dollars to expand some high technology cardiac units. All the projects were worthwhile and some necessary. But the overall long-term effect would be to emphasize the specialized and high technology aspects of his hospital, as well as to increase the per diem rate to well above that of surrounding hospitals. Since this community hospital was situated in one of the poorest areas of one of the most turbulent cities in America, the unintended consequences of this set of actions could well be difficult at some time in the future.

A process for enabling managers to arrive at policy conclusions which is particularly appropriate where the group of decision makers may have diverging if not conflicting interests is that of the Odyssey process (Sheldon and McIver, in press). It is difficult for a group of decision makers to come to important conclusions, if their interests diverge, for their conclusions will be based as much on group process as on an intelligent internalization of information. Moreover, they will tend to dismiss staff data, especially if it fails to confirm their point of view.

The Odyssey process is essentially a sequence of individual consideration of data, followed by exchange of that data anonymously through a written questionnaire, followed by group discussion. Relevant information is assembled into digestible form and provided to the participants who are requested to comment on the critical elements of the data through carefully designed questionnaires. The results of these questionnaires are collected anonymously, analyzed, and recirculated to the group for comment and reanalysis, as many times as are felt to be desirable to obtain clarification of the key issues, and of consensus or dissensus (and the reasons) on them. At the end of the process the group meets to ratify the agreements and to explore further and attempt to resolve the disagreements. The sequence of events for policy formulation will usually be (1) analysis of present policy against likely future trends, (2) conclusion about need for change, (3) analysis of alternative strategies, and (4) choice of strategy. This process encourages critical review of forecasts and avoids the trap of presenting unpalatable data to disinterested managers to ignore, for they have to arrive at action decisions based on their own conclusions about the data and not those of some staff group.

CANTON STATE UNIVERSITY
ACADEMIC MEDICAL CENTER (C)

In April, 1972, Dr. John Gray, Dean of the School of Medicine and Vice President of Health Sciences at Canton State University (CSU), was reviewing events in the process of organizational change of the CSU Medical Center and wondering what steps to take to continue the process. [See Canton State University (A) and (B) for background information on the organization.] Early in April about fifty members of the Medical Center attended a workshop and discussed the Medical Center's goals and priorities, demands upon it from its environment, and the adequacy of the organization for meeting these demands. The participants left this workshop with high enthusiasm for changing the organization. However, only three Medical School department chairmen had attended, and participants were skeptical that any change would occur. Dr. Gray knew that it was important to involve the charimen in the change process, but the questioned the specific steps he sould take.

The Initial Steps in
the Change Process

In 1971 CSU was included at the request of Dr. Gray in a four-site Study of Organization and Management of Academic Medical Centers. After the Study Team presented their initial findings to a meeting of representatives of the four sites, Dr. Gray decided he wished to provide detailed feedback to his faculty. He hoped to find a better way to organize the Medical Center and for members of the organization to work together.

In March, 1972 members of the Study Team presented their findings to a meeting of the faculty of the School of Medicine. They answered questions about the theoretical basis of the study, data collection methods, and specific findings. Following this meeting Dr. Gray appointed a faculty committee to consider whether there should be a pursuit of the possible implications of the Study. The committee decided that a larger and more representative group from the School and its affiliated hospitals should meet. The committee thus became a planning committee for a workshop held at the Fox Farm resort in early April.

The Fox Farm Workshop

The planning committee developed the agenda for the workshop in cooperation with members of the Study Team, who agreed to act as consultants and to run the initial phases of the program. Invited to participate were department chairmen, administrators from the School and the hospitals, other faculty who represented some of the existing programs, house staff, medical students, and other personnel including deans of the Colleges of Nursing and Pharmacy.

On Friday and Saturday, April 7 and 8, a group of about fifty individuals met at Fox Farm. The group was fairly representative of all parts of the professional staff of the Medical Center. However, only three department chairment attended.

Fox Farm provided an informal setting several hours' drive from CSU. The planning committee hoped that its location away from interruptions from telephones and regular work demands, together with its setting, would be conducive to open discussion.

Dr. Gray began the workshop at 10 A.M. Friday by welcoming the participants. He expressed his hope that the group would immerse themselves in analyzing the nature of the system that the Medical Center represented and the demands placed upon it. He then introduced the consultants, who continued the meeting.

The consultants first stated that at the end of the first day the participants would have the option of continuing for at least a second day or of terminating the workshop at that point. They then asked each participant to introduce himself to the group. For their first task the participants formed into four groups, each containing a mix of individuals from different parts of the Medical Center.

They were told:

> Identify the CORE MISSION which unites people in this room. But first—Spend ten minutes discussing in your group how you will handle such "blocking behavior" as people who talk too much, change the subject (flee the task), don't talk at all. How will you handle status differences? . . . make sure all are clear about the task? Who will do summarizing and control the easel? Who will make sure you observe time limits?

> Also, a ground rule: Be aware of differences in values, feelings, perceptions that others have, and try to accept these as legitimate, though you may differ.

> Spend 50 minutes arriving at a definition of the core mission, which all can accept for the time being (not final—we'll come back to it.) Post your definition on a single flip chart sheet. When you return put the sheet up on the wall. Look at each other's work. Note the common themes.

The groups had some initial difficulty in getting into their tasks, but all developed a definition of the core mission. All of the groups agreed that for the Medical Center providing health care, training health personnel, and performing research in health care were essential and interdependent. Some groups placed priorities on the three missions, while others did not.

Analyzing Demands on the Organization

After a break for lunch the participants formed groups of eight to consider the demands placed on the organization from different parts of its environment. The groups were also asked to rate the organization's response to those demands using the following scale:

1) Totally inadequate
2) Inadequate
3) So-so
4) Fairly adequate
5) Fully adequate

The groups each returned with a problem census and adequacy ratings, summarized in Table 1 below (See Apendix A for detailed list).

Initial Reaction to the Exercises

Toward the end of the day some clinical faculty confronted the consultants, saying, ". . . This was a waste of time. There are expert answers [that you, the consultants, have] to these problems, and you should supply them instead of doing all these Mickey Mouse small group exercises."

"You call that data?" one physician said, looking at the mass of flip sheets. I say it's bul . . ."

The consultants countered that only they, the people in the organization, could decide whether the stuff on the walls was worth dealing with or not. This led to a tense dialogue, with various participants speaking heatedly pro and con for continuing down this track. Finally one physician, who had opposed the methodology at every step, said, "Whatever you call that stuff on the wall, the fact is we've got a lot of problems and we aren't dealing with them very well." Most participants nodded their heads in agreement. The hour was late, and the consultants proposed that they vote the next morning on the decision to proceed.

Dr. Donald James, a well respected member of the Department of Surgery, and Dr. William Barker, a newly appointed program director who had excellent academic credentials, decided to leave.

On saturday morning the participants voted almost unanimously to continue. They organized into four groups around interest: patient care, use of the mixed-model of organization,* development of a problem census, and conflict of management.

---

*See Canton State University Academic Medical Center (B). The terminology "mixed-model" was used interchangeably with "matrix" organization.

Table 1

Demands on the Medical Center Organization

Source of Demand	Adequacy in Meeting Demand (Average)
Private Practitioners	3.8
Other Medical Facilities	3.5
Professional Societies	3.7
Licensing Boards	3.8
Local Agencies	3.7
Media	3.5
Employees – Medical School	3.0
Students	3.5
House Staff	3.5
City	3.1
Community	3.1
Insurance	3.9
Minority Groups	2.7
Sick People	2.8
Employees – Hospital	2.5
Federal Agencies	4.0
State	3.75
Accreditation	4.0
Scientific Community	2.5
Faculty: Medical School	2.3
Health Care Facility	2.5
Regents: Medical School	3.5
Health Care Facility	2.4

Results of Second Day Sessions

The groups summarized the major problems into six categories:
1) No long-term planning
   a) Financial
   b) Personnel
   c) Programs
2) Inadequate resources at all levels
3) No formalization of goals—long or short
4) Institution lacks priorities
5) Dehumanizing of patient care
6) No system of implementation

The group focussing on the Hospital and patient care noted five problem areas:
1) Crises (many, planning is non-existent)
2) Goals (none, personalities rather than system, poor understanding of system)
3) Forum (poor communication, ill-defined decision-making)
4) Priorities (no good system for setting)
5) Conflicts (many, poorly defined, unresolved hostility)

They also proposed three solutions:
1) Delegation (accepting *responsibility, authority, accountability*)
2) Medical director and administrator act as one with dual leadership
3) Department charimen *different* than service chiefs
The group felt that the strategy for change should, *"Stress the good, not the bad."*
Throughout the day the groups worked hard and enthusiastically. However, skeptical observations that only three deparment charimen had come were voiced periodically. As committment of the group to start changing things rose, so did the anxiety that without support of the charimen nothing would happen. The Dean repeated his intention to support change.

Formation of a "Continuity Committee"

Dr. Gray indicated that he would like a "Continuity Committee to evaluate the organization of the Medical Center and to consider an alternate organizational format" that would lead to better performance. He offered to let the group pick its own committee. They insisted he name it himself. After some thought he named six physicians and a basic scientist, all of whom had been active (pro and con) in the meeting. The committee included a chief of a major hospital service, an acting department chairman, chairman of the Curriculum Committee, directors of a pediatric clinic and student health service, and repsected members of the Departments of Surgery and Medicine.

The Dean gave the following charge to the Committee:
1. Educate themselves in Organization Development (OD) language and ways of thinking.
2. Set priorities for dealing with the problems.
3. Recruit task forces to work on various issues.
4. Report progress to all periodically.
5. Transmit requests for action to the Dean.
The Dean in filling his part of the "contract" with the Committee agreed to respond to their requests in one of four ways:
1. Yes. We will do it. I assign (*person/group*) to act by (*date*).
2. No, because (*reason*).
3. We need more data (*kind*) from (*person/group*) by (*date*).
4. I need time to decide. I will respond on (*date*) by (*method*).

The Committee began their first meeting as a committee at the workshop. They grouped in the center of the room, and other workshop participants observed the process of their meeting.* The committee decided to draft a report of the meeting to distribute throughout the Medical Center (See Appendix B) and to ask the Dean to convene a meeting with the department chairmen to discuss their task and what stance the chairmen would take toward them.

As the participants left the workshop, enthusiasm was high, especially among members of the Continuity Committee. However, several participants expressed doubt that anything would happen at all.

Comments of Participants
at the Fox Farm Workshop

Several people expressed their views on the Fox Farm Workshop. Philip Kraft, M.B.A.,Administrator of CCH, noted: "Fox Farm was useful in promoting communications. This had never taken place before."

Dr. Gray said: "There was not much substantial accomplished at Fox Farm. We got a feeling and momentum going. Getting the Continuity Committee appointed and giving it that particular name was very significant. I think that signified to the skeptical faculty that we intended to follow through."

Paul Queen, Ph. D., a member of the Department of Psychiatry, expressed some reservations:

> Too many people there were relatively uninformed. To have to try to educate so many people was a poor utilization of time, especially where we didn't know where we were going. Retreats had been universally unsuccessful.

> The meeting was too non-directed. It was an uncomfortable way of doing things. The thing that was so disturbing (especially in small groups is that it's dangerous. Who knows when to say stop? There are some things that may not be forgiven. These meetings can often pick up steam. Whe someone is picked on, the weak ones jump on him. After putting it into motion, how do you ever stop it? It puts demands on people in leadership roles that they may not be able to meet.

Jack Collins, M.D., a member of the Continuity Committee and of the Department of Surgery, said:

> My first involvement with the change process was at Fox Farm. Compared to other medical schools I thought even before that this was more open. So we had a fairly good start. At Fox Farm I think people at the Medical School began to do more talking with each other and began to look at the structure and whether it is right for the function. No one in any medical school that I know of ever looked at the goals. We have these "motherhood" goals that are not made explicit.

*The actual process was similar to the "Fishbowl," described in O.D. literature. As used in the workshop, it was intended to focus participants on the process of their interactions in addition to the content issues of the meeting.

Les Jones, M.D., Chief of Surgery at the CVAH, commented:

> What I was subjected to as a rank neophyte at Fox Farm was—these people are out of their minds. The second day I decided there were two things that bothered me. One, lack of organizational structure. For example, who does the Medical Director talk to? Who is he responsible to or accountable to? Who are the chairmen of department responsible to? Second, what bothered me even more, was the total lack of understanding the faculty had for the organization and particularly the role they played in it.

Dr. Gray's Problem

Following the Fox Farm Workshop Dr. Gray was faced with the problem of continuing the change process and meeting his commitment to the Continuity Committee. The Committee had asked for a meeting with the department chairmen. As Dr. Gray reviewed previous events in the change process he wondered whether such a meeting was the appropriate next step. What were the desired outcomes of such a meeting, and how should the meeting be run?

Canton State University School of Medicine

Organization Planning Workshop

Friday, 8 April 1972

Work Session: Problem Census
(On an "Adequacy Scale" of 1 through 5)

1. Private Practitioners (3.8)
   a) Continuing Education
   b) Consultation and referral resource
   c) Pressure to influence graduate and undergraduate education
   d) Not to be economically competitive
   e) Expect clinical appointments
   f) Expect children to be admitted to medical school
   g) Expect assistance for scutwork and technical assistance
   h) Want recognition — to teach in programs

2. Other Medical Facilities (3.5)
   a) Umbrella accreditations of medical school
   b) Coverage by housestaff and residents
   c) No competition
   d) Dumping unwanted and non-paying patients
   e) Expect educational participation for accreditation

3. Professional Societies (3.7)
   a) Specify standards for training programs
   b) Demand certain facilities for accreditation
   c) Demand participation in programs
   d) Same pressures as from individual physicians
   e) Expect support in time and effort

4. Licensing Boards (3.8)
   a) Inflexible licensing restrictions

5. Local Agencies (3.7)
   a) Compliance with local ordinances — e.g., building code, Fire Department, Police Department, District Attorney
   b) Coroner expects autopsy space and assistance of pathologist
   c) VFW, etc., exert pressures

6. Media (3.5)
   a) Direct — expect interviews and appearances
   b) Indirect — raise expectations and demand conformity to national image and/or popular concepts

7. Employees (3.0)
   Wages, security, fringe benefits, rewarding work experiences, prestige quality, personal recognition

8. Students (3.5)
   Quality education and patient care. Academic honesty from faculty, voice in content and process of teaching and administration, realistic role models, more student spaces, education which fits what they want to know (relevance), MD degree, hospital resources (patient care and educational), greater community role (CSU and CCH), fringe benefits (hospitalization and parking), security of position (promotion?), financial support for students, raising number of minority group places, special programs for needs of minority groups, new system for student and faculty evaluation.

9. House Staff (3.5)
   Employee demands, variation in patient material, organized curriculum. Faculty time and supervision. Allowance to develop to their own capabilities. Faculty flexibility relating to educational needs. Recognition of growth of his own ability, community involvement.

10. City (3.1)
    a) Care of city indigent patients
    b) Accountability for use of funds
    c) Maintenance and operation of hospital

11. Community (3.1)
    a) Demands for supplies, innovations and delivery of services by various ethnic and business groups
    b) Asking medical service input into community health projects
    c) Requesting educational programs (e.g. sex education, drug abuse, etc.)

12. Insurance (3.9)
    a) Identifiable service by fully qualified physician
    b) Efficient, auditable service
    c) Proper utilization

13. Minority Groups (2.7)
    Quality care at a competitive price.

14. Sick People (2.8)

    a) Good care, pleasant surroundings, concerned physicians
    b) Ready availability of care
    c) Continuity of care, understanding of how to function in system of university hospital
    d) Care at a reasonable price

15. Employees (2.5)

    a) Competitive wage
    b) Better working conditions
    c) Employment opportunities without discrimination
    d) Pressures for training programs
    e) Professional status, respect

16. Nursing School

    a) More space
    b) What do they want?

17. Pharmacy School

    a) More space
    b) Inclusion in medical school team
    c) New teaching programs (coordination with clinical pharmacology programs)

18. Allied Health Profession Schools
    We ran out of gas here

19. Federal Agencies (4)

    a) Grants — Accountability; Evaluation and demonstration for service and research more than teaching maintenance of program when present grant runs out
    b) Focus on nation rather than state (Insufficiency of indirect costs.)
    c) Physician Augmentation in quantity more than quality

20. State (3.75)

    a) More rural primary care
    b) Higher student–faculty ratio
    c) More state students
    d) Political influence on admissions
    e) Inadequate but high per capita funding

21. Accreditation (4)

    a) Curriculum emphases
    b) National Boards leads to conformity rather than experiences

22. Scientific Community (2.5)
    a) Continuing Education
    b) Set standards for publication (primary promotion route)
    c) Currency of expertise — Faculty
    d) Consultation and committee work

23. Faculty
    a) Medical School
        1. Resources (salary, fringe, space, equipment (3))
        2. Career advancement (recognition) (2-3)
        3. Autonomy — leadership (3)
        4. Quality (all efforts) (2)
        5. Priority of demands (time roles) (2)
    b) Health Care Facility
        1. Resources (2)
        2. Health care delivery service (2)
        3. Quality (2)
        4. Special favors (5)

24. Regents
    a) Medical School
        1. Don't compete with private sector (5)
        2. Admit select students (4)
        3. Make own money (3)
        4. Stay out of trouble (4)
        5. Be innovative (4)
        6. Identify and respond to state needs (economical, effective, efficient (3)
        7. Quality (4)
    b) Health Care Facility
        1. Administration of CCH and CMHC (economical, effective, efficient) (2)
        2. Cooperation with Medical School (3)
        3. Special personal favors (4)

25. University Administration
    a) Fiscal Responsibility
    b) Compliance with regulations
    c) Conformity with rest of University
    d) Bring in outside funds

26. Internal Conflicts
    a) Intra-departmental
    b) Inter-departmental
    c) Intra-faculty
    d) Etc.

Canton State University School of Medicine
Fox Farm Workshop

7 & 8 April 1972

REPORT TO THE SCHOOL OF MEDICINE FACULTY

Background

As presently structured, schools of medicine have difficulty in responding to demands and expectations made upon them both from within and from without. The frustration felt in identifying problems and resolving conflicts led to the participation of our School in a study of the organization of medical schools . . .

The results of this study were disclosed to the faculty at a meeting on 6 March and in a report which was distributed on 24 March. Dean Gray appointed a committee to determine whether there should be pursuit of possible implications of the study. The committee decided that a larger and more representative group from the School and its affiliated hospitals should meet. Thus the Fox Farm Workshop was conceived.

The planning committee developed the agenda for the Workshop in co-operation with the study team, who agreed to act as consultants and to run the initial phases of the program. Invited to participate were department chairmen, administrators from the School and the hospitals (CCH, CVAH and CMHC), other faculty who represented some of the existing programs, members of clinical faculty, house staff, medical student body, other personnel and the deans of the Colleges of Nursing and Pharmacy.

7 & 8 April 1972

A group of about fifty individuals met to consider the organization of the Health Sciences Center and the influence of that structure on its efficiency and effectiveness. The group considered the functions of the center, and concluded that **providing health care, training health care personnel,** and **research in health care** were essential and interdependent.

The participants then identified the groups and agencies which place demands on the Health Sciences Center. The list ranged from patients through employees to community groups and governmental bodies, and included the demands of each group on the system and an evaluation of how well these demands were met.

Our efforts to perform these functions and to meet these demands were

288

considered in relationship to the organization of the center. Quickly pinpointed were areas in which the organization appeared to create conflicts and confusion. This posed the questions:

1. Does the present organization prevent good people from doing their jobs, or
2. are the people incompetent, or
3. are both the people and the organizational structure at fault?

The consultants explained how organizational format affects performance in industrial situations, and reviewed another organizational structure (matrix organization) which potentially may increase efficiency and effectiveness. Having expressed its willingness to pursue matters, the group identified problems with the Health Sciences Center and its patient care areas, and looked at the influence of the organization and its ability to solve these problems.

At the request of the group, Dean Gray appointed a committee to assist him. He named Drs. Butcher, Collins, Kaminsky, Lash, Morsehead, Randolf and Smith to evaluate the organization at the Health Sciences Center, and to consider an alternative organizational format so that it and its sub-units could optimally fulfill their missions. He stressed the need to recruit assistance from the Health Center staff, and to provide frequent progress reports.

Committee Plan

1. The Committee will educate itself; e.g., background information from literature, other organizational systems, new language and way of thinking.

2. The Committee will set priorities for itself regarding the order in which it deals with things (i.e., somebody must decide what order things are dealt with, even if it is wrong).

3. The Committee will recruit task forces to gather and evaluate data from all departments and programs.

4. The Committee will communicate its progress with all members of the Health Sciences complex.

5. The Committee will transmit its recommendations (requests for action) to the Dean who will act according to the following:

   a) Yes. We will do it. I assign __(person/group)__ to act by ____(date)____ .

   b) No. Because _____ .

   c) Need more date __(kind)__ from (person/group) by ____(date)____ .

   d) Need time. Will respond on ____(date)____ by____(method)____ .

CANTON STATE UNIVERSITY
ACADEMIC MEDICAL CENTER (D)

In the Spring of 1973 a search committee at the Canton State University (CSU) School of Medicine was looking for a new dean. (See Canton State University Academic Medical Center (A), (B) and (C) for background information on the organization.) The former Dean, Dr. John Gray, had resigned as dean but continued as vice president for health sciences. In the previous year, under Dr. Gray's leadership, members of the Medical Center had begun to look at their organization and behavior and had made a number of organizational changes. The search committee knew that their choice of dean would have a major influence on this change process.

Dr. Gray and strongly supported the original study of the CSU Medical Center organization and the continuing efforts of members of the organization to study their own relationships and organizational arrangements. Many members of the organization had a significant investment in both time and emotion in the change process. However, not everyone agreed that it was necessary or even desirable to make changes.

The Change Process

In 1971 Dean Gray asked that the CSU Medical Center be included in a four-site Study of Organization and Management of Academic Medical Centers. In 1972 the Study Team presented their findings to representatives of the four sites and recommended a mixed-model of organization, where faculty are responsible not only to their department chairmen but also to program directors.* After the Study Team presented their findings at a meeting of medical school faculty, fifty faculty and administrators met with members of the Study Team at a workshop held at Fox Farm.*

At the workshop Dean Gray appointed a "Continuity Committee" as one vehicle for analyzing the organization and continuing the change process. One of the major concerns of the Committee and of the workshop participants was that only three department chairmen had attended the Fox Farm Workshop. Before leaving the workshop the Committee asked Dean Gray to set up a meeting with the department chairmen.

Activities of the Continuity Committee

Following the workshop the Committee began meeting twice weekly at 7 A.M. They decided to call themselves "ACCORD—A Continuity Committee on Review-

*See Canton State University Academic Medical Center (B).

*See Canton State University Academic Medical Center (C).

ing Organizational Design.'' In the first week ACCORD began to acquaint itself with O.D. literature. They prepared a report on the workshop to be distributed to the faculty and set priorities on problems to be considered. The most urgent problems, they determined, were those within the health care facilities CCH and CVAH.

ACCORD asked members of the Health Center to serve on four task forces: 1) CCH, 2) CVAH, 3) CMHC, and 4) School of Medicine (SOM). Members of ACCORD were to act strictly in a consultant capacity as *ex officio* members within the four groups. In addition to the ACCORD members, a total of twenty-eight faculty and administrators and one student participated in the task forces.

The charge developed for the task forces was read at a general faculty meeting in mid-April. The minutes of ACCORD reflect is perceptions of the faculty's involvement and response:

> . . . Although specific questions were addressed to various faculty members on aspects of structural reorganization, the summary of the Fox Farm Workshop, and overall views concerning organizational development, few of the conflicts and problems, identified at the workshop were discussed at any length or with any depth. The Committee noted that persons who did not attend the meetings at Fox Farm do not yet share the interest and momentum which is felt among those who did attend. Hence, there can be little dialogue until everyone becomes more aware of the problems and conflicts and resolves to find solutions. The task forces, through their charge, should be able to reach many individuals and dispel the apathetic feeling of some faculty members. The committee also agreed that the meeting with department chairmen will be an important step in that it will hopefully inform and involve individuals who will be most essential to the progress of any organizational development within the Health Center.

Meeting of ACCORD and Department Chairmen

Early in May members of ACCORD, the department chairmen and two of the consultants held a two-day meeting at Chatham Villa, an hour's drive from Canton. At this meeting the consultants met individually with ACCORD and with the group of chairmen, and they worked with the groups together. Each group first went into a separate room with one of the consultants and made lists of what they expected from the other group if they were to proceed. When they met together, they found the two lists were very similar.

ACCORD made a ''contract'' with the chairmen in which the chairmen agreed that anything that ACCORD or any of its task forces recommended could be implemented by the Dean acting alone so long as they (the chairmen) had an opportunity to influence the shape of that final decision and to dissent from it publicly if they wanted.

In July one of the consultants interviewed members of the organization. Several members of ACCORD expressed their views on the meeting, the contract, and ACCORD's relations with the chairmen.

Al Butcher, Ph. D., a member of ACCORD and of the Department of Microbiology, said:

> The first time we ran into anything we thought would be trouble was [at Fox Farm]
> when we said, "Where the hell are all the department chairmen?" We were trying to
> use "process" and actually I don't think we were using any at all. We got a real
> sensitivity about how the chairmen felt about us. Some of the chairmen made com-
> ments about us being the red guard.

> The Chatham Villa meeting went well maybe because of our meticulous preparation.
> We came out with a contract. This was a high point . . .

Rick Smith, M.D., a member of ACCORD and of the Department of Pediatrics,
commented:

> One of the things people worried about was that none of the chairmen were at Fox
> Farm. We spun our wheels for a long time out of fear about whether we would ever get
> them together. Finally we took the bull by the horns and met with them at Chatham
> Villa, and formed a decent contract. They said we were a valid force. The chairmen
> agreed to work with us and us with them. One chairman said he wasn't going to play
> this chicken-shit game. He's impatient with us. I don't think he's bought into it.

Henry Morsehead, M.D., a member of ACCORD and of the Department of
Medicine, spoke of the contract negotiated at Chatham Villa:

> The contract was negotiated with the department chairmen. That was a huge positive
> forward step. I didn't think we could get that far. I thought it was pie in the sky. I
> didn't think the chairmen would get together with themselves or ACCORD. ACCORD
> represented a bunch of young upstarts upsetting the power structure,. . .

> The contract between the chairmen and ACCORD recognized ACCORD as a vehicle
> for change. Not the only vehicle . . .

Dr. Gray said:

> ACCORD took very seriously their responsibility to report to the faculty and deal with
> the absent chairmen. They knew they couldn't as a group develop a blueprint for the
> School and present it to the faculty. The Chatham Villa meeting was highly significant.
> The chairmen came and that gave a validation to ACCORD. Having [the consultants]
> sit with ACCORD and with chairmen in two separate rooms and then coming together
> reassured the chairmen that they would have an important role and told ACCORD that
> they would be listened to.

> The fact that I went to ACCORD and spoke publicly and privately made it clear to the
> chairmen that I was serious. I was fearful that we might only get a revolution rather
> than planned change.

Subsequent Events

ACCORD and its task forces continued meeting through May, June, and July.
The consultants worked with ACCORD on improving the process of their meetings

and on confronting issues. In late June ACCORD held a joint meeting with the department chairmen and the CCH Task Force to discuss progress to date.

In June, Dr. Gray announced that he would resign as Dean but remain as Vice President of Health Service. He also announced that he would go on sabbatical in September. Raymond Posner, Ph. D., was chosen as Dean Pro Tem.

In July the CCH Task Force recommended that a full-time medical director be appointed, as a peer to the Dean, with both reporting to the Vice President of Health Sciences. The Task Force described the complex relationships between Dean, Medical Director, Hospital Administrator and service chiefs in the context of a mixed model of organization (See Exhibit 1). After a joint meeting with ACCORD, the chairmen agreed to ACCORD's recommendations with only minor changes.

Without consulting ACCORD on his choice, Dr. Gray appointed Dr. Donald James as Medical Director. ACCORD confronted the Vice President around the process of his choosing the Medical Director. While supporting his choice, they wanted more influence in the decision. Dr. Gray responded that administration must go on and could not wait for this involvement. He said:

You can't define the job description in the abstract, and then find the person. You have to do it in real time with real people.

Comments on the Change Process

During interviews in July several members of ACCORD commented on the appointment of the medical director and on the change process.

Jack Collins, M.D., a member of ACCORD and of the Department of Surgery noted: ". . . I was really let down when the Dean jumped the gun on the Medical Director. You learn to work with each other by telling how we feel when they do something like that. I feel much closer to the Dean than I did before."

Rick Smith commented:

We've been pushed to define relations and the job of medical director, and process has fallen to the wayside.

. . . [there was] the hassle that we got into with the Dean having people look at the position of medical director while we're trying to define a job. The Dean had individuals interviewing service chiefs, etc. It turned several of us off. Maybe our feelings were hurt. We had a confrontation with the Dean. The positive thing was that we were able to have that confrontation.

Rich Smith's views of the change process were similar to those of several people interviewed in July. He said: "It's not the same place it was four months ago."

He described the spreading of the change process through the Center:

Part of the problem in getting interest generated is that the Continuity Committee hadn't done anything. We're feeling our way. The first real accomplishment was putting down for the department chairmen the role of medical director, chiefs, chairmen, etc. Some departments have defined service chiefs separate from chairmen already. And they've defined steps in case of conflicts . . . Now people can start seeing what those guys [ACCORD] are doing over there.

The fact that this process went on here is 100 percent dependent on the Dean. I can't imagine it happening any other way. [Before the Study] we already dealt with each other in a pretty open way . . . I never heard of O.D. before all this started. From where I sat the organization didn't need any development.

Philip Kraft, Administrator of CCH, was concerned that few people were involved in the change process. He said: "The follow-up since Fox Farm has been sort of elitist. A small group has become possessive of data and techniques."

Dr. Gray commented:

We're not yet doing a good job of specifying problems in problem terms. The task forces don't have the message at all. ACCORD hardly has the message. That kind of deficiency is most serious. You can make some changes, but changing the culture takes a long time. It won't happen unless others own the idea of changing the culture. To a limited extent I could do it by insisting on problem definition before accepting answers. I didn't have enough idea early on about the O.D. area or about the complementary aspects of personal development and organizational development. I think we slipped into this through the back door. I would have made this a more pedantic approach.

Dr. Posner, Dean Pro Tem, said:

One of my concerns is that the development of all these mechanisms of change where everyone is told that conflict is something to be brought into the open . . . Although interesting, people have to understand this is a mechanism and says nothing about the quality of what is done . . . I'm not sure that "closed warfare" in contrast to open conflict—is consistent with excellence or mediocrity. I'm concerned that no one is addressing the question of quality. I hope that people don't feel that just having a good mechanism insures quality.

Al Butcher, who was Chairman of the Curriculum Committee as well as a member of ACCORD, remarked:

Each time one of the consultants came out we got the feeling we knew how to do it, but when he left we couldn't make it work. At times some members felt we weren't accomplishing anything. I never felt that way. I felt we were having better meetings than we ever had before. We're building up confidence. There's insecurity every person has. You don't want to make an ass of yourself following something you've never tried before.

I'm scared to introduce process into the Curriculum Committee. Things are going there as well as they ever have, and I'm afraid.

My fears are that the enthusiasm might start to die before we get everything going. It's a hell of a problem. I could take all night and read . . . but I can't do that because I've got students waiting for me over in the lab. But what we do is that we've got our scratch pad over there and we brainstorm [use problem-solving process]. I'm just concerned about the time you've got to put into it.

Howard Davis, M.D., a faculty member in the department of Surgery commented: "Most of us function very well autonomously. We try to do that in a group, and it doesn't work."

Bob Randolf, M.D., member of ACCORD, Director of the Clinical Laboratories in the CCH, and a member of the Department of Pathology, spoke of the change process:

> For a long time I have felt that change is good. After a while it was clear that the consultants were showing us a new religion. It was easy but at the same time hard to put into operation because so much goes against what we've learned.

> One of my frustrations is that I see people who haven't bought the contract. They're on the outside and we need them. But there are fewer and fewer of them. I think they will get trampled in the stampede.

Jerry Samuelson, M.D., Chairman of the Department of Medicine attended neither the Fox Farm Workshop nor the Chatham Villa meeting. He commented:

> A fair number of people have gotten "committeeitis." They don't see patients or write papers. That's a negative thing. It's hard for me to get some of the people involved in this to do their regular work . . . Basically I think it will be a positive effort. It has been good in pointing out some of the deficiencies in the hospital.

> I have felt that there's a little bit of tendency that planning has been taken out of the hands of the chairmen . . . Why should there be fifty thousand committees telling me what to do? There's been too much matrix [organization]. If they know so much what to do, why don't they do it. The way things are going now ACCORD is running the school. It's emasculated the chairmen. We haven't had a meeting with the chairmen and Dean for three months. ACCORD is dealing with the Dean, and we're not. All we have to do is sit in here and have them gripe to us . . ..

> I resent being by-passed all the time. The whole thing about a healthy organization is good communication. Maybe there's some hope because there's a new dean. It's rather hypocritical for a dean to set up this whole study and take off our clothes and confront the problems and have no meetings with the chairmen. The Dean likes to avoid conflict and have everything placid . . .

Richard Gregory, M.D., Chairman of the Department of Surgery, experienced a different opinion: "Somebody's got to do the legwork, and the chairmen don't have the time. ACCORD has done an excellent job. They've kept us informed. I don't feel threatened at all. I would be annoyed if we didn't have the opportunity to influence decision making. If we don't, it's our fault."

Henry Morsehead, who was a member of Dr. Samuelson's Department, commented:

It's not the role of ACCORD to force Samuelson. I see the role as change agent, as a recommending group that doesn't make policy but makes recommendations for consideration by the Committee of Chairmen. ACCORD sees their role as a catalyst in trying to spread the process—to change the climate.

Mark Kaminsky, M.D., a member of ACCORD and of the Department of Surgery, spoke of Dr. Samuelson: "Jerry Samuelson—no matter what he says—has made some changes in his own department—like making Henry Morsehead the Education Director."

Department of Surgery Retreat

In July the Department of Surgery met off-site with one of the consultants for a two-day team building session. Two members of ACCORD were members of the Department, and ACCORD agreed that the team building could be a good demonstration. As one outcome of the sessions, the Department Chairmen agreed to delegate more tasks, including the job of service chief at CCH, to others. The Chairman, Departmental Director of Undergraduate Education, service chiefs at CCH and CVAH, Departmental House Staff Coordinator, and Department Teaching Coordinator each prepared a new description of his job. These descriptions included accountabilities, responsibilities, methods of performing the job (such as attending all Curriculum Committee meetings), relationships within and outside of the Department, and qualifications needed for the job. All then agreed to each other's statement of his job.

Several people mentioned the Department of Surgery retreat and the resulting reallocation of responsibilities. While no other departments utilized the format of a retreat, several did appoint individuals other than the department chairman to administer departmental clinical and educational programs.

Comments on Dr. Gray's Resignation

Nearly all of the faculty interviewed in April commented on Dr. Gray's resignation as dean. Many people expressed feelings similar to those of Bob Randolf:

There's been some things separate from the process that have upset some people. The biggest was the Dean's saying he's going on sabbatical. I personally felt let down and angry. Part of the reasons relate to this process and the committment we have. He's leaving when we need him.

Dr. Calvin Lash, a member of ACCORD and the Department of Psychiatry, said: "I'm afraid the Dean won't come back. Is that bad? It's bad because he could have waited six months when this is jelled. He has a major influence on our morale—the School and the Continuity Committee."

On the other hand, Paul Queen, Ph.D., a member of the Department of Psychiatry, said: "I think the Dean's resigning has helped to get people to take their own initiative. He's bailing out of a ship that isn't sinking. Maybe his leaving, or threats of leaving, was necessary to get the initiative off his desk."

Mark Kaminsky commented: "If a guy gets a thing going and it's good, it will keep going whether he's there or not."

Events During the 1972-73 School Year

In September, 1972 John Gray left CSU for a year's sabbatical, and Ray Posner continued as dean pro tem. Throughout the year ACCORD and its task forces continued their efforts, but the relative infrequency of their meetings was a reflection of the slower pace of the change process.

Representative of the feelings of members of ACCORD, its task forces, and faculty and administrators are the following comments made in April, 1973.

Jack Collins said:

> [The change process] has almost stopped. We had completed our projects, and there was a lull. People were tired. We need to know how much the Dean and Director of the Hospital want to be involved. We [ACCORD] spent two evenings saying, "What the hell is ACCORD, and what is our function?"

> It's vague what we're doing, still. Are we seeing if this kind of committee can change the structure and climate of the Medical School? If so, we have to convince the Dean to keep using this mechanism.

Rick Smith said:

> Some of the people who were excited at Fox Farm haven't been involved in anything since. ACCORD has had its own problems with its identity and hasn't spread the word as it should.

> Much of the time involvement and committment began getting to people [on AC-CORD] . . . We may have lost much of the team spirit we had earlier.

> Having to reestablish its identity every two weeks—or feeling you have to—has made it difficult to do things. We need solid leadership at the top.

Paul Richardson, M.D., Chairman of the Department of Pathology, had returned to CSU in the 1972-73 academic year. He commented:

> People run meetings differently now—generally more effectively.

> There's a lot of faculty who haven't appreciated what ACCORD has done. Probably a lot . . . never knew they did [the reorganization of the CCH administrative structure].

> It has taken a fair amount of time of faculty. Perhaps it was not worth the effort . . . A number of colleagues get mad at them [ACCORD members] for even being involved.

Dr. Joseph Parker became acting chairman of the Department of Neurology during the 1972-73 academic year. He also had attended the Fox Farm Workshop and served on the V.A. Task Force. He commented:

We've gone through all the steps of the game plan. I'm not sure all the time has been most productive. If we got some bread and butter lectures on organization, it might have been as effective.

I can't see that meetings run more effectively. Most are pointless and structureless.

Richard Simon, Ph. D., Chairman of the Department of Pharmacology, said:

ACCORD has had no impact on me personally. I get blurbs [from ACCORD] and can't make sense out of them. "This guy is making contracts with that guy, and . . ." I'm glad I'm not in it.

It's so gunked up with terminology and catch phrases. I throw it in the wastebasket.

Academic Promotions

In early 1973 Al Butcher came up for academic promotion. In the review by the Promotion Committee, composed of other faculty members from a number of departments in the School, Dr. Butcher's promotion was denied. Dr. Butcher had been active on a number of committees in the School. He continued to be active on ACCORD. He commented on the promotion decision and on ACCORD and the change process:

I've been told by several chairmen to get off those committees and do research. I've done a good job teaching and spend a lot of time on committees.

I still think there are a lot of faculty who haven't felt anything about us [ACCORD]. They are in their own world and don't care.

A lot of people in ACCORD are disappointed because of the slowness of things. [The consultants] said it would take a long time.

We get feeling sorry for ourselves and fall back into our old ways [of running meetings and dealing with each other].

Martin Rini, Ph. D., Acting Chairman of Microbiology (Dr. Butcher's department) commented:

Working on ACCORD doesn't contribute to professional development in any way. It's like taking an artist and putting him in a machine shop and telling him to grease cars . . . If we do this to young [faculty], we should tell them, "You're going to lose a year . . . You're going to be judged by your peers." We should have a clear distinction between academics and organization. We should have people in this area to advise us [rather than using faculty for looking at the organization].

Many members of ACCORD and its task forces had experienced intense pressure in trying to meet the demands of teaching, research and patient care, while participating actively in the organization development effort. Rick Smith described how he discussed this problem with the chairman of his department, reaching a more favorable outcome than Al Butcher had achieved:

> There was a time when I was really feeling the crunch and wondering whether I should resign from ACCORD. I went to talk to my boss and he agreed with my feelings. ACCORD comes first. I miss grand rounds and conferences. People said, "We understand that, the commitment you make to ACCORD will save us time later." I was able to get out of other commitments. Essentially I was redefining my interest. I had a tremendous relief and boost after that.

Donald James commented on academic promotion: "Our criteria for promotion are more appropriate for an English professor, but we've never straightened that out."

Functioning of the New Medical Director at CCH

By April of 1973 Donald James had been medical director at CCH for several months. He appeared to have changed his feelings about Organization Deveopment from the time a year earlier when he had walked out of the Fox Farm Workshop. When asked in April whether he would use O.D. methods, he said:

> We have. We have task forces with goals to be met in a certain period of time . . . People are talking now.

> My contract with ACCORD was I should set up a committee to look at Hospital problems. It was the means by which physicians who are heads of cost centers can have input to the budget. For the first time we have a budget committee.

> A big task was to look at all outpatient areas and the Emergency Room. We are ready to implement the Committee's recommendations. The big test is whether I can institute their reorganization plan. The test is really of me—whether I can implement it with the department chairmen. I'm going to tell them what their faculty are going to do to deliver medical care at this hospital.

When asked whether he felt it was better to have different people in the roles of department chairman and chief of the hospital service, he said: "What a department does [with that arrangement] is much more balanced. What the service chief does really represents the service function. The department chairman may have a conflict of interest in wearing two hats."

Joint Meeting of the Curriculum Committee and the Chairmen

One event mentioned by several people was the joint meeting of the Curriculum Committee and the Committee of Chairmen. For example, Dr. Smith said:

"There's no question that the climate around here is different. The fact that the Curriculum Committee met with the Committee of Chairmen for the first time in history is something."

When asked how the Committee of Chairmen finally met with the Curriculum Committee, Dean Posner said, "by [my] fiat. I thought the Curriculum Committee should meet with the Chairmen." One the effects of recent organizational changes he felt that "the clinical service and teaching have improved." His feelings about ACCORD were that it was "A useful mechanism," but not the only mechanism for change.

The Search Committee's Problem

As the Search Committee attempted to narrow down its choices and select a candidate for Dean of the School of Medicine, it questioned the importance of the Dean in the process of organizational development. Was the on-going process of organizational self-diagnosis and change leading to more effective performance of the Medical Center's goals? What were the personal and organizational costs of this process? Was there a better way to change the organization? Did the organization need changes at all? Finally, should a candidate's expressed support of the O.D. effort be necessary for him to be considered by the committee as a serious candidate for the position as Dean at CSU?

Exhibit 1

**CSU Academic Medical Center
Top Administrative Structure**

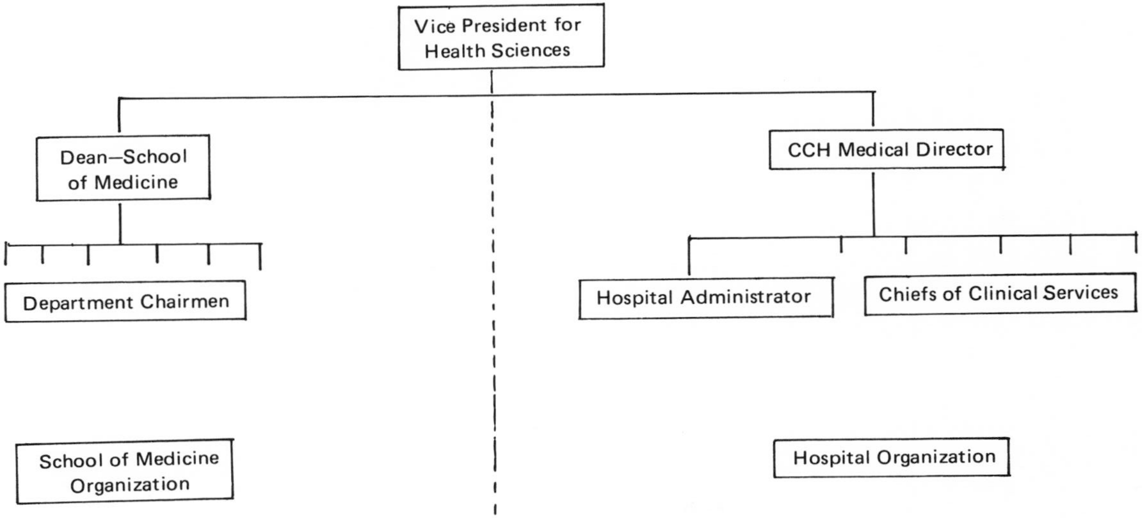

Note for "Turner Hospital"

Description

This case describes the functioning of a renal dialysis unit in a large adult medical-surgical hospital which is closely affiliated with a medical school and loosely affiliated with several specialty hospitals. Specifically it focuses on the decision the hospital administrator must make as a result of a general feeling she has that something is wrong on the unit. The hospital and its affiliations are described, as are the history, functioning and personnel of the unit. A number of specific incidents involving both unit personnel and patients are detailed. Exhibits include a floorplan, a schedule of the unit's activities, and organization charts of the hospital and the unit.

Methodology

This presents a morass of small problems which imply much larger problems. The organizational design of the unit; the lines of responsibility in the unit, the hospital and the medical school; the interpersonal relationships; the emotional demands of work on such a unit can be inferred from the case in such a way that a student could make decisions despite the complexity of data presented. It is recommended that the case be used as a general management case, perhaps at the end of a course when the students can best draw on their learning about a variety of organizational approaches and issues.

TURNER HOSPITAL

In February 1974, the Administrator of Turner Hospital, Ms. Laura Maxwell, decided that the time had come to do something about the situation on the renal dialysis unit. Quite what, however, she had not decided.

For months a succession of small incidents and problems had occurred, no one of which was very significant, but which added up to a matter of some concern. While there were frequent "rumblings" from the employees on the unit, these expressions of dissatisfaction were not evidenced in employee turnover. Yet, Ms. Maxwell felt that the situation needed sorting out, especially because the unit's problems sometimes affected its interfaces with other parts of Turner.

Turner Hospital

Turner Hospital, located in a large midwestern industrial city, was one of six teaching hospitals affiliated with the City University Medical School. These hospitals, which formed the University Medical Group (UMG), provided a complete spectrum of hospital services. The members of UMG included four specialty hospitals (Children's, Eye and Ear, Women's, Midwestern Psychiatric) and two adult medical-surgical hospitals (Turner with 562 beds, and City Hospital with 474 beds). Although the six hospitals theoretically cooperated in providing medical services to the community and learning situations to students in the health professions, a certain amount of rivalry existed between Turner and City because they generally performed the same services for the same patient population. As in most university-affiliated hospitals, the staff physicians in all six hospitals were members of the Medical School faculty, and medical students, residents and interns worked in the hospitals under supervision of the clinical faculty of the Medical School.

Despite duplication of many services by Turner and City, some specialty areas were unique to one or the other. Most UMG renal patients, for example, were channeled through Turner Hospital, as were renal patients from the entire central area of the state. Although there were a few beds for renal patients receiving dialysis treatment in City Hospital and in other hospitals in the area, the renal unit at Turner Hospital clearly led the area in number of patients seen in level of medical expertise available.

The Turner Dialysis Program

Four groups of patients were served by the Turner dialysis unit. First, there were in-hospital patients who came from other units in Turner for treatment. Second, were ambulatory patients who came into the hospital only for dialysis and who would continue to receive treatment on the unit indefinitely or until they received a transplant. Third were ambulatory patients who received treatment in the Hospital, but who also received training which, would enable them to dialyze at home. Each of these patients was accompanied by a "back-up," a family member who trained with them and would share responsibility with the patient for home treatment. Finally, there were successful home patients who came in for the Wednesday clinic where they were checked and tested approximately once a month.

Turner Hospital's original three-bed unit, opened in 1966, accepted only patients who could be trained for home dialysis, that is, patients with no medical complications, with stable emotional and home lives, and who had a back-up person available. Because treatment facilities were so limited, the staff felt they could help a maximum number of people by accepting only home training patients who would be out of the Hospital and on their own in three to six months.

By 1973, the unit had expanded to twelve beds. The staff consisted of a medical director, three other staff physicians, a fellow, one resident, three interns, nine RNs, one LPN, one nurse's aide, two technicians, a unit manager and two unit clerks, two secretaries and a housekeeper. In addition two floating clinical specialists (RNs specializing in renal care) often consulted with the regular staff. Approximately fifty patients per week received treatment (120 procedures per week). No longer were only home training patients accepted; many of the patients would continue to come in for dialysis indefinitely.

Exhibit 1 diagrams patient and staff activities during a typical week; Exhibit 2 provides a floorplan of the unit.

Administration and
Structure of the Unit

The organizational structure of the renal unit reflected both the structure of the Hospital and its relationship with the Medical School. Responsibilities for administration of the unit were not clearly defined, in part because of the complex set of relationships between the physicians. (See Exhibits 3 and 4 for organization charts of the Hospital and the unit.)

Dr. Oakes and Dr. Karan were both members of the Department of Nephrology at the Medical School. Both had offices on the unit and provided a limited amount of direct renal patient care. However, they had primary responsibility for teaching and working with residents and interns and for consultation in transplant cases. Dr. Oakes was Chairman of the Division of Nephrology and consequently had administrative responsibilities in the Medical School but responsibilities were not clearly defined on the unit.

Dr. Pardo had first come to the renal unit in 1972 as a Fellow. In 1973, he became a staff physician with responsibility for home dialysis patients. He originally conceived of this role as one which would involve extensive in-center patient care with an emphasis on training patients for home dialysis, followed by contact with these patients after they left the hospital. However, he was often the only physician on the unit during the day so he spent most of his time treating rather than training patients or following up on home patients. His responsibilities were thus somewhat nebulous. In February 1974, he had announced his intention of leaving the hospital in June and returning to Argentina, his native country. His immediate reason for leaving was a problem with his visa.

The fourth physician involved in the renal unit administration was Dr. Bell. He came to the unit as Director of Renal Therapy in 1970. As Dr. Bell understood his position at that time, he was to integrate dialysis and transplant activities throughout the entire University Medical Group as well as establishing an interface with the community in the form of satellite dialysis units under the Regional Medical Program. After four years as director however, he did not feel that he had the authority or support necessary to carry out these activities. Furthermore, certain areas for which he initially had responsibility had been removed from his control, e.g., the kidney transplant program at Turner.

In addition to the attending physicians, a Fellow in Nephrology was also attached to the renal unit, spending time in both the transplant and dialysis programs. He was an employee of the University with responsibility for patient care similar to that of the attending physicians. Specifically, he was one of the most active physicians in terms of delivery of actual patient care.

While the physicians in the renal unit were responsible for the medical care of transplantation patients, the actual surgical procedure and immediate pre- and post-transplant care was the responsibility of Dr. Rivers, a member of the department of surgery, who usually specialized in another area. The surgery department was actively recruiting a kidney transplant surgeon so that Dr. Rivers could be freed from this responsibility.

Other Staff Members

Besides the physician group, there were a number of other groups which contributed to the functioning of the unit.

The nurses. The nine RNs, one LPN and one nurse's aide attached to the unit worked under the supervision of the head nurse, Marie Frederick, who in turn was responsible to one of the three assistant directors of nursing in the Hospital. As in most dialysis centers the nurses were responsible for the actual dialysis of patients. They received orders from the physicians and assistance with equipment from the technicians but they had the most patient contact and a great deal of expertise in dialyzing. The nurses, with the help of the technicians, also trained potential home care patients, answered questions from home patients, and consulted with patients who attended the Wednesday clinics. Each nurse was assigned certain patients whose medical problems and personality she came to know over the course of treatment. If more than one nurse was needed for one patient at any time, another nurse or the head nurse usually provided assistance.

In addition to backing up the staff nurses as they dialyzed patients, Ms. Frederick also supervised patient care, evaluated the nurses' performances, counselled them on personal and professional problems, acted as liaison with the physicians and trained nurses from other hospitals in dialysis techniques.

Evening (3 RNs) and night shifts (2 RNs) were usually supervised by a charge nurse. This position was assumed by one nurse on each shift, most often at that time, by Frieda Waters.

Besides the staff nurses and the head nurse, two other members of the nursing department, Susan Fox, and Mary Day were often present on the renal unit. There were clinical specialists in renal services reporting directly to an assistant director of nursing. As clinical specialists they taught in the graduate program in the school of Nursing, headed staff development programs within the Hospital, were available for consultation on renal patients throughout UMG and followed specific renal patients during their association with UMG. As a result of this last area of interest, they often worked with patients in the renal unit, sometimes as a consultant and sometimes in the delivery of direct care. Although they had no administrative responsibility in the unit, they worked closely with Ms. Frederick. Finally, there were several visiting nurses who worked with home dialysis patients exclusively.

The Technicians. Two technicians, Bob Miller and Charlie Lawrence, worked on the renal unit, one on the day shift and one on the evening shift. Both had similar responsibilities: they kept the machinery in working order, worked with the nurses in putting patients on the machines and taking them off, and provided technical instruction and assistance to patients and backups training for home dialysis. The day technician, Mr. Miller, had additional responsibilities for preparation of home care facilities (testing water and electrical power available, for example), meeting with salesmen of machines and supplies, and coordinating patient care with the nurses. He was designated chief technician and was responsible directly to Dr. Bell.

Both technicians felt that they were an integral part of the patient care team and that their responsibilities frequently overlapped with those of the nurses. In addition they felt they were better able to establish personal contact with some patients or back-ups who responded poorly to the nurses and social workers.

Social workers. Two social workers, Sara Sinclair and Helen Mason, worked with the renal unit. Both worked under Dr. Bell and the Director of Social Work for the Hospital. They saw candidates for the dialysis program and evaluated their home situations, mental health, and financial capabilities. They counselled patients with problems in any area that might impede their medical progress or ability to move to home dialysis. They also worked with the visiting nurses when home dialysis patients had personal or financial problems relevant to their treatment, especially those requiring contacts with community agencies.

Unit Management. Turner Hospital used a system of unit managers whereby each unit or a set of units was administered by a unit manager who had responsibilities for ordering supplies, requesting lab tests, making out requisitions and charges to patients, and generally coordinating paperwork which had previously been handled by the nurses, as well as coordinating the efforts of the various nonprofessional groups who worked on the unit and handling the interface between the unit and the rest of the Hospital. Betsy Back, the Unit Manager, had served in that capacity on another unit for one and a half years before moving to the renal unit. She felt that the renal unit was unique in terms of specialty and cost of supplies and equipment, relationships of various sections of the staff, kind of service provided (i.e., repeating outpatients rather than inhouse patients), and in other areas. Because of the special needs and structure of the unit, Ms. Back had some problems in relating to the Director of Unit Management to whom she was officially responsible. She often discussed unit problems with Dr. Bell, who in turn approached the administrator of the Hospital. Sometimes problems were solved at the top management level; sometimes they were referred back to the Director of Unit Management and then to Ms. Back again.

Two unit clerks also worked on the unit and reported to Ms. Back. The day clerk, Connie McCarthy, made appointments, answered the phones, wrote out requisitions, kept patient charts, etc. The evening clerk, Florence Barton, had more general responsibilities in such areas as accounting and billing.

Others. In addition to the groups of staff members described above, the renal unit employed several other people. A full-time dietician, Gloria Denver, consulted with outpatients on diet restrictions and requirements. Two secretaries worked for Dr. Bell. Nancy Ford acted as his private secretary and also took phone calls and made appointments in cooperation with the day clerk. Karen Chambers worked with Dr. Bell on Regional Medical Program activities such as planning satellite dialysis units and arranging for training of nurses from other hospitals in dialysis techniques. Mamie Burns performed regular housekeeping duties on the unit. Virginia Day worked with Dr. Bell in the position of lab technician in his laboratory research work.

Other Groups. In addition to the regular full-time staff, members of several other groups were also usually on the unit. One group consisted of nurses from other hospitals in the region who were learning dialysis techniques under the auspices of the Regional Medical Program. Medical students from the City University Medical School formed a second group. Finally, there were residents (three in February 1974) and interns (one) who were continuing their training under the Medical School but all of whom had responsibility for providing patient care.

The Work of the Unit:
Problems, Processes and People

Wednesday Morning. Late Wednesday morning, February 20, 1974, the regular Wednesday clinic was almost over. Dr. Pardo was in the nurses station talking to one of the last patients when Connie McCarthy, the unit day clerk. and a middle-aged woman came in. "Dr. Pardo," Ms. McCarthy said, "this is Ms. Lloyd. She was supposed to come here during the clinic this morning to talk to a lot of different people about becoming a dialysis patient. She had appointments with Dr. Bell, Dr. Rivers, Sara Sinclair, Betsy Back and Dr. James, the psychiatrist, who consults with us."

"And I was here right on time," interjected Ms. Lloyd. "I came right up here and some older man in a white coat asked me what I was here for. I told him for the clinic—to see some people." And he said, "Well, you should be at the other clinic, down at the health center." "So I went down there and waited and they didn't know who I was either. Then I came back up here and finally found this nice young lady who said she had been looking all over for me and so had all those other people I was supposed to see."

"I'm terribly sorry," said Dr. Pardo. "I don't know exactly how we can salvage your appointments. Perhaps Connie would take you down to talk to Nancy Ford, Dr. Bell's secretary. She usually makes these appointments."

"But I made these," Ms. McCarthy interrupted. "That's why I was looking for her this morning."

"I still think Ms. Lloyd should talk to Nancy," said Dr. Pardo firmly. "She is the only one who knows what Dr. Bell's schedule is like now. And Ms. Lloyd should talk to Dr. Bell first."

Ms. McCarthy escorted Ms. Lloyd to Ms. Ford's office. Dr. Bell was in catching up on some correspondence, and was able to talk to Ms. Lloyd right away. She went into his office and he closed the door.

"What a mess," Ms. McCarthy said. "I don't even know any more what I'm supposed to do and what you're supposed to do. Come on Nancy, let's go down to the kitchen and get some coffee." The two women went into the staff kitchen and sat down on stools in a corner. One of the RNs, Peggy Foster, who had been in the nursing station when Ms. Lloyd came in was already in the kitchen.

"I don't know," said Ms. Ford. "I never saw her before and I don't know a thing about her. I guess Dr. Bell forgot to tell me she was coming."

"Well, I certainly hope she's not going to be a permanent in-center patient," said Ms. Foster, setting down her empty cup. "There are already so many. It's getting very depressing. I came to this unit to teach people and now nobody ever goes home. It will just get worse as these patients accumulate. I've always thought if we had any problems we could go to Marie or to Dr. Bell and everything would be worked out. But these in-center patients . . . I'm sure there's some good reason why we have to take them, but I'm getting discouraged." She looked at her watch. "Is it really 11:30? I've got to run." She left the kitchen.

Ms. Ford and Ms. McCarthy looked at each other. "The nurses have their problems but at least they know what they're supposed to do," said Ms. McCarthy. "That poor lady today. I felt responsible for her and I don't know if I was or not."

"Connie, it wasn't your fault. If the doctors forget to tell us what's happening, we can't be expected to read their minds. I've been trying for a year to get them to write things down or to follow some procedures for admitting patients or scheduling interviews. But they can't even seem to work out their problems with each other, much less agree on policies that they don't see as important."

Wednesday Conference. On Wednesday afternoons from 3:30 to approximately 5:00 all personnel on the renal unit who were directly involved with patients or patient care usually attended a unit conference. These meetings begun in 1971 by Dr. Bell, had sometimes been used as a forum for discussing intra-staff problems but generally they had provided an opportunity for the staff to evaluate potential patients in terms of the the the likelihood of their becoming home dialysis patients. At some undefined time, however, the staff became aware that they were not really choosing patients any longer but were accepting anyone for whom they had space. In fact, Dr. Bell had announced at a meeting in 1973 that policy had changed. In February 1974, the meetings were consequently devoted to discussing problems of current home and in-center patients.

For the meeting of February 20, members of the staff began assembling in the conference room at 3:30. The meeting did not officially begin until Dr. Bell and Dr. Pardo returned from an outpatient renal clinic session which they and the other nephrologists conducted at a clinic affiliated with UMC. Meanwhile, most of the nurses from the day and evening shifts (with the exception of the head nurse who was attending another meeting), both technicians, one of the social workers, two visiting nurses, the unit manager and the evening unit clerk, the unit medical fellow, one of the medical students and Dr. Bell's lab assistant came into the conference room. Some people chatted, some discussed patients, some sat and rested. The room was crowded but a seat at the head of the conference table was left for Dr. Bell and a seat on one side for Dr. Pardo. At the foot of the table was Freida Waters, the RN who most often acted as evening supervisor. At 4 p.m., Drs. Bell and Pardo came in and Dr. Bell asked Ms. Waters to get the cardex files on the patients. She left, returned several minutes later, gave the name of the first patient, and described the problems the nurses had had with him during his last evening dialysis.

The patient complained of pain early in the evening and asked for an extra injection. When Ms. Waters said she could not give him extra medicine except under a doctor's order, he told her that he had permission to come off dialysis an hour early if he was in pain. Ms. Waters phoned the doctor on call to ask about extra medication and shortened dialysis. The doctor said the patient could have an injection later but should be dialyzed for the full time. Ms. Waters reported this conversation to the patient and told him that he could not have an injection for three hours and at that time he would have to make the request again. The patient became angry and said she was playing games with him. The patient did not speak to the nurse again; he received no extra medication and he dialyzed for his full time.

As the case was discussed in the meeting, Dr. Pardo (who had not been on call that night) said he had told the patient that he could come off dialysis early if he felt it necessary. Ms. Waters pointed out that permission had not been written into the physician's orders for the patient, nor had the physician on call any way of knowing of the permission. Dr. Pardo said that he was reluctant to write permission for shortened treatment into the orders because then the patient would be likely to take advantage of the orders often and that such a situation would be medically unsound. He had given the patient the option of ending dialysis early so the patient would feel he had some control over his treatment, a feeling which would usually result in the patient dialyzing for a full eight hours, because this particular patient's pain, he felt, was the result of anxiety over lack of control rather than the result of a medical problem.

A brief discussion of communication problems on the unit followed, with an ensuing agreement among the physicians that they would try to write down tentative or special orders in certain cases.

Other patients were then discussed. After 45 minutes Dr. Bell turned the meeting over to Dr. Pardo and left the room. During his absence, one of the visiting nurses described serious problems with a home dialysis patient. Then Ms. Back, the Unit Manager, asked if everyone in the group still believed that home dialysis was the best way of treating renal patients in light of the emotional strain it caused for patients and their families. Ms. Sinclair, the social worker, said she thought it was. Several other people made brief comments and discussion then turned to another patient.

Around 5 o'clock, Drs. Karan and Oakes came in and shortly thereafter Dr. Bell returned accompanied by Dr. Rivers. The latter quickly described surgical procedures and developments with several patients and left.

Charlie Lawrence, a technician, then brought up a problem which had occurred during the past week on the evening shift.

"I was making my rounds of the patients, checking their machines, asking if they had any problems and chatting with patients I knew well. I came to one bed where Roberta (an RN) was preparing to put a patient, Jerry Pollack, on a machine. I said, 'I don't think that machine is ready yet. It was just turned on and the water circulation is not up to full power. Wait a few minutes before you put Jerry on.' Then I went to another patient.

"Twenty minutes later there was suddenly an alarm from Jerry's machine. Freida, Roberta and I ran over. The patient was having trouble. His blood pressure was down and the machine's alarm was sounding. We made some adjustments and in ten minutes the treatment and patient were back to normal. I told Roberta that machine wasn't ready and she put him on anyway. That's why he had trouble and it could have been much worse."

Ms. Waters said, "I looked at that machine too. It said ready. Charlie, it's your responsibility to keep those machines in order. Roberta did the best she could be expected to do."

"My job isn't only working with machines," Mr. Lawrence said. "It's also applying my knowledge of the machines and their quirks to actual patient care. I told you it wasn't ready and you should have listened to me. Besides I don't think you looked at the machine, too, Freida. Why would you have been with Roberta on a routine start-up?"

"Are you implying that I'm lying?"

"Wait, wait," interrupted Dr. Bell. "There's absolutely no way to prove what actually happened. Freida and Roberta, please make sure you listen to what Charlie says. Charlie, check the controls on that machine and adjust it so it indicates what's really happening. Now, let's go on to the next patient."

The meeting continued for another half-hour, during which time a number of people left the room, mostly to get back to the treatment rooms to handle patients who were coming in for evening dialysis.

Thursday. The morning after the conference began routinely with the twelve regular dialysis patients coming in between 7 and 9 a.m. to begin their treatments. The nurses and technician on day shift were busy starting the patients on dialysis and continually checking on their progress. The head nurse, Marie Frederick, spent an hour working with one of the RN's, Christine O'Malley, who was having trouble getting dialysis started with a new patient. Finally, things began to go smoothly and Ms. Frederick returned to the nursing station. She took a phone call from an in-center patient and hung up the phone, shaking her head.

One of the patients who lived over a hundred miles away was afraid he could not get enough gas to come into the Hospital because of the current gas shortage. Ms. Frederick realized that this could be a problem for both patients and staff. She felt that she should do something about the situation, but she didn't know what to do. She was reluctant to talk to Dr. Bell: he had other things to worry about. And no other unit in the Hospital would have exactly the same problems so she didn't think the administration would help.

Once again she experienced the feeling that there was no place she could turn, no one she could rely on except herself. The unit and its problems were so unique. She decided to worry about it later. Now there were too many immediate decisions about patient care that took precedence.

Meanwhile, at the end of the hall, Betsy Back, the Unit Manager, was reviewing the unit's capital budget expenditures to date and making a list of requests for the new fiscal year to submit to the budget committee. As she looked through her file, she found a carbon copy of a letter to Dr. Bell from the capital budget committee dated ten months before. It said in part that the committee had reconsidered the renal unit's request for an allocation of $7,000 to replace their water purification system and that the funds would become available on July 1, 1973.

Ms. Back remembered what had led up to that letter very well. She had included the request when she prepared the 1973 budget which Dr. Bell would submit. The committee had turned down the request, saying that the unit had not documented a definite need for the equipment. She and Dr. Bell had both discussed their frustration with the administrative assistant to the Hospital administrator who had been doing an in-house consulting report on the unit at the time. When the AA submitted his report on the unit to top management, he had described the incident and detailed the need that Dr. Bell, Ms. Back and the other staff members believed existed. A month later the letter had appeared.

"We never did order that system," she thought. "Everyone was so eager to get it, so upset when the request was rejected. But then we got permission and nothing ever happened. Dr.

Bell hasn't said anything; Bob Miller hasn't said anything. It is old.''

Her thoughts were interrupted by a knock on the door. It was Ms. Frederick. "Do you have time for a cup of coffee?" she asked. "I want to talk to you about something. Maybe we could go into Dr. Pardo's office where we won't be interrupted. He's on the unit right now and he wouldn't mind."

A few minutes later the two women settled down in Dr. Pardo's office. "I want to talk to you unofficially," Ms. Frederick said. "In the middle of everything else I just got a phone call from Charlie. He said he had to talk to me before tonight's shift. He went by Mr. Lockwell's house yesterday to check the water quality in preparation for installing the home dialysis machine. Apparently Mr. Lockwell poured out his heart to him about the problems at home, with his wife and children, his job, everything. He wanted someone sympathetic to talk to. Charlie's been in situations like this before. He is a good listener."

"So he wants some advice before he comes in tonight?" asked Ms Back.

"I don't think he wants advice as much as he wants to make sure someone else knows the situation. He wants to have good patient and family contact, but restricted to working hours."

"I know he has good patient contact," said Ms. Back, "because at the Wednesday conferences he often has some facts about a patient's home life that no one but the social workers know. I'm sure he shares his information with Sally Sinclair, but one day she said that sometimes he knows more than she does."

"It seems that way," Ms. Frederick lowered her voice. "But the patients who talk to him, instead of to Sally, the black patients. I'm afraid there is getting to be a racial split between those patients and some of the staff. After all, all the doctors, all but two nurses, and both social workers are white. If I were Mr. Lockwell, I probably wouldn't feel like Sally understood me and my life and my problems. The men can't talk man-to-man to those two nurses so that leaves Bob and Charlie."

"If you really think the problems are getting worse," signed Ms. Back, "you'll just have to bring it up the next time we meet with Dr. Bell and Bob. But it is a terribly sensitive issue and I wouldn't want to embarrass Charlie. Bob and Charlie are just sorting out their relationship and if anyone implied that Charlie has a better rapport with the patients . . . ."

"I will bring it up," said Ms. Frederick. "I'll just have to hope that Bob sees this as a professional rather than a personal issue."

"Sometimes I think we all need to look at issues from that point of view," said Ms. Back, smiling.

Exhibit 1

Turner Hospital

Schedule for Dialysis Unit

Day of Week	Time of Day	Services	Number of Patients	Attending Staff
Mon.	7 a.m.–3 p.m.	In-center dialysis for permanent and home training patients	12	1 head nurse (8–5) 4 RNs 1 technician 1 unit clerk 1 MD*
	3 p.m.–11 p.m.	In-center dialysis for permanent and home training patients	12	3 RNs 1 technician 1 unit clerk 1 resident* 1 MD on call*
	11 p.m.–7 a.m.	Late in-center patients from 3–11 shift come off dialysis	varied	2 RNs 1 MD on call*
Tues.	7 a.m.–3 p.m.	In-center dialysis for permanent and home training patients	12	1 head nurse (8–5) 4 RNs 1 technician 1 unit clerk 1 MD*
	3 p.m.–11 p.m.	In-center dialysis for permanent and home training patients	12	3 RNs 1 technician 1 unit clerk 1 resident* 1 MD on call*
	11 p.m.–7 a.m.	Late in-center patients from 3–11 shift come off dialysis	varied	2 RNs 1 MD on call*
Wed.	7 a.m.–3 p.m.	Clinic for home dialysis patients	15–30	1 head nurse (8–5) 4 RNs 1 technician 1 unit clerk 1 MD*
	3:30–5:00	Unit Meeting	none	entire staff

Day of Week	Time of Day	Services	Number of Patients	Attending Staff
	5:00–11:00	In-center dialysis for permanent and home training patients	12	2 RNs 1 technician 1 unit clerk 1 resident* 1 MD on call*
Thurs.	7 a.m.–3 p.m.	In-center dialysis for permanent and home training patients	12	1 head nurse (8–5) 4 RNs 1 technician 1 unit clerk 1 MD*
	3 p.m.–11 p.m.	In-center dialysis for permanent and home training patients	12	3 RNs 1 technician 1 unit clerk 1 resident* 1 MD on call*
	11 p.m.–7 a.m.	Late in-center patients from 3–11 shift come off dialysis	varied	2 RNs 1 MD on call*
Fri.	7 a.m.–3 p.m.	In-center dialysis for permanent and home training patients	12	1 head nurse (8–5) 4 RNs 1 technician 1 unit clerk 1 MD*
	3 p.m.–11 p.m.	In-center dialysis for permanent and home training patients	12	3 RNs 1 technician 1 unit clerk 1 resident* 1 MD on call*
	11 p.m.–7 a.m.	Late in-center patients from 3–11 shift come off dialysis	varied	2 RNs 1 MD on call*
Sat. to Mon.	7 a.m. 7 a.m.	Emergency patients only	varied	1 RN on call 1 MD on call*

*The Nephrology Fellow spent three months of his rotation in dialysis training. During this period he was generally available on the unit from 7 a.m. to 3 p.m. The medical director was on the unit during the day when he was not teaching, in his research lab or in conference elsewhere. While no physician was formally assigned to the unit at a specific time, responsibility to be on call from 3 p.m. to 7 a.m. rotated between residents, the fellow and the attending physicians.

Exhibit 2

Turner Hospital

Partial Floor Plan

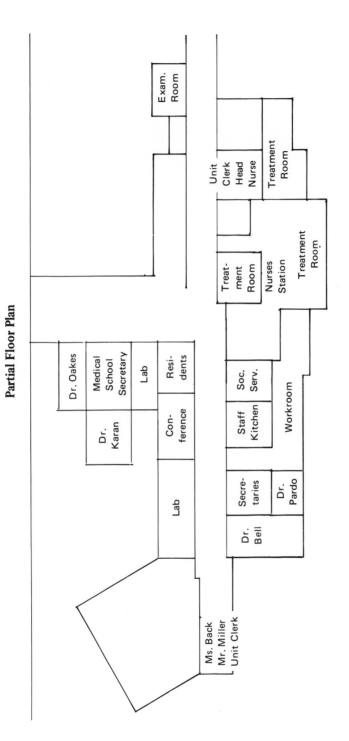

Exhibit 3

Turner Hospital

Organization Chart

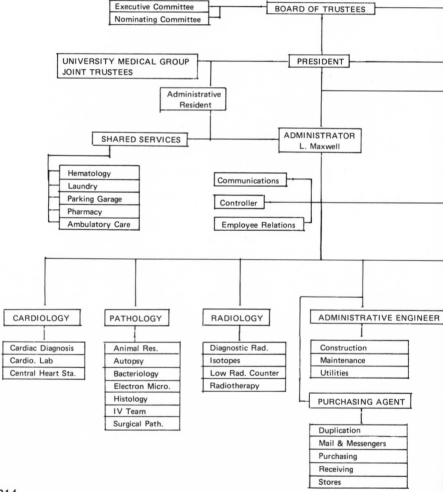

314

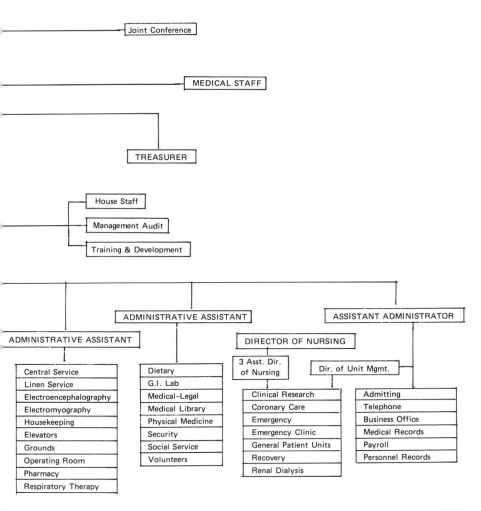

Joint Conference

MEDICAL STAFF

TREASURER

House Staff

Management Audit

Training & Development

ADMINISTRATIVE ASSISTANT

ASSISTANT ADMINISTRATOR

ADMINISTRATIVE ASSISTANT

DIRECTOR OF NURSING

| Central Service |
| Linen Service |
| Electroencephalography |
| Electromyography |
| Housekeeping |
| Elevators |
| Grounds |
| Operating Room |
| Pharmacy |
| Respiratory Therapy |

| Dietary |
| G.I. Lab |
| Medical–Legal |
| Medical Library |
| Physical Medicine |
| Security |
| Social Service |
| Volunteers |

3 Asst. Dir. of Nursing

Dir. of Unit Mgmt.

| Clinical Research |
| Coronary Care |
| Emergency |
| Emergency Clinic |
| General Patient Units |
| Recovery |
| Renal Dialysis |

| Admitting |
| Telephone |
| Business Office |
| Medical Records |
| Payroll |
| Personnel Records |

315

316

Exhibit 4

Turner Hospital

Organization Chart – Renal Unit*

*Casewriter's interpretation

CHAPTER 6

LEADERSHIP: STYLE AND TASKS

WHO DOES A LEADER HAVE TO BE? MANAGERIAL AND LEADERSHIP STYLE

Studies of leadership and theories of leadership may be divided into three groups. There are those which treat leadership as primarily a function of the personality of the leader, of inborn traits or traits developed early in life. This is the "great man" school or trait approach. In terms of the influence model (Chapter 2), this would emphasize the importance of the internal constraints on the manager as he attempts to diagnose and suit his behavior to fit the situation. Although this approach seems outdated for a world in which the influencer and leader must more often negotiate and mediate in order to lead than to play out his basic personality, it is definitely an important variable in determining effective leadership, for many organizations are still largely shaped by the personality of their leader. Thus the international reputation of one English mental hospital grew from the innovations in the role of outpatient psychiatric nurses instituted by the hospital director. But his emphasis on nursing power at the expense of his psychiatric colleagues led to their resignation and the consequent decline of the hospital. This argument allows that a personality can be relatively open and unconstrained to permit the leader to be comfortable with a variety of styles appropriate to the situation. In short the personality of the leader is the first funnel or source of influence behavior intended to ultimately result in behavior by other consonant with organizational goals.

Trait theorists suggest that the leader should be superior in: verbal facility, judgment, scholarship, I.Q., physical stature, initiative, self-assurance, individuality, perceptiveness, self-awareness, and ability to communicate. This approach suggests one set of traits for all situations.

The personal-behavioral approach says that leadership is a function of the interaction of the leader and those whom he leads. This social-psychologial approach suggests that effective leadership is a function of the fit of personality with expectations and personality characteristics of subordinates and group needs.

Blake's grid (1969) (task-person orientation) and Tannenbaum and Schmidt's (1973) boss-subordinate centered approaches are both of this kind. Each of these allows the manager to characterize managerial style along specified dimensions. Blake proposes a two-dimensional typology, more or less concern with task, and more or less concern with people, each on a 1-9 scale. While the ideal manager might be thought to be the 9-9 (high on task and people), in fact the flexible manager will display different emphasis in different situations. Tannenbaum and Schmidt's approach characterizes the extent to which a manager is prepared to delegate. These approaches suggest some important dimensions of behavior, but not the situations under which any particular behavior is useful.

The implication of Schein's "complex man" is that the leader must diagnose the people, groups, task, organization structure, and environment in order to choose appropriate behavior to lead. This is called the situation or contingency approach, i.e., "it all depends." The situation dictates the required behavior subject to modification by the leader's own predilections. Fiedler's (1967) research has found for instance that task-oriented leadership is best under very favorable or very unfavorable conditions but person-oriented leadership is best for inbetween situations.

Leadership therefore, in terms of the influence model, is the effort of an individual to influence an organization toward determined ends, taking into account the people, groups, tasks, organization, and environment as influences on his preferred style in so doing. The author's four-f theory of leadership is flippantly supposed to remind the manager that if there is not a favorable "fit" between the kind of people he will have to manage, the task, and his own predilections, or if he does not have sufficient "flexibility" to change himself when required, he had better "fly" to some more fitting situation or he will "foul up" either the task or himself. This last is in fact no joke, for poor fit may well result in poor performance or physical or psychological consequences.

Zaleznik (1963) has dealt compellingly with the problems that leaders so often have in coping with the power at their disposal. He points out the common fear of success and of failure, and the need to acknowledge in oneself that one has diverse motivations. The leader has to come to terms with his identity and to be constant in his relationships while selective in his actions. He has to be able to communicate effectively and accept the cyclical nature of his life pattern. McClelland (1970) pursues a similar theme, pointing out that many people shy away from leadership because of their feeling that power is exploitation. He points out that effective leadership is one which turns followers into leaders and does not just dominate them as a dictator might. This is very much in line with May's concept of affirmation.

The leader inevitably has to acquire, retain, and use power and in doing so must come to some degree something of a politician. Whether he reflects the best or worst connotations of either word is a matter for him to choose. He may either represent and enhance others, or manipulate and modify them.

WHAT DOES A LEADER HAVE TO DO

Managership is the efficient, effective solving of today's problems. Leadership is the identification of tomorrow's problems, and the setting in place of the problem solving mechanisms needed today, i.e., the creation of an adaptive organization through altering an organization's dynamics.

The leader must be able to deal with the simplifying assumptions that produce the kind of rhetoric that goes on in organizations, with the organizational mythology and ideological (and resource) territoriality described in Chapter 2, and the trivial changes in technology and reorganization that his subordinates may make.

The top manager must not only work on managing tasks and people, the two traditional kinds of work but engage in a "third work," the reexamination of boundaries (actual or idealogical) and the review of organizational mechanisms in the light of environmental change. Since the organization's adaptive response may be to overreact disastrously, or to engage in pseudo organization where defensive management abounds; since an information system can be as well used to defend against the supra-system as to manage; since a control system can be used to exclude creative deviance, the leader's task is to keep the system honest and aware of its own bad habits. In a hospital merger situation for example, the speed of decision-making was so slow and cumbersome, because each hospital had a board of trustees who had to ratify each decision, that by the time any decision was near, the significant environmental factors had already altered and the decision was meaningless. After a decade with little movement, a new administrator finally saw this and came up with a new decision-making system utilizing a smaller group and faster processes.

Top-down decisions are efficient and fast, but the need to involve more people in an increasingly complex environment suggests more bottom-up or side-to-side kinds of decision-making processes. These increase the amount of information but also the variety and disturbance and delay. Decisions are better, but much harder to arrive at, because the system seems so open that it can never be closed enough for a decision to be made. One of the questions for the leaders is: what do you do to be efficient, and what to be in touch? What parts (and when) do you keep stable and closed and what parts open? It is obviously important to have stable enough sub-systems to develop a stable infrastructure and thus allow decisions to be made and operations to continue in a reasonable way. In the hospital merger situation the need for variety (each hospital was specialized in a different set of clinical areas, but not financially viable) to create a more diverse (and therefore adaptable to a diverse environment) organization, compounded diversity of interest and therefore complicated the decision-making process.

The complexity of modern organizations is such that most decisions can no longer be made by the single leader in isolation. The decisions are interdependent both with other managers within his organization and with other decision makers outside his organization. The complexity may be such that, as in Children's Hospital, he decides to create an office of the president which may take one of several forms. Generally speaking, a dyadic form is the most stable, and role differentiation is between Mr. inside and Mr. outside. Triadic arrangements tend to be unstable, but at least one has been described (Hodgson *et al.*, 1965). This involved a mental hospital with a triad consisting of one manager coping with the internal operating environment, a second with research and innovation, and the third with the outside world.

The issue of management succession is a final and often ignored topic. The outgoing leader must consider the tasks to be done, and the style of contenders in relation to his organization's style and his own. He must be prepared to deal with his own possible ambivalence about stepping down and to work through the feelings of his subordinates about his departure and his choice (e.g., Webber General Hospital).

The incoming leader often has a choice of how to handle a situation in which his predecessor may well have left not inconsiderable residues of success or failure. He may choose to play the waiting game, learning the organization and the people before making his move to put his mark on the organization. This has the advantage of convincing his managers that he is prepared to learn before acting, but may equally communicate to them that he is weak and uncertain. He may alternatively choose to make a dramatic act to assert his leadership position, to draw attention of the organization to him and to demonstrate his credibility and competence. This, while making it clear who is the boss, runs considerable risks if the action taken turns out to be hasty or unwise.

To summarize, the leader must: scan and span (manage) and review the boundaries between the organization and its environments, external (key relationships) and internal (keep in touch), for trends, fit, and problems. He must review the distinctive competence of his organization (what it is best at) and its necessary competence (what it has to be good at) as well as the appropriateness of its organizational mechanisms (e.g., decision-making processes) for present and future function. He must recognize the profound importance of his role as symbol, and stabilizing focus of attention, as well as the limited aspects of his role as shaper of action in a complex world rather than action taker. Finally, he must know himself, his preferences, his skills, his motives, and his blind spots, and thus know where he needs complementing and who should succeed him.

Note for Children's Hospital Medical Center

Description

This case describes the evolution of Children's Hospital Medical Center (CHMC) over a decade of leadership by Dr. Leonard Cronkhite, a well-known and colorful hospital administrator. The case focuses on Dr. Cronkhite's leadership style, and the effects of this style on the Medical Center, on responsibilities and definitions of other staff positions in the hospital, and on interpersonal relationships of certain staff members. The case situation involves a decision about responsibility for a certain situation facing the hospital.

Teaching Objectives

Because the case is oriented around Dr. Cronkhite, a first set of issues can be raised concerning leadership style.

—What constitutes leadership style?

—Why does an individual choose a particular style?

—What is the correlation between the style of a leader or manager and the evolution of his position; how do style and job definition affect one another?

—How is the style of a particular individual reflected in the style of his subordinates?

A second set of issues involves interpersonal relationships within CHMC.

—What is the relationship between Dr. Cronkhite as Executive Vice President and the current director?

—What are the effects of delegation of authority within the management system? Where do responsibilities lie in such a system?

—How does the concentration of external affairs of CHMC affect handling of internal affairs by various staff members?

Another set of issues revolves around organizational structure. In the course of the evolution of the hospital Dr. Cronkhite' title changed from ''Director'' to ''Executive Vice President,'' a change which reflected his increasing interaction with the external environment (regulatory agencies, other hospitals, the community, etc.). These questions can be reaised:

—What is the role of a hospital in its community?

—What effects are changes in governmental attitudes toward health delivery systems likely to bring about?

—What responsibilities does the top management of a hospital have for influencing the entire health delivery system?

This case is designed to be used alone or with background readings on leadership style and organizational structure.

CHILDREN'S HOSPITAL MEDICAL CENTER

In December 1972, Dr. Leonard Cronkhite, Executive Vice President of Children's Hospital Medical Center (CHMC), was discussing his role in the hospital and the changes of the past eighteen months with a casewriter from the Harvard Business School. Since 1962, Dr. Cronkhite had been Director of the hospital and deeply involved in its day-to-day operations. In February 1971, he had become Executive Vice President and his role in the hospital and hsi relationship to the Associate Directors had changed substantially as he removed himself from direct operations. Concurrently, the new Director of the hospital, David Weiner, had assumed more responsibility. (See Exhibit 1 for organization chart of CHMC in 1972.)

During the eleven years of Dr. Cronkhite's directorship, the hospital had grown dramatically both in physical plant and in reputation. In 1969, however, this growth had been slowed by the combination of a down-swing in the economy and legislative pressures to reduce the ever-increasing percentage of the GNP going to health care. (Exhibit 2 provides data on health costs during the 1960's and early 1970's.) Dr. Cronkhite felt that the resulting holding period in the hospital's development had affected the feelings of the staff both about the hospital and about his role in it.

Some people here are wishing for the good old days which were really free-wheeling and free-swinging. We have to say "no" more often than "yes" now.

I think a few of them are wondering whether or not I will be able to shorten this period of inactivity by coming up with innovative concepts which are consistent with the environment in which we live now. In other words, can I get a second wind? I think some of them will wonder about that—whether anybody can get a second wind, for that matter.

CHMC in the 'Sixties

In the spring of 1962, CHMC was having serious difficulties. The plant was old and dilapidated, sprawled in an old-fashioned cottage system over eleven acres of land. The hospital had very low occupancy and consequently was in fiscal trouble. The management of the hospital had neither the depth nor the expertise to pull CHMC together and correct the increasingly pressing problems. Not only were the financial and personnel practices out of date; because the institutional goals had not been clearly defined for years, there was no touchstone for setting policy and making changes.

The Board of Directors of CHMC became aware of the magnitude of these problems as a result of an extensive management study of the hospital by a large consulting firm. When submitting their report, the consultants also advised hiring a new director. One of the candidates they suggested was Leonard Cronkhite.

Dr. Cronkhite had graduated from Bowdoin College after spending seven years in the Army during and after World War II. He had attended Harvard Medical School and trained at Massachusetts General Hospital in internal medicine. After some years in private practice, he returned to the Army during the Berlin crisis in 1961, having retained his membership in the Army Reserves in the interim. He was not, however, activated as a physician but rather as an infantry commander.

When he was approached as a candidate for the directorship, Dr. Cronkhite had some idea of the problems CHMC was facing. He was advised by friends not to get involved with the hospital because its problems could not be solved. However, he was by then determined not to return to private practice but instead to go into management because, as he put it, "I wasn't going to influence the shape of the world from the armchair in my office." He saw Children's as having no place to go but up. He took the post, becoming Director of CHMC in 1962.

Ten years later, in late 1972, he described what he had done during his first years at CHMC.

> The first thing I had to do was to really revitalize the plant. We acquired by hook or crook $45 million over a five-year period and completely rebuilt most of the plant. Working with the architects and planners, I designed the master plan for this rebuilding.

> Second, it just happened by pure coincidence that many of the chiefs of service who were also Harvard professors retired (CHMC is Harvard's major affiliate in pediatrics) so it gave me an opportunity to have a hand in the rebuilding of the senior scientific and clinical staffs.

> Third, we had to achieve a critical mass in pure scientific investigation of children's diseases. The scientific effort in this country had been directed toward the degenerative diseases of aging rather than the diseases of the newborn, genetics, etc. So we created quite a large number of tenured research posts which we filled with adequate people. Our research budget has grown from $3 million to $10 million in this decade. We have first class facilities and probably the largest mass of scientific talent bearing on children's diseases in the world.

The fund-raising begun by Dr. Cronkhite went into a major capital campaign which financed, over the next ten years, new ambulatory care facilities, parking facilities, an apartment building for employees who needed quick access to the hospital, a hotel and restaurant for families of patients, and major research facilities. In acquiring money for this growth, Dr. Cronkhite had shown great sensitivity in planning for programs which would fit in with areas in which federal money, in particular, was available. Rudman Ham, Associate Director, who had been at the hospital even before Dr. Cronkhite, described part of this growth:

> Until 1957 or 1958, most of our energies had been directed toward new in-patient facilities. That left our research facilities fully inadequate. Federal monies for the kind of thing we were interested in were reasonably liberal during the middle '60's so the next thrust was to move in that direction. Out of that grew the research building.

Dr. Cronkhite had been able to steer the development of the hospital to meet its most pressing needs by thoroughly utilizing external resources.

Leonard Cronkhite as a Manager

"No one feels on the fence about Leonard Cronkhite. He has a very distinctive shoot-from-the-hip style. (Joanne Bluestone, Director of Patient Services)."

As Director of Children's Hospital, Dr. Cronkhite not only established a national reputation for the hospital; he also established a reputation for himself as a strong and visionary manager. Dr. Julius Richmond, Chief of Psychiatry at Children's, described him as resourceful, vigorous, and innovative.

> The very nature of the buildings that were built under his administration indicates his pragmatic approach to planning and to administration. He identified the needs that sorted out as the highest

priorities, put these into some perspective in terms of future projection, and then moved. He has a capacity to conceptualize problems and is very articulate and orderly in stating them.

His support of the decision to fund three professorships in association with the Medical School reflects a kind of statesman-like orientation to the use of one's resources. He could have elected to maintain those funds in the province of Children's Hospital rather than make them available to the Medical School for major staff developments.

Dr. Juda Folkman, Head of Surgery, described some situations which characterized Dr. Cronkhite's approach to managing the hospital and his method of both predicting problem areas and planning for solutions. A typical situation revolved around the rapid influx of Spanish-speaking families into the area surrounding the hospital. Dr. Cronkhite first became aware of the increased number of such families as the result of a demographic study CHMC sponsored yearly. Although other staff members had questioned the continued allotment of funds to the study, Dr. Cronkhite had felt that it would eventually pay off.

The payoff came when Dr. Cronkhite realized that as non-English speaking families came into the area at the rate of 200 per week, non-English patients would begin coming into the hospital. He offered a $5 raise to any employee who successfully completed a Spanish course and he arranged for courses to be offered at Children's in the evening. When the expected rush began, there were enough Spanish-speaking employees at all levels, from the receptionist to the doctor giving special care, to deal with the families who came to the hospital.

Dr. Cronkhite described his early training as a manager in the Army as germane to his style at Children's.

One of the first stylistic attributes of a good army manager is to be sure that he has developed his subordinates to the point where the unit will still do well even if he gets killed the first day. That means that you attract people around you who share your beliefs, who have the ability to give you great personal loyalty and who follow you, sometimes even blindly. In turn you give them tremendous latitude and loyalty and you don't manage tightly in the sense of looking over their shoulders all the time. You take full responsibility but you don't bug them on a daily basis because some day they're going to have to get along without you.

In the Army we don't call that management, we call it leadership. But it really is a form of management. It works well, I think, when you have a very clearly conceived goal which all people in the organization can agree on and you have the assets to reach that goal in very speedy fashion.

I tend to define the piece of cloth one of my associates is to run with, give him great latitude in how he wants to do it, from him periodically in terms of progress, back him up when he makes the same mistake again, but generally make him feel that I'm supportive but not a constraint on his activities.

Rudman Ham described how he experienced Dr. Cronkhite's style of management when Dr. Cronkhite was Director.

We had informal get-togethers to give me a sense of his direction: a *sense* of direction, not specific directions. We'd usually meet early in the morning, before things started to fly, at 7:45 or 8 o'clock over coffee. I'd get the feel of how he saw something in general and then go ahead and do it, being consistent with the way I thought he would like it done. We had very few formal meetings. I rarely wrote a memo; he rarely wrote one to me.

In looking for people who could assume responsibility and successfully work with him,

Dr. Cronkhite relied on his "gut feeling about the nature of the man rather than his credentials." He had learned in the Army that high performance could come from unlikely people—that a person didn't need a Harvard MBA to be an effective manager. He described his current crop of managers as very diverse, with different backgrounds, but as all ambitious, sharing the desire for a great deal of responsibility and latitude in their work, and sharing a belief in him, "the leader of the moment."

> I think both they and I have to be reasonably secure in order to operate the way we do. We don't try to make group decisions and we don't try to diffuse blame. When we make a mistake I want to know exactly who did it and I want him to be man enough to take the blame for it and take the corrective actions necessary. If you're making decisions by consensus, you can't ever really pinpoint where the process went wrong and it is much harder to correct it because everybody says, "It's not me. I didn't make the decision therefore I can be held blameless."

Besides maintaining close contacts with his immediate subordinates, the policy makers, Dr. Cronkhite also maintained his visibility with the hospital's policy implementers, some of whom were as many as 18 levels below him in the organizational hierarchy. In maximizing his span of control and influencing the greatest possible number of people, he relied on the kind of informal communication he used as General in charge of Massachusetts Army Reserve troops.

> I wander around, get to know a few people who are willing to say hello and so on, impress on them that my door is open, and hopefully at least once a month I do something good for somebody that the grapevine will carry through the system. Now word of mouth is very efficient; it's much better than a mimeograph machine. If one of my short-order cooks has a daughter that needs an abortion and I arrange it, everybody in the hospital will know about it by the next day. That's no systems analyst approach to management but it's a way of making an impact on a maximum number of people. I think if you tend to stay in your office, and talk only to your immediate subordinates you have really lost your intelligence system and you've lost your ability to affect people's attitudes. You've got to show the flag, you've got to be a reasonably resilient person, but with some degree of humanism of responsiveness.

Besides making himself accessible and visible, Dr. Cronkhite felt that he had to do a few other things that were "purely showbiz," that were symbolic.

> We seem to be living in an age of symbols and they are very useful if used properly, I think. If you have an opportunity to put a woman in a high position in administration, goddam it, well then do it. You may concede that perhaps she was the next best available, but you still ought to do it, as long as you know she is competent. That is a symbolic gesture to give everybody the general idea of where you stand in terms of an equity position or people of equal brilliance but of different sexes. I think that's a bending to current social forces which is completely compatible with the organization's survival.

Those who worked closely with Dr. Cronkhite described his style in slightly different ways. Mr. Weiner said: "First and foremost he's a general. He expects to run the show and he has a high sense of ego, as most people in leadership positions have to have. He enjoys the acclaim but also is willing to assume the responsibility for the major decisions."

Ms. Bluestone modified this somewhat: "Leonard Cronkhite is probably one of the most incredibly complex men I've ever met. There is the split between his medical career and his military career. He doesn't play the General's role here very much, but he must be different when he goes off to be a soldier. He is really a very compassionate physician—not nearly as cynical as he would have people believe. He has a tremendous feel for people."

Working with Leonard Cronkhite

Dr. Cronkhite's strongly personal style of management affected both how his subordinates handled their responsibilities and how they dealt in turn with their subordinates.

Mr. Weiner described some of the characteristics of this style.

> Dr. Cronkhite has given me tremendous freedom to grow in my role as director. He is not afraid to delegate both authority and responsibility. But if a person can't handle that responsibility, really do a job with the faith of others beneath him, then Dr. Cronkhite has no hesitancy about drawing it back.

Dr. Neuhauser, who had been at CHMC since the 1940's, recalled that Dr. Cronkhite had had some difficulty at first in finding people who were "sympathetic to the problems of the staff who went to them. So the staff began to by-pass them. These Associate Directors eventually left and were replaced by good people."

One of the Associate Directors who had not met the staff needs successfully had left CHMC shortly after Mr. Weiner became Director. A well-known administrator who had been in a very responsible position before coming to CHMC, he was not able to do what needed to be done at Children's. He chose, therefore, to do what he could do, which was to head one of the professional associations in the state. Ms. Bluestone commented on this kind of situation:

> When this internal responsibility is passed on, some people can deal with it and some people cannot. Those of us who can have survived, but there have been some people who haven't. It is delegating and letting a person run with the ball, but if he falls he sometimes has to figure out how to get up again himself. The people that have perished, I guess, are those who have not been as self-sufficient or as independent as those who have stayed. They were willing but maybe not able to go it alone.

The Director, Mr. Weiner, and the Associate Directors had also delegated as much authority as their subordinates could handle. Ms. Bluestone described her use of her Assistant Directors.

> Because things were in utter chaos at first, I took back the line responsibilities for all of my areas and used my Assistant Directors in a staff capacity. I was out on the line to everybody for a year. By then I was able to identify where the problems were, what needed to be done and which areas I wanted to parcel out. Now my Assistant Directors carry heavy loads for the departments within the area while I have continued to carry all of the responsibilities for the professional service area.

Her use of the Assistant Directors for operational responsibilities reflected her own approach to managing which was essentially "to stay home and mind the store." Mr. Ham, who was more oriented towards interactions of the hospital with other institutions and the community, used his assistants slightly differently although he too delegated as much responsibility as possible.

> I have an assistant whom I encourage to take very active roles in areas broader than Children's. For example, he is working with the American Hospital Association to establish emergency communications throughout the country for hospitals. That's a commitment by Children's that takes a lot of his time. He also has worked on the establishment of the Medical Area Service Corporation (MASCO). Sponsored by eight hospitals and the Harvard Medical School, MASCO eventually will provide parking, specialized mainteance, warehousing, telephone systems, training, electricity, steam and chilled water and transportation for area institutions. I don't know frankly if these outside interests weaken our day-to-day operations or not. I have a feeling you keep and interest better people if you can excite them with motion like this.

Changing Times

After almost a decade of tremendous expansion under the directorship of Leonard Cronkhite, in 1969 CHMC faced, for the first time, some serious limitations on its growth and development. A recession combined with increasing governmental questioning of the spiralling cost of medical health care had resulted in the curtailment of money directed to the health system.

Dr. Cronkhite described how changes resulting from the cutbacks in the goals of CHMC affected him and his actions:

> For the last three years, I've been undergoing a voluntary forced change in style. We're probably not going to be able to grow and innovate at the rate we did in the sixties and the emphasis is on survival: cost cutting and fiscal stability. In that arena personal charisma is not nearly as important as careful and precise analysis of what the nature of the problem is and the establishment of quite precise priorities and tough judgements on what you give up doing.

He described the people he had looked for over the past three years to help implement new strategies as pragmatic, systems-oriented people who could adapt to these growth limitations while realizing that they were temporary. He felt CHMC was in a pattern that was characteristic of all industries: expansion followed by a stand-fast period. Thus he saw the immediate goal as maintaining solvency. To achieve this goal, he said, "You have to look to a different kind of person and you have to behave in a little different way yourself."

As part of his strategy for dealing with the increasing demands of legislative and governmental agencies, Dr. Cronkhite began to concentrate more heavily on the external affairs of the hospital. If the hospital industry was in disrepute in the public eye then spending would be cut back more and more. The best way of counteracting the pressure for increased external limits on growth was for hospitals to start policing themselves.

> Each hospital has by tradition been totally autonomous and very insular in outlook, wanting to own everything it needs for its own well-being. The whole phenomenon of merging institutions and having common management and common government is a thrust which I think will characterize the '70's.

In addition to believing that it was necessary to deal more directly with external relationships, Dr. Cronkhite felt that it was time to change his orientation:

> I wouldn't want to run the same organization in an intimate day-to-day fashion for twenty years. I'm damned sure that I would get bored. I've learned in the first seven years how to do it, and the last three years how to chuck it off onto other people. And since there is another job yet to be done, I'm about ready in my own growth and development to take on a new task . . . a rather indefinable one because it really didn't exist before.

As he became more involved with the external affairs of the hospital, his role in day-to-day affairs changed. As Mr. Weiner described it:

> Dr. Cronkhite is a medical statesman of the highest calibre with a national reputation. He travels regularly, making speeches, attending new committee sessions, etc. One of the reasons for his promotion was that the Board thought there was a broad range of external functions that required more of a commitment of Dr. Cronkhite's time: relationships with the Board itself, with state and federal government, with legislative committees on heath care—that Dr. Cronkhite was a natural for. At the same time they felt there was a great need for somebody on the premises as the on-going director of operations.

At the recommendation of Dr. Cronkhite, the Board of Directors chose Mr. Weiner to succeed him as Director of CHMC. The Board gave Dr. Cronkhite the title of Executive Vice President.

The Relationship of
Dr. Cronkhite and Mr. Weiner

As the organizational change was explained to and discussed with us, we were going to have a Mr. Inside and a Mr. Outside. Perhaps that is too simplistic an explanation of it but that was the spirit behind it. That's why to some extent Dave Weiner spends more time on internal operations, meeting with head nurse groups and various departments. But he also spends a substantial amount of time representing Children's at the National Children's Hospitals Association or the Massachusetts Hospital Association and on issues of joint medical programs with Harvard and so forth. (Rudman Ham).

In December 1972, Mr. Weiner had been Director of CHCM for eighteen months. He and Dr. Cronkhite had, in the latter's words, "never bothered to write down a split of our job. We evolved it over the last 18 months. I think today we are both comfortable in it although its evolution is not entirely complete."

Mr. Weiner described this evolution:

At an early stage we came to an understanding that in the broadest sense possible he would respond to the many external influences on the Medical Center and I would be responsible for the operations of the Center. We decided that the strength in our relationship depended upon a sense of mutual respect. He can become involved in operations and I can become involved in external relationships, particularly those related to operations.

He has felt free to assign a great deal of responsibility to me. I have felt totally free to disagree with him and to develop new directions for internal programs. But I've always discussed my ideas with him at length before going ahead. I have recognized that by right he still was my boss and responsible for reporting to the Board on these final things. We've come up with compromises on many things, with him giving in on some things and me giving in on others. There has been conflict but it always was resolvable.

The staff of the hospital who dealt directly with the two men generally made the transition of loyalties smoothly. Some older members of the staff continued at first to go to Dr. Cronkhite for operations decisions but within six months had begun to approach the new Director more consistently. Several Associate Directors were hired directly by Mr. Weiner and therefore clearly worked through his office.

One drawback to the arrangement in the eyes of those who had dealings with the two men was Dr. Cronkhite's decreasing availability. Dr. Richmond described his view of the situation:

I think that what has developed operationally since Dr. Cronkhite became Vice President has been a considerable withdrawal from the internal administrative affairs of the hospital. I can see this in both positive and negative terms. It is positive in that the lines of responsibility are now quite clear; Mr. Weiner is definitely the administrator. the negative side, Dr. Cronkhite isn't as available to people as he was, so one doesn't have the benefit of his experience and advice as Director. Having been an administrator, though, I hasten to add that I think this is very good, in that I think that it's of responsibilities never leading on to new and more complex responsibilities.

David Weiner as Director

> Mr. Weiner could be underestimated. He is quite different from Dr. Cronkhite. He is unflappable, quiet, a play-it-down type of person. He is liked by everyone but he never loses his effectiveness. (Dr. Neuhauser, Head of Radiology.)

Mr. Weiner came to CHMC as Assistant Director in Patient Services reporting to the Associate Director after attending the Yale program in Hospital Administration and working for the Public Health Service. When the Assistant to the General Director retired, Mr. Weiner assumed this post, which he held for eight months until he was appointed Director.

Mr. Weiner described the immediate impact of his promotion and its effect on him. He knew that he would immediately have to alter his style of management somewhat. He felt that CHMC needed some radical changes: new programs, reorganization of the Board of Directors, increased awareness of the community, a more democratic approach to decision-making. But he also realized that "if I was to remain as Director for more than two months, I would quickly have to learn that my ideals had to be balanced by a clear sense of reality."

> I had to be sensitive to the strong influence of the Associate Directors whom I had just inherited. They were terribly loyal to Dr. Cronkhite over the years; now they had somebody else to report to. I anticipated difficulty in allowing as much of a laissez faire approach toward management as Dr. Cronkhite had exercised over the years—total autonomy to each Associate Director for his functional area. The trustees were afraid that we were eating into the endowment too much and so they were expecting some consolidation from the administration.

> I was a dreamer in a sense and so these expectations quickly imposed on me a different responsibility. I realized that one of my first tasks would be to pull the associates' efforts together and give a new sense of coordination to the institution, but at the same time leave the associates with the feeling that I wasn't really usurping their responsibilities. We've had our conflicts at times, but I have recognized that you just can't impose loyalty to yourself. Loyalty has to be won.

Mr. Ham described Mr. Weiner as an unusual man who was very easy to work with, who understood the issues, and who worked hard. He felt that the change in directors had been facilitated by the spirit of working together that existed in the hospital as well as by Mr. Weiner's efforts.

> I think in the hard corporate world this sort of evolution of management responsibility causes all kinds of corporate turmoil. There's something else here, though, that hangs it all together. There's a real mission that is very much stornger than just one person. There's a commitment to making this a superb place for giving medical care, doing research and teaching. I think this overrode any potential problems.

Results of Organization Restructuring

Although the change of Directors had generally gone smoothly, by December 1972 some areas of staff-director relationships needed further clarification. Although Mr. Weiner did not see himself as having a laissez faire approach to management, he too had delegated a great deal of responsibility. Ms. Bluestone described the effect of this policy.

> I think that as Dr. Cronkhite moves more into external affairs, the rest of the top administration has begun to shift its jobs. David now, for instance, bears a lot of responsibilities for dealing with

the other directors of the Harvard teaching hospitals, with the Massachusetts Hospital Association, and the American Hospital Association. This means that the responsibility for the internal operation of the institution has been shifted somewhat. In the two years that I have been here, my responsibilities have increased and I feel it's time a redefinition of what the real function of my office is.

Mr. Ham felt that although he had continued going ahead and doing things, . . . probably over the next year or so Dave and I will have to formalize our relationship more than we've done in the past. Things are a little more tense now, not between us personally, but because of an acuteness of regulations and sensitivities imposed by serious financial problems.''

Although Ms. Bluestone and Mr. Ham felt competent to handle their responsibilities they felt an increasing need to spend more time with Mr. Weiner making major decisions and keeping him up to date on their actions.

Ms. Bluestone described her situation:

I never have enough time with David to sit down and work through policy decisions. That makes a person who is really out on the line begin to feel a little nervous, because some policy is sometimes being made off the cuff. When I see him I have a laundry list of many different issues, and we go down the list: yes, no, maybe, what do you think?

Mr. Ham, too, felt that there was an increasing need for clearer and more extensive communication.

I think our style has to be tightened up. We've got to test things more carefully. Money is tighter. Priorities have to be weighed. We just can't do everything that everyone requests. These changes will dictate formal or at least communication between the chap who's going to have to face the music and be very visible and myself: my free-lancing, damn-the-torpedoes approach. This style, which has characterized many of us, will have to go by the boards.

He specified the kind of changes he felt would be necessary.

The complexities of the problems Dave has to deal with put an enormous burden on his time. Perhaps some of the activity outside of what really are operations might be split up a little better between Len and Dave, to give the latter more time to work with us. We could spend an hour in the management meeting we have every Tuesday morning talking about the ramifications of City Hospital closing. That's very interesting and clearly we ought to be thinking about it yet there are many things—decisions which ought to be made about the hospital functions today and tomorrow—that need attention too.

Both Mr. Weiner and Dr. Cronkhite realized the needs of the staff, particularly of the Associate Directors, for strong policy leadership. But they were not certain of how they could balance responsibilities between themselves, answer the challenges of the increasingly complex environment, and still give the Associate Directors the support and direction they needed to continue successful operations.

A problem calling for immediate action on the part of Mr. Weiner and Dr. Cronkhite centered on the management of the apartment tower tenanted by CHMC employees. Working with the Board of Trustees and the Financial Officer, Mr. Ham had put through a rent increase. The tenants organized rapidly to oppose the increase and Mr. Weiner and Dr. Cronkhite, neither of whom had participated directly in the decision-making, were caught between the Board, which was anxious to increase revenue, and the tenants, who in fact were employees of the same organization they were organizing against. Dr. Cronkhite and Mr.

Weiner had to act at once to answer a set of complex challenges and they also had to set some policy for dealing with the results of decisions made by the Associate Directors without the specific involvement of the Director and Executive Vice President.

Exhibit 1

Children's Hospital Medical Center

**Partial Organization Chart
for Administration of CHMC**

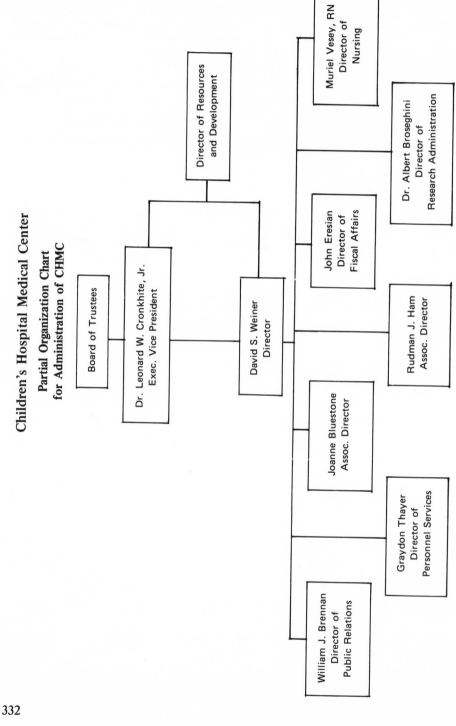

332

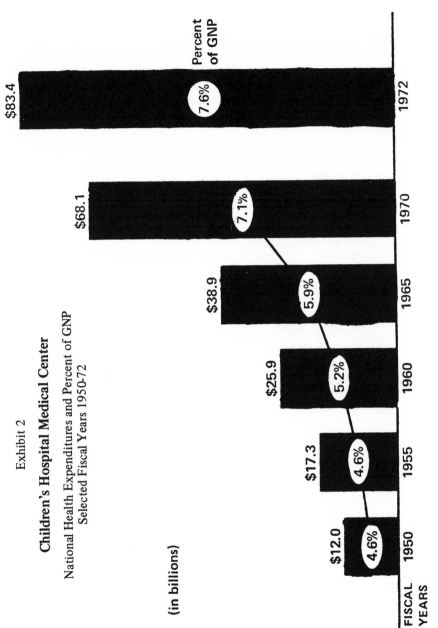

Exhibit 2

Children's Hospital Medical Center

National Health Expenditures and Percent of GNP
Selected Fiscal Years 1950-72

(in billions)

Percent
of GNP

$12.0	$17.3	$25.9	$38.9	$68.1	$83.4	
4.6%	4.6%	5.2%	5.9%	7.1%	7.6%	
1950	1955	1960	1965	1970	1972	

FISCAL
YEARS

Source: U.S. Social Security Administration, *Social Security Bulletin*, V. 36, No. 1,
January 1973, p. 4.

Note on Webber General Hospital

Description

This case focuses on a set of decisions which must be made by the Executive Director of a 400-bed general hospital as he anticipates his retirement. A history of the hospital, the Director's role in its development, and a description of members and functions of the top management group are followed by detailed descriptions of the decisions to be made. First, the Director must decide whether to retire completely or gradually and whether to stay in the community or move elsewhere. Second, he must make recommendations to the Board of Trustees concerning his successor and possible related changes in the organizational structure of the hospital.

Methodology

Webber General Hospital provides an opportunity to discuss not only issues centering on retirement (i.e., predominantly personal issues confronting a manager), but also issues of management succession. The case provides sufficient data to enable students to defend a number of alternatives, which can then be weighed for their effect on individuals in management, the internal development of the hospital, and the hospital's ability to adapt to projected environmental pressures, such as possible governmental regulations.

The case could also be used to explore the impact of personality and personal goals (the Executive Director's) on management decisions.

WEBBER GENERAL HOSPITAL

In February, 1974, Dr. Keith Andrews, Executive Director of Webber General Hospital, was vacationing with his wife and eight-year-old daughter in Cuernevaca, Mexico. Dr. Andrews had designed his vacation with more than relaxation in mind. He hoped to be able to gain some perspective on the hospital, its top administration, and his own future role in Webber General. There were a number of decisions he wanted to make which hinged on his impending retirement from the directorship. Although his current contract with the hospital extended for two more years, the potential impact of his decisions was great enough to necessitate some immediate action in his part. Specifically, he wanted to set a tentative date for his retirement and decide what recommendations to make to the Board of Trustees concerning his successor.

Dr. Andrews and Webber General Hospital

In 1974, Dr. Andrews was 65 years old. He had served as Executive Director of Webber for the past ten years. Prior to assuming that position he had most recently served as Chief of Staff and Chief of Surgery since coming to the hospital in 1946.

Dr. Andrews was a native of Webber, an industrial community of 90,000, located twelve miles south of Wilmington, Delaware. He had grown up in a working class family and attended college and medical school at Columbia University. After serving a five-year surgical residency at Bellevue Hospital in New York, he had joined the Armed Forces during World War II. While in the Army, he had responsibility for the training programs in all branches of a large general hospital. It was this experience that had made him seem highly desirable to the Board of Trustees at Webber General as a possible Chief of Staff.

Dr. Andrews' first intention at the end of the war had been to go into the private practice of surgery in New York City. But when he was approached by the Board of Webber he had reconsidered. First, he had found that the performance of routine surgical procedures could become boring. The possibility of acting both as a surgeon and an administrator was much more appealing. Second, the hospital, which at the time had 250 beds, was anticipating a period of growth which would include the construction of a new wing. Dr. Andrews was interested in this plan and the challenges of both planning the facility and raising funds for it. Third, the University of Delaware was interested in establishing a medical school in Wilmington and Dr. Andrews thought Webber General might be considered as a possible affiliated teaching hospital. Finally, the Board of Trustees offered Dr. Andrews extensive authority to reorganize surgical services and the medical staff.

In 1946, after three months of private practice, Dr. Andrews left New York City and went to Webber General as Chief of Surgery and Chief of Staff. With him were his wife and their two small daughters.

The Development of Webber General

Dr. Andrews' first two years as Chief of Surgery and of Staff were marked by some significant changes in the hospital which were attributable to his influence, at least in part. Webber General, the only hospital in the community, had traditionally allowed general practitioners to perform surgery. Gradually these GPs were reviewed as to their surgical competence and their surgical privileges were phased out. Webber General became affiliated with the University of Delaware Medical School, with residents and interns coming into the hospital and some hospital staff joining the Medical School faculty. A fund raising drive was initiated by the hospital and plans to construct another addition to the plant got under way. Dr. Andrews was responsible for a complete revision of the staff by-laws, rules and regulations. In 1948 a group of staff physicians from Webber joined Dr. Andrews in establishing a multispecialty private group practice near the hospital.

Throughout the next fifteen years, the hospital continued to grow and develop. Dr. Andrews continued to work closely with the lay administrator who directed the hospital. When the administrator resigned in 1963, Dr. Andrews was an obvious choice as his successor. He was offered the position that he be granted a one-month leave of absence so he could attend an intensive training course at Columbia designed for hospital administrators.

1964-1974

In 1974, Webber General had grown to a 400 bed hospital with a staff of 1100, including 400 nurses, 32 full time physicians and a house staff of 45 interns and residents. Several new wings had been added to the hospital building and a remodeling program was under way. A 52 unit apartment building had been constructed for the house staff. Bed occupancy was around 90% with length of stay averaging seven days. A new psychiatric unit with in- and out-patient facilities had just been opened. The School of Nursing was being phased out to allow resources to be concentrated in other areas.

Since Dr. Andrews had become Executive Director, he had attempted to build a strong management team in the hospital. Central to this team were the Associate Director, Harold Harrison, who directed fiscal affairs; and the Assistant Director, Peter Phillips, who was responsible for operations. (See Exhibit 1 for an organization chart at this time.) Both of these men had been members of the hospital's administration since the 1950's and both worked very closely with Dr. Andrews throughout his directorship.

Mr. Harrison was the financial wizard of the hospital, according to the other members of the management group. His handling of increased pressures from government, third party payers and consumer groups had been excellent and he had a reputation throughout the state for his financial expertise. Until 1973, he had had almost total responsibility for fiscal affairs; in that year a controller had joined the staff and had gradually assumed some responsibilities for financial operations. Mr. Harrison had continued to handle fiscal planning and to oversee all money matters.

Mr. Phillips had joined the Webber staff in 1956 after receiving an MHA degree. He had known Dr. Andrews most of his life; his parents and Dr. Andrews were friends, as were Dr. Andrews' parents and Mr. Phillips' grandparents. Mr. Phillips had great personal admiration for Dr. Andrews and often served as a kind of sounding board for him when Dr. Andrews wanted to discuss sensitive issues. Mr. Phillips' career at Webber had been characterized by his responsibilities being greater than his title indicated. He was not interested in titles or in moving to another hospital as director. He described himself as someone who liked being a "second banana" and who intended to maintain that role.

Dr. Andrews, Mr. Harrison and Mr. Phillips met twice a week to discuss problems and exchange information. They were referred to in the hospital as "The Triumverate." Dr. Andrews had intentionally formulated the relationships in such a way that the three men presented a united front and interpersonal relationships between them had been consistently good. Dr. Andrews, however, continued to take responsibility for ultimate decision-making and sometimes acted contrary to the advice of the other two men, although he did so only after thorough discussions with them both on their points of view.

The other principal members of the management team were drawn from both staff and line positions in the hospital. Martin Bakst, Adminstrative Assistant to Dr. Andrews, was a young man who had recently received an MHA from Duke University. His responsibilities, which included a variety of secondary services, centered on acting as liaison with the medical staff. Prior to 1970, the medical staff had worked directly with Dr. Andrews but there had been a Medical Director with responsibility for patient care from 1970 to 1973 and subsequently Mr. Bakst had acted as liaison with Dr. Andrews maintaining close contact through his role as Secetary of the Medical Staff. Dr. Andrews anticipated Mr. Bakst's leaving Webber within a few years to assume greater responsibilities elsewhere.

The Personnel Director, Sally McGinnis, had come to Webber in 1960 after working in New York for many years, principally in the field of labor relations. She had first worked with Dr. Andrews when he was Chief of Staff and had continued to respect his interest in and ability to deal with people. Together, Ms. McGinnis and Dr. Andrews had developed a number of innovative means of dealing with staffing problems, such as the creation of a nursery school during a nursing shortage so mothers would be freed to return to work, and the establishment of annual meetings between Dr. Andrews and all hospital employees.

Rosemarie Trepo, Director of Nursing, had been hired by Dr. Andrews when he became Executive Director. She had developed a management team in her own area which included a Director of the School of Nursing, two Associate Directors of Nursing, and a strong group of supervisors and head nurses. She had joined Webber's staff because Dr. Andrews had promised support of nurses in the hospital. She felt that he had kept his promise and that the staff nurses liked and admired him because of his support of their area and his personal involvement with them and in their work.

Ms. Trepo and Ms. McGinnis each met once a week with Dr. Andrews to discuss problems and new ideas. They both found these brainstorming sessions extremely useful, especially since Dr. Andrews was inclined to take their ideas seriously and move quickly to test them. As Ms. McGinnis said, "You'd better make sure you're serious about what you suggest to Dr. Andrews because he'll probably do it."

The final member of the central management team was Ezra Caldwell, Systems Engineer. Mr. Caldwell joined the staff of Webber in 1972 after working at the hospital as a consultant off and on over several years. Although he reported directly to Dr. Andrews, Mr. Caldwell frequently worked closely with the other managers when problems developed in their areas. Specifically Mr. Caldwell evaluated various management practices and operational functions and made recommendations, especially in the area of cost reduction. He presented his findings and proposals in outline form to Dr. Andrews and anyone whose area of responsibility was involved. Once the outline was approved, development and execution of the detailed plans were up to Mr. Caldwell and other appropriate management team members. Like Ms. Trepo, Mr. Caldwell had chosen to work for Webber in large part because of Dr. Andrews. Mr. Caldwell respected Dr. Andrews' skill as a manager, in particular his ability to blend the community service aspects of the hospital's functioning with a highly developed business sense.

Although she was not a member of the management team, Ms. Rebecca Freund, Assistant to Dr. Andrews, was involved extensively with top management, especially in her role as recording secretary for the Board of Directors, and the Medical Staff Executive Committee. She had worked with Dr. Andrews since he became Executive Director and planned to retire within a few years also.

Dr. Andrews' Alternatives

As Dr. Andrews considered possible actions and recommendations, he decided to divide his thoughts into two areas. First, what personal decisions should he make? Second, what should he recommend for the hospital?

In the first area, he considered a number of options which could be exercised over a fairly long period of time. He could leave the hospital gradually, staying on for a while (even a number of years) as a member of the Board of Trustees or as a consultant to the hospital. If he chose such an arrangement, he and his family would continue to live in Webber. His young daughter would grow up in an average town and he would be able to maintain contact with his other older children and eventually his grandchildren. He could take long vacations, play golf often, and generally be a respected older member of the community. His second option was to withdraw completely from the hospital within two or three years and move to another area. In Cuernevaca, for instance, his pension and savings would finance an elegant and leisurely life. He would have plenty of time to spend with his wife, who was somewhat younger than he and who had tremendous energy and a desire to share her experiences with him. Their daughter would grow up in an unusual setting, and it would take time to make the kind of friends they had in Webber. And Dr. Andrews wasn't sure he was ready for so much leisure time. But he was eager to enjoy life, to reap the rewards of a successful career and to take advantage of his excellent health.

The other set of decisions was harder in some ways but easier in others. His at least partial retirement from the hospital was a necessity. Some responsibilities were becoming a chore rather than a pleasure and he had no desire to do a less than excellent job as Executive Director. He needed to formulate some concrete proposals to submit to the Board of Trustees who were almost certain to follow his advice.

First, he considered the lack of any other physicians in top management in the hospital. He felt that it was important that the medical staff relate to an MD at some level. There were several difficult physicians who might split the staff or put undue pressure on a layman to increase the size and power of their departments. So the Executive Director should be a physician or there should be a new Medical Director who worked well and closely with the Executive Director.

If a new Medical Director came in, the Executive Director could be drawn from the present management group. He considered the three men at the top. He felt that Mr. Bakst was too yound and inexperienced to head such a large hospital. Mr. Phillips had clearly stated his desire to maintain his present status and also it would be difficult to find a replacement who handled both the mechanics of operation and the people involved at different levels so effectively. Mr. Harrison was an excellent fiscal man and the next ten years would bring even greater financial pressure to bear on hospitals. However, his dealings with people sometimes were less than expert. He had been in several serious disagreements with staff physicians, for example. Dr. Andrews felt that he could better judge Mr. Harrison when he returned to Webber because Mr. Harrison had assumed total responsibility for the hospital in Dr. Andrews' month-long absence, this being the first time he had an opportunity to work completely on his own.

Finally, there was the option of bringing in an outside adminstrator, perhaps from a smaller hospital in Delaware. Dr. Andrews remembered a comment Ms. Freund had recently made about Mr. Harrison and Mr. Phillips: "They're almost like two sons vying for your attention and recognition," she had said. Employing an outside administrator would maintain the balance between the two men, a balance which had proven very effective for the past decade. Also, an outsider with strong experience might be well equipped to deal with the sometimes difficult physician group. There were two drawbacks to this approach. Mr. Harrison would be disappointed that he had not been promoted and Dr. Andrews would have a hard time establishing just the right relationship with a new manager. He would have to teach the new person the ropes and yet not dominate his or her development. It would take a unique person to feel comfortable working under these conditions.

Dr. Andrews was suddenly very glad he'd gotten away for a while. He had a chance to gain better perspective on both personal and organizational options, and the rest of the administration had a chance to begin to work things out without him.

BIBLIOGRAPHY

Ackoff, R.L. and Emery, F.E. (1972). *On Purposeful Systems*. Aldine Atherton, Chicago.

Allen, T.J. and Cohen, S.I. (1969). Information Flow in Research and Development Laboratories. *Administrative Science Quarterly*.

Allison, D. (Ed.) (1969). *The R&D Game Technical Men. Technical Managers, and Research Productivity* M.I.T. Cambridge.

Anthony, R.N. (1965). *Planning and Control Systems, A Framework for Analysis*. Division of Research, Harvard Business School.

Bales, R.F. (1954). In Conference. *Har. Bus. Rev.* 32, 2, pp. 44-50.

Banfield, E.C. Wilson, J.Q. (1963). *City Politics*. Vintage Books, New York.

Barker, R.G. and Kaplan, B. (1961). "Studying Personality Cross-Culturally," *Behavior Units for the Comparative Study of Cultures*, Chapter 15, pp. 471-473.

Beckhard, R. (1969). *Organization Development: Strategies and Models*. Addison-Wesley, Mass.

Bennis, W.G. (1969). *Organization Development: Its Nature, Origins, and Prospects*. Addison-Wesley, Mass.

Bennis, W.G. (1973a). *The Leaning Ivory Tower*. Jossey-Bass, San Francisco, Calif.

Bennis, W.G. (1973b). *Beyond Bureaucracy*. McGraw Hill, New York.

Berrien, K.F. (1968). *General and Social Systems*. Rutgers University Press, N.J.

Blake, R.R. and Mouton, J.S. (1969). *Building a Dynamic Corporation Through Grid Organization Development*. Addison-Wesley, Mass.

Blau, P.M. (1955). *The Dynamics of Bureaucracy*. University of Chicago Press, Chicago, Ill.

Blauner, R. (1964). *Alienation and Freedom*. University of Chicago. Chicago, Ill.

Blake, R.R. and Mouton, J.S. (1964). *The Managerial Grid*. Gulf, Houston, Texas.

Bolt, R. (1960). *A Man for all Seasons*. Vintage Books, Random House, New York.

Brady, R.H. (1973). MBO goes to Work in the Public Sector. *Har. Bus. Rev.* 51, 2, pp. 65-74.

Bright, J.R. (ed.) (1968). *Technological Forecasting for Industry and Government: Methods and Applications*. Prentice-Hall, Englewood Cliffs, N.J.

Bronowski, J. (1956). *Science and Human Values*. Harper & Row, New York.

Brown, W. (1971). *Organizations*. Heinemann, London.

Buckley, W. (1967). *Sociology and Modern Systems Theory*. Prentice-Hall, Englewood, N.J.

Burger, J. (1967). *A Fortunate Man*. Allen Lane, The Penguin Press.

Burns, T. and Stalker, G.M. (1961). *The Management of Innovation*. Tavistock, London.

Chamberlain, N.W. (1965). *Private and Public Planning*. McGraw-Hill, New York.

Charns, M.P. (1974). *The Organization and Management of Hospital Patient Units*. Carnegie Mellon.

Cockcroft, Sir J. (Ed.) (1965). *The Organization of Research Establishments*. Cambridge University, London.

Crosby, A. (1968). *Creativity and Performance in Industrial Organization*. Tavistock, London.

Crozier, M. (1964). *The Bureaucratic Phenomenon*. University of Chicago, Ill.

Dalton, G.W., Barnes, L.B. and Zaleznik, A. (1968). *The Distribution of Authority in Formal Organizations*. Division of Research, Har. Bus. Sch., Boston, Mass.

Davis, N.P. (1968). *Lawrence and Oppenheimer*. Simon & Schuster, New York.

Drucker, P.F. (1974a). *Management-Tasks, Responsibility, Practices*. Harper & Row, New York.

Drucker, P.F. (1974b). New Templates for Today's Organizations. *Har. Bus. Rev.* 52, 1, pp. 45-53.

Duhl, L.J. (1968). *The Parameters of Urban Planning; in S. Anderson Planning for Diversity and Choice*. pp. 64-73. M.I.T. Cambridge, Mass.

Emery, J.C. (1969). *Organizational Planning and Control Systems*. MacMillan Co., New York.

Emery, F.E. and Trist, E.L. (1973). *Towards a Social Ecology*. Plenum, London.

Evan, W. (1963). Indices of Hierarchical Structure of Industrial Organizations. *Management Sciences*.

Fielder, F.E. (1967). *A Theory of Leadership Effectiveness*. McGraw-Hill, New York.

Field, H.H. (1965). *Organizing the Planning Process*. Ann. N.Y. Acad. Sci. 128: 2.

Folger, A. and Gordon, G. (1962). Scientific Accomplishment and Social Organization, a Review of the Literature. *Am. Behav. Sci.* 11, pp. 51-58.

Freidson, E. (1970a). *Profession of Medicine*. Dodd Mead.

Freidson, E. (1970b). *Professional Dominance*. Atherton.

Friedmann, J. (1967). A Conceptual Model for the Analysis of Planning Behavior. *Administr. Sci. Quart.* 12: pp. 225-252.

Glaser, B.G. (1964). *Organizational Scientists, their Professional Careers*. Bobbs-Merrill, New York.

Goggin, W.C. (1974). How the Multidimensional Structure Works at Dow Corning. *Har. Bus. Rev.* 52: 1, pp. 54-65.

Gordon, G. (1966a). The Identification and Use of Creative Abilities in Scientific Organizations, presented at *The Seventh Nat. Res. Conf.* of Creativity. Greensboro, N.C.

Gordon, G. (1966b). Organizational Setting and Scientific Accomplishment, presented at the *Am. Sociol. Assoc. Annual Meeting,* Miami, Florida.

Gordon, G. and Marquis S. (1966). Freedom, Visibility of Consequences and Scientific Innovation. *Am. J. Sociol.* 72: pp. 195-202.

Gordon, T.J. and Hayward, H. (1968). Initial Experiments with the Cross Impact Matrix Method of Forecasting. *Futures: J. Forecast. Planning.* 1: 2.

Greiner, L.E. (1967). Patterns of Organization Change. *Har. Bus. Rev.* 45: 1, pp. 119-128.

Greiner, L.E. (1972). Evolution and Revolution as Organizations Grow. *Har. Bus. Rev.* 50: 4, pp. 37-46.

Greiner, L.E. (1973). What Managers Think of Participative Leadership. *Har. Bus. Rev.* 51: 2, pp. 111-117.

Griffith, H.R. and Rees, E.T. (1963). *Hinges of Administration*. Oxford University, London.

Gruber, W.H. and Marquis, D.G. (Eds.) (1969) *Factors in Transfer of Technology*. M.I.T., Cambridge, Mass.

Hainer, R.M., Kingsbury, S. and Gleicher, D.B. (Eds.) (1967). *Uncertainty in Research, Management, and New Product Development*. Arthur D. Little, Reinhold, Cambridge, Mass.

Hall, R.H. (1962). Intraorganizational Structural Variables. *Administrative Science Quarterly*. December.

Harrison, R. (1972). Understanding Your Organization's Character. *Har. Bus. Rev.* 50: 3, pp. 119-128.

Harvey, E. (1968). Technology and the Structure of Organizations. *American Sociological Review*.

Helmer, O. (1966). *Social Technology*. Basic Books, New York.

Herzberg, F. (1968). One More Time: How Do You Motivate Employees? *Har. Bus. Rev.* 46: 1, pp. 53-62.

Hodgson, R.C., Levinson, D.J. and Zaleznik, A. (1965). *The Executive Role Constellation*. Division of Research, Har. Bus. Sch., Boston, Mass.

Hollingshead, A.B. and Redlich, F.C. (1958). *Social Class and Mental Illness*. Wiley; New York.

Homans, G.C. (1950). *The Human Group*. Harcourt, Brace, New York.

Huxley, J. (1970). *Memories*. Allen & Unwin, London.

Janis, I.L. (1972). *Victims of Groupthink*. Houghton Mifflin, Boston.

Jantsch, E. (1966). *Technological Forecasting in Perspective*. OECD.

Jantsch, E. (1968). *Perspectives of Planning* Organization for Economic Cooperation and Development.

Jaques, E. (1956). *Measurement of Responsibility*. Tavistock, London.

Jones, R.V. (1967). Evolution of the Laboratory. *Science Journal*. 3: 30.

Jouvenel, B. de. (1967). *The Art of Conjecture*. Basic Books, New York.

Keeling, D. (1972). *Management in Government*. George Allen and Unwin. London.

Laframboise, H.L. (1971). Administrative Reform in the Federal Public Service: Signs of a Saturation Psychosis. *Canadian Public Administration*. Vol. 14, Fall, pp. 303-325.

Lawrence, P.R. (1969). How to Deal with Resistance to Change. *Har. Bus. Rev.* Jan-Feb. pp. 4-12.

Lawrence, P.R. and Lorsch, J.W. (1967a). *Organization and Environment*. Division of Research, Har. Bus. Sch., Boston, Mass.

Lawrence, P.R. and Lorsch, J.W. (1967b). New Management Job: The Integrator. *Har. Bus. Rev.* 45: 6, pp. 142-151.

Lawrence, P.R. and Lorsch, J.W. (1969) *Developing Organizations: Diagnosis and Action*. Addison-Wesley, Mass.

Leavitt, H.J. (1972). *Managerial Psychology*. University of Chicago, Chicago, Ill.

Lerner, M. (1958). *America as a Civilization*. Jonathan Cape, London.

Levinson, H. (1970). Management by Whose Objectives? *Har. Bus. Rev.* Jul.-Aug. pp. 125-134.

Levinson, H. (1973a). *The Great Jackass Fallacy*. Graduate School of Bus. Admin., Harvard University, Boston, Mass.

Levinson, H. (1973b). Asinine Attitudes Toward Motivation. *Har. Bus. Rev.* 51: 1, pp. 70-76.

Likert, R. (1967). *The Human Organization: Its Management and Value*. McGraw-Hill, New York.

Litterer, J.A. (1969a). *Organizations: Systems Control and Adaptation*. (Vol. 1). Wiley, New York.

Litterer, J.A. (1969b). *Structure and Behavior*. (Vol. 2). Wiley, New York.

Litterer, J.A. (1973). *The Analysis of Organizations*. Wiley, New York.

Logan, R.F.L., Ashley, J.S.A., Klein, R.E., and Robson, D.M. (1972). *Dynamics of Medical Care. The Liverpool Study Into Use of Hospital Resources*. William Davidson & Son Ltd, London.

Lorsch, J.W. and Allen, S.A. (1973). *Managing Diversity and Interdependence*. Harvard University, Boston, Mass.

March, J.G. (Ed.) (1965). *Handbook of Organizations*. Rand McNally, Chicago, Ill.

May, R. (1972). *Power and Innocence*. Houghton, New York.

McCelland, D.C. (1970). The Two Faces of Power, *J. International Affairs*. 24, 1, pp. 29-47.

McLaughlin, C.P. and Sheldon, A. (1974). *The Future and Medical Care*. Ballinger Books, Boston, Mass.

McMurry, R.N. (1973). Power and the Ambitious Executive. *Har. Bus. Rev.* 51:6, pp. 140-145.

McNair, M. (1954). *The Case Method of Harvard Business School*. McGraw Hill, New York.

Medawar, P.B. (1969). *Induction and Intuition in Scientific Thought*. Methuen, London.

Meyers, S. (1964). Who Are Your Motivated Workers. *Har. Bus. Rev.* Jan-Feb.

Miles, S.B. Jr. (1961). The Management Polician. *Har. Bus. Rev.* 39:1, pp. 99-104.

Miller, E. and Rice, A.K. (1967). *Systems of Organizations*. Tavistock, London.

Miller, S.J. (1970). *Prescription for Leadership*. Aldine.

Mintzberg, H. (1972). *The Nature of Managerial Work*. Harper & Row, New York.

Morse, J.J. and Lorsch, J.W. (1970). Beyond Theory Y. *Har. Bus. Rev.* May-June, pp. 61-68.

Murnhehan, J.H. and Talalay, P. (1967). John Jacob Abel and Crystalization of Insulin. *Perspect. Biol. Med.* 10, pp. 334-380.

Neuhauser, D. (1972). The Hospital as a Matrix Organization. *Hospital Administration*. pp. 8-25.

Ozbekhan, H. (1968). *The Triumph of Technology: "Can" Implies Ought; in S. Anderson, Planning for Diversity and Choice*, pp. 204-219. M.I.T. Cambridge, Mass.

Pelz, D.C. and Andrews, F.M. (1966). *Scientists in Organizations*. Wiley, New York.

Plumb, J.H. (1972). *Sir Robert Walpole Vol. 1 The Making of a Statesman*. Allen Lane, Penguin, London.

Polanyi, M. (1967). *The Tacit Dimension*. Routledge & Kegan Paul, London.

Prehoda, R.A. (1967). *Designing the Future: The Role of Technological Forecasting*. Chilton, New York.

Rapoport, R.N. (1970). *Mid-Career Development*. Tavistock, London.

Reader, W.J. (1966). *Professional Men*. Basic Books, New York.

Rhenman, E. (1973). *Organization Theory for Long Range Planning*. Wiley, New York.

Rice, A.K. (1963). *The Enterprise and Its Environment*. Tavistock, London.

Roe, A. (1956). *The Psychology of Occupation*. Wiley, New York.

Roemer, M.E. and Friedman, J.W. (1971). *Doctors in Hospitals*. John Hopkins, Baltimore, Md.

Roethlisberger, F.J. (1965). The Foreman: Master and Victim of Double Talk. *Har. Bus. Rev.* 43: 5, pp. 22-32.

Sapolsky, H.M. (1972). *The Polaris System Development*. Harvard, Cambridge.

Schein, E.H. (1969). *Process Consultation: Its Role in Organization Development*. Addison-Wesley, Mass.

Schein, E.H. (1972). *Organizational Psychology*. Prentice Hall, Englewood, N.J.

Schmookler, J. (1966). *Invention and Economic Growth*. Harvard, Cambridge, Mass.

Schon, D.A. (1967). *Technology and Change: The New Heraclitus*. Dell, New York.

Seiler, J.A. (1967). *Systems Analysis in Organizational Behavior*. R.D. Irwin and the Dorsey Press, Homewood, Illinois.

Shils, E. (Ed.) (1968). *Criteria for Scientific Development, Public Policy and National Goals*. M.I.T. Cambridge, Mass.

Shonfield, A. (1969). Thinking about the Future. *Encounter*. 32: 15-26.

Smith, B.L.R. (1966). *The Rand Corporation*. Harvard, Cambridge, Mass.

Smith, B.L.R. and Hague, D.C. (1971). *The Dilemma of Accountability in Modern Government*. MacMillan, London.

Sofer, C. (1972). *Organizations in Theory and Practice*. Basic Books, New York.

Sprague, L., Sheldon, A. and McLaughlin, C. (1973). *Teaching Health and Human Services Administration by the Case Method*. Behavioral Publications, New York.

Tannenbaum, R. and Schmidt, W.H. (1973). How to Choose a Leadership Pattern. *Har. Bus. Rev.* 51: 3, pp. 1-10.

Taylor, G.R. (1968). *The Biological Time Bomb*. Thames and Hudson, London.

Thompson, P.H. and Dalton, G.W. (1970). Performance Appraisal; Managers Beware. *Har. Bus. Rev.* Jan.-Feb. pp. 149-157.

Towl, A.R. (1969). *To Study Administration by Cases*. Har. Bus. Sch., Boston, Mass.

Trist, E.L. *el al.* (1963). *Organizational Choice*. Tavistock, London.

Turner, A.N. and Lawrence, P.R. (1965). *Industrial Jobs and the Worker*. Har. Bus. Sch., Boston, Mass.

Uyterhoeven, H.E.R. (1972). General Managers in the Middle. *Har. Bus. Rev.* 50: 2, pp. 75-85.

Vickers, Sir G. (1965). *The Art of Judgment*. Basic Books, New York.

Vickers, Sir G. (1967). *Towards a Sociology of Management*. Basic Books, New York.

Vickers, Sir G. (1968). *Value Systems and Social Process*. Basic Books, New York.

Vollmer, H.M. and Mills, D.L. (1966). *Professionalization*. Prentice Hall, Englewood, New Jersey.

Walker, A.H. and Lorsch, J.W. (1968). Organizational Choice: Product vs. Function. *Har. Bus. Rev.* Nov.-Dec. pp. 129-138.

Walton, R.E. (1969). *Interpersonal Peacemaking: Confrontations and Third Party Consultation*. Addison-Wesley, Mass.

Watson, J.D. (1968). *The Double Helix*. Atheneum, New York.

Weed, L.L. (1969) *Medical Records, Medical Education & Patient Care*. Press of Case Western Reserve University of Chicago, Chicago, Ill.

Weick, K. (1969). *The Social Psychology of Organizing*. Addison-Wesley, Reading, Mass.

Weinberg, A.M. (1967). *Reflections on Big Science*. M.I.T., Cambridge, Mass.

Weiss, R.S. (1956). *Processes of Organization*. Institute for Social Research, University of Michigan, Ann Arbor, Mich.

Whyte, W. (1957). *Organization Man*. Jonathan Cape, London.

Wilmott, P. and Young, M. (1960). *Family and Class in a London Suburb*. Routledge. p. 122.

Woodward, J. (1958). *Management and Technology*. Her Majesty's Printing Office, London.

Woodward, J. (1965). *Industrial Organization Theory and Practice*. Oxford, London.

Young, M. (Ed.) (1968). *Forecasting and the Social Sciences*. Heinemann, London.

Zaleznik, A. (1963). The Human Dilemmas of Leadership. *Har. Bus. Rev.* 41: 4, pp. 49-55.

Zaleznik, A., Christensen, C.R. and Roethlisberger, F.J. (1958). *The Motivation, Productivity, and Satisfaction of Workers*. Har. Bus. Sch., Boston, Mass.

Index